A-Level Year 1 & AS
Biology
Exam Board: AQA

Let's face it, Biology is a tough subject. You'll need to get to grips with a lot of difficult concepts, and have plenty of practical skills up your lab-coat sleeve.

But don't worry — this brilliant CGP book covers everything you'll need for the new AQA courses. It's packed with clear explanations, exam practice, advice on maths skills and practical investigations... and much more!

It even includes a free Online Edition to read on your PC, Mac or tablet.

How to get your free Online Edition

Go to **cgpbooks.co.uk/extras** and enter this code...

3310 0285 7994 5443

This code will only work once. If someone has used this book before you, they may have already claimed the Online Edition.

Contents

Exam Help

Reference

How to use this book

Learning Objectives

- These tell you exactly what you need to learn, or be able to do, for the exams.
- There's a specification reference at the bottom that links to the AQA specification.

Maths Skills Examples

There's a range of maths skills that you could be expected to apply in your exams. Examples that show these maths skills in action are marked up like this. There's also a Practical and Maths Skills section at the front of the book.

Exam Tips

There are tips throughout the book to help with all sorts of things to do with answering exam questions.

Learning Objectives:

- Be able to use this formula to calculate magnification:
$$\frac{\text{size of image}}{\text{size of real object}}$$
- Know the difference between magnification and resolution.
- Know the principles and limitations of optical microscopes and transmission and scanning electron microscopes.
- Appreciate that there was a considerable period of time during which the scientific community distinguished between artefacts and cell organelles.
- Understand how cell fractionation and ultracentrifugation are used to separate cell components.

Specification Reference 3.2.1.3

3. Analysis of Cell Components

Investigating cells, and what's in them, involves digging out your microscope.

Magnification and resolution of microscopes

We all know that microscopes produce a magnified image of a sample, but resolution is just as important...

Magnification

Magnification is how much bigger the image is than the specimen (the sample you're looking at). It's calculated using this formula:

$$\text{magnification} = \frac{\text{size of image}}{\text{size of real object}}$$

Examples — Maths Skills

Calculating magnification

If you have a magnified image that's 5 mm wide and your specimen is 0.05 mm wide the magnification is:

$$\text{magnification} = \frac{\text{size of image}}{\text{size of real object}}$$
$$= \frac{5}{0.05} = \times 100$$

Calculating size of image

If your specimen is 0.1 mm wide and the magnification of the microscope is × 20, then the size of the image is:

$$\text{size of image} = \text{magnification} \times \text{size of real object}$$
$$= 20 \times 0.1 = 2 \text{ mm}$$

Calculating size of real object

If you have a magnified image that's 5 mm wide and the magnification is × 50, then the size of the real object (i.e. the size of the specimen you're looking at) is:

$$\text{size of real object} = \frac{\text{size of image}}{\text{magnification}} = \frac{5}{50} = 0.1 \text{ mm}$$

When you're calculating magnification you need to make sure that all lengths are in the same unit, e.g. all in millimetres. When dealing with microscopes these units can get pretty tiny. The table below shows common units:

	Unit	How many millimetres it is:	
To convert × 1000	Millimetre (mm)	1 mm	To convert ÷ 1000
× 1000	Micrometre (μm)	0.001 mm	÷ 1000
	Nanometre (nm)	0.000001 mm	

Example — Maths Skills

To convert from a smaller unit to a bigger unit you divide by 1000.
So to convert 6 micrometres to millimetres you divide 6 by 1000
= 0.006 mm. To go from a bigger unit to a smaller unit you times by 1000.

Exam Tip

If you find rearranging formulas hard you can use a formula triangle to help:

All you do is put your finger over the one you want and read off the formula. E.g. if you want the size of the real object, you put your finger over that and it leaves behind size of image ÷ magnification.

Cancer

Mitosis and the cell cycle are controlled by genes. Normally, when cells have divided enough times to make enough new cells, they stop. But if there's a mutation in a gene that controls cell division, the cells can grow out of control. The cells keep on dividing to make more and more cells, which form a tumour. Cancer is a tumour that invades surrounding tissue.

Tip: Mutations are changes in the base sequence of an organism's DNA (see page 221).

Cancer treatments

Some treatments for cancer are designed to control the rate of cell division in tumour cells by disrupting the cell cycle. This kills the tumour cells. These treatments don't distinguish tumour cells from normal cells though — they also kill normal body cells that are dividing. However, tumour cells divide much more frequently than normal cells, so the treatments are more likely to kill tumour cells.

Tip: Cancer is basically uncontrolled cell division.

Examples

Some cell cycle targets of cancer treatments include:

G_1 (cell growth and protein production)
Some chemical drugs (chemotherapy) prevent the synthesis of enzymes needed for DNA replication. If these aren't produced, the cell is unable to enter the synthesis phase (S), disrupting the cell cycle and forcing the cell to kill itself.

S phase (DNA replication)
Radiation and some drugs damage DNA. At several points in the cell cycle, the DNA in the cell is checked for damage. If severe DNA damage is detected, the cell will kill itself — preventing further tumour growth.

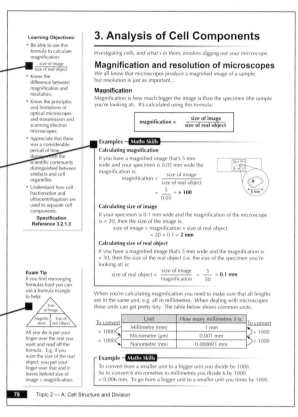

Figure 7: Cancer of the knee — the tumour is sticking out of the leg.

Tip: Rapidly dividing cells, like hair cells and cells that line the gut, are often affected by cancer treatments. This can cause side effects like hair loss.

Practice Question — Application

Q1 Methotrexate and vincristine are drugs used to treat cancer. Methotrexate blocks the formation of nucleotides within cells and vincristine prevents the formation of spindle fibres within the nuclei of cells. Which stage of the cell cycle is disrupted by:
a) methotrexate   b) vincristine?

Tip: Don't let the tricky names of the drugs throw you when answering Q1 here. Just apply your knowledge to the information given in the question.

Practice Questions — Fact Recall

Q1 What is the cell cycle?
Q2 Why is mitosis needed?
Q3 In what stage of the cell cycle does all the DNA unravel?
Q4 Describe what happens during prophase.
Q5 Describe what happens during telophase.
Q6 What is cytokinesis?
Q7 What is cancer?

Examples

These are here to help you understand the theory.

Practice Questions — Application

- Annoyingly, the examiners expect you to be able to apply your knowledge to new situations — these questions are here to give you plenty of practice at doing this.
- All the answers are in the back of the book (including any calculation workings).

Practice Questions — Fact Recall

- There are a lot of facts you need to learn — these questions are here to test whether you know them.
- All the answers are in the back of the book.

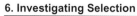

6. Investigating Selection

You can carry out practical investigations into the effects of antimicrobial substances (substances that kill microorganisms, e.g. antibiotics, antiseptics or disinfectants) on microbes. These investigations should show you whether the microbes have evolved resistance to these substances or not.

Learning Objective:
▪ Be able to use aseptic techniques to investigate the effect of antimicrobial substances on microbial growth (Required Practical 6).

Specification Reference 3.4.4

Testing the effects of antibiotics
REQUIRED PRACTICAL 6

Antibiotics are medicines that are designed to kill bacteria. This makes them a type of **antimicrobial substance**. You can investigate the effects of different antibiotics on bacterial growth using the following method. The whole investigation must be carried out using **aseptic techniques**. These are explained on the next page.

1. The bacteria you will use are likely to have been grown in a liquid broth (a mixture of distilled water, bacterial culture and nutrients).
2. Take a wire inoculation loop that's been sterilised in a Bunsen burner flame (see next page) and use it to transfer the bacteria from the broth to an agar plate — this is a Petri dish containing agar jelly. Spread the bacteria over the plate using the loop.
3. Place sterile paper discs soaked with different antibiotics spaced apart on the plate. Various concentrations of antibiotics should be used. You also need to add a negative control disc soaked only in sterile water.
4. Tape a lid onto the Petri dish (without completely sealing it), invert, and incubate the plate at about 25°C for 48 hours. This allows the bacteria to grow, forming a 'lawn'. Anywhere the bacteria can't grow can be seen as a clear patch in the lawn of bacteria. This is called an **inhibition zone**.
5. The size of an inhibition zone tells you how well an antibiotic works. The larger the zone, the more the bacteria were inhibited from growing.

Tip: Make sure you carry out a full risk assessment before you carry out this practical. It's also really important that you understand how to use aseptic techniques properly before you start.

Tip: A negative control is not expected to have any effect on the experiment — see page 2 for more.

Tip: Don't completely seal the Petri dish with tape before incubation — it will prevent oxygen from entering the dish, which may encourage the growth of anaerobic disease-causing bacteria. Don't open the dish after incubation.

— Example —

Figure 1 shows an agar plate after it has been incubated with paper discs soaked in the antibiotics meticillin, tetracycline and streptomycin.

Figure 1: *An agar plate used to investigate antibiotic resistance.*

125 mg 250 mg — Inhibition zone
Meticillin
Tetracycline — Agar plate
— Disc soaked in antibiotic
Streptomycin — Lawn of bacteria
Negative control (soaked in water)

▪ The tetracycline discs have no inhibition zones, so the bacteria are resistant to tetracycline up to 250 mg.
▪ The streptomycin discs have small inhibition zones, with the zone at 250 mg slightly larger than the one at 125 mg. So streptomycin inhibits the growth of some of the bacteria.
▪ The meticillin discs have the largest inhibition zones, so meticillin inhibits the growth of most of the bacteria.
▪ The negative control has no inhibition zone, which shows that the other results must be due to the presence of the antibiotics, not the paper disc.

Figure 2: *A bacterial culture plate with clear inhibition zones where an antibiotic has stopped the bacteria from growing.*

Topic 4 — B: Diversity and Selection **231**

Required Practicals

There are some key practicals that you'll be expected to do throughout your course. You'll need to know all about them for the exams. Information about these practicals is marked up with a Required Practical stamp.

Practical Skills

There are some key practical skills that you'll not only need to use in your Required Practicals, but that you could be tested on in the exams too. These skills are covered in the Practical and Maths Skills section at the front of the book.

Tips

These are here to help you understand the theory.

Exam-style Questions

▪ Practising exam-style questions is really important — you'll find some at the end of each section.

▪ They're the same style as the ones you'll get in the real exams — some will test your knowledge and understanding and some will test that you can apply your knowledge.

▪ All the answers are in the back of the book, along with a mark scheme to show you how you get the marks.

Exam Help

There's a section at the back of the book stuffed full of things to help with your exams.

Glossary

There's a glossary at the back of the book full of all the definitions you need to know for the exams, plus loads of other useful words.

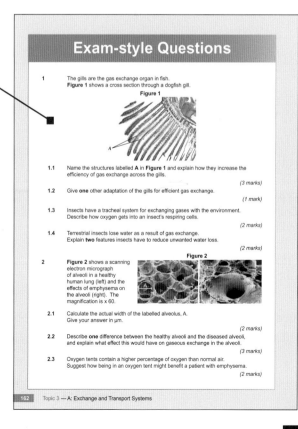

Exam-style Questions

1 The gills are the gas exchange organ in fish.
Figure 1 shows a cross section through a dogfish gill.

Figure 1

1.1 Name the structures labelled **A** in **Figure 1** and explain how they increase the efficiency of gas exchange across the gills.
(3 marks)

1.2 Give **one** other adaptation of the gills for efficient gas exchange.
(1 mark)

1.3 Insects have a tracheal system for exchanging gases with the environment. Describe how oxygen gets into an insect's respiring cells.
(2 marks)

1.4 Terrestrial insects lose water as a result of gas exchange. Explain **two** features insects have to reduce unwanted water loss.
(2 marks)

Figure 2

2 **Figure 2** shows a scanning electron micrograph of alveoli in a healthy human lung (left) and the effects of emphysema on the alveoli (right). The magnification is x 60.

2.1 Calculate the actual width of the labelled alveolus, A. Give your answer in μm.
(2 marks)

2.2 Describe **one** difference between the healthy alveoli and the diseased alveoli, and explain what effect this would have on gaseous exchange in the alveoli.
(3 marks)

2.3 Oxygen tents contain a higher percentage of oxygen than normal air. Suggest how being in an oxygen tent might benefit a patient with emphysema.
(2 marks)

Published by CGP

Editors:
Charlotte Burrows, Christopher Lindle, Christopher McGarry, Sarah Pattison,
Claire Plowman, Rachael Rogers and Hayley Thompson.

Contributors:
Gloria Barnett, Paddy Gannon, Liz Masters, Steven Phillips, Adrian Schmit, Anna Fe Williamson.

ISBN: 978 1 78294 319 8

With thanks to Joe Brazier, Janet Cruse-Sawyer, Ellen Shores,
Camilla Simson and Karen Wells for the proofreading.
With thanks to Laura Jakubowski for the copyright research.

Printed by Elanders Ltd, Newcastle upon Tyne.
Clipart from Corel®

Practical and Maths Skills

1. Planning an Experiment

You have to do practical work in class as part of your course. You'll be asked about it in exams too, so you need to know how to plan the perfect experiment.

Testing a theory

Before you start planning an experiment, you need to be clear about what you're trying to find out. Like all scientists, you should start off by making a **prediction** or **hypothesis** — a specific testable statement, based on theory, about what will happen in the experiment. You then need to plan a good experiment that will provide evidence to support the prediction — or help disprove it.

┌ **Example** ────────────────────────────────

Theory — enzymes have an optimum temperature. They work fastest at this temperature.

Prediction — the rate of the activity of an enzyme will be fastest at its optimum temperature, and slower at higher and lower temperatures.

Experiment — measure the rate of an enzyme's activity at various temperatures.

Getting good results

A good experiment is one that will give results that are:

- **Precise** — Precise results don't vary much from the mean. Precision is reduced by **random error** (the unpredictable way in which all measurements vary).

- **Repeatable and reproducible** — Repeatable means that if the same person repeats the experiment using the same methods and equipment, they will get the same results. Reproducible means that if someone different does the experiment, using a slightly different method or piece of equipment, the results will still be the same.

- **Valid** — Valid results answer the original question. To get valid results you need to control all the variables (see below) to make sure you're only testing the thing you want to.

- **Accurate** — Accurate results are really close to the true answer.

Here are some things you need to consider when designing a good experiment:

1. Variables

Variables are quantities that have the potential to change, e.g. temperature, pH. In an experiment you usually change one variable and measure its effect on another variable.

- The variable that you change is called the **independent variable**.
- The variable that you measure is called the **dependent variable**.

All the other variables should be controlled — when you're investigating a variable you need to keep everything else that could affect it constant. This means you can be sure that only your independent variable is affecting the thing you're measuring (the dependent variable).

Exam Tip
At least 15% of your AS Biology marks will come from assessment of Practical Skills in the exams — so you really do need to know this stuff.

Tip: The results of your experiment can't be used to <u>prove</u> that your theory is right, but can be used as evidence for or against it. There's more about what results mean on pages 15-18.

Tip: Precise results are sometimes referred to as reliable results.

Exam Tip
Examiners love getting you to comment on experimental design or suggest improvements to methods — e.g. how a method could be improved to make the results more precise.

Tip: There's more on how enzymes work on pages 35-46.

Example

For an investigation into how temperature affects enzyme activity:

- Temperature is the independent variable.
- Enzyme activity is the dependent variable.
- pH, volume, substrate concentration and enzyme concentration should all stay the same (and the quantities should be recorded to allow someone else to reproduce the experiment).

2. Controls

Negative controls are used to check that only the independent variable is affecting the dependent variable. Negative controls aren't expected to have any effect on the experiment.

Exam Tip
If you get an exam question asking why a control is important in a particular experiment, make sure your answer is specific to that experiment (not just about why controls are good in general).

Example

When investigating how temperature affects enzyme activity, you should measure a negative control at each temperature you're investigating. The controls should contain everything used except the enzyme. No enzyme activity should be seen with these controls.

Positive controls can also be used. They should show what a positive result of the experiment should look like, to check that it is possible.

Example

If you're testing for the presence of starch in a solution, you would carry out an iodine test (see page 26). You could test a solution you know contains starch before you start to show what a positive iodine test result looks like. This is your positive control.

In studies, **control groups** are used. The subjects in the study are split into two groups — the experimental group and the control group. The control group is treated in exactly the same way as the experimental group, except for the factor you're investigating.

Tip: In a study with human participants, you should try to keep the variables of all the participants the same, e.g. they should all be the same age, sex, etc.

Example

If you were investigating the effect of margarine containing omega-3 fish oils on heart disease, you'd have two groups — an experimental group that would be given margarine containing omega-3 fish oils, and a control group that would be given margarine without fish oils. This is done so that you can tell any reduction in heart disease is due to the fish oil, not some other substance in the margarine.

Tip: When testing a new drug to see if it works, the control group is given a placebo instead of the drug. A placebo is a dummy pill or injection that looks exactly like the real drug, but doesn't contain the drug. It's used to make sure that people don't improve just because they think they're being treated.

3. Repeats

Taking several repeat measurements and calculating the mean can reduce the effect of random error on your experiment, making your results more precise. Doing repeats and getting similar results each time also shows that your data is repeatable. This makes it more likely that the same results could be reproduced by another scientist in an independent experiment.

Example

For an investigation into how temperature affects enzyme activity, the experiment should be repeated at least three times at each temperature used. A mean result should be calculated for each temperature (see page 5).

Repeating measurements also reduces the likelihood that the results are due to chance — see next page.

4. Sample Size

Sample size is the number of samples in the investigation, e.g. the number of people in a drug trial. As with carrying out repeats, having a large sample size reduces the likelihood that the results are due to chance (e.g. if you get the same result twice it might be because of chance, but if you get it 100 times it's much more likely that it's not due to chance).

Tip: Scientists can use statistical tests to figure out if a result is likely to be due to chance or not. See page 9 for more.

Taking accurate measurements

When you're planning an experiment you need to decide what it is you're going to measure and how often you're going to take measurements.

Example

If you're investigating the rate of an enzyme-controlled reaction, you could either measure how fast the product is made or how quickly the substrate is used up. You could take measurements at, e.g. 30 second or 60 second intervals.

Then you need to choose the most appropriate apparatus, equipment and techniques for the experiment.

The measuring apparatus you use has to be sensitive enough to measure the changes you're looking for. For example, if you need to measure small changes in pH, a pH meter (which can measure pH to several decimal places) would be more sensitive than indicator paper.

The technique you use has to be the most appropriate one for your experiment. E.g. if you want to investigate plant cells undergoing mitosis, it's best to prepare a stained squash slide so you see the chromosomes clearly under the microscope (see page 88).

Figure 1: *pH meters can be used to measure small changes in pH.*

Risk assessments

In order to work safely, you need to carry out a risk assessment for your experiment. To do this, you need to identify:

- All the dangers in the experiment, for example any hazardous chemicals, microorganisms or naked flames.
- Who is at risk from these dangers — this could be you and your lab partner, but it could also be anyone who is in the same room or building.
- What can be done to reduce the risk. You should wear a lab coat and goggles as a standard precaution, but you may need to take other safety precautions, such as carrying out your experiment in a fume cupboard or using aseptic techniques (see page 232).

Ethical issues

You also need to consider any ethical issues in your experiment.

Figure 2: *Chemicals marked with hazard warning signs.*

Example

If you're using living animals (e.g. insects) you must treat them with respect. This means handling them carefully and keeping them away from harmful chemicals, extreme heat sources and other things that might cause them physical discomfort.

---

2. Carrying Out an Experiment

As part of your AS or A-level in Biology, you're expected to carry out Required Practicals and be familiar with the techniques and apparatus involved in each one. You could be asked about the skills you've learnt in your exams.

Using the correct apparatus and techniques

Examiners could ask you about a whole range of different apparatus and techniques. Make sure you know how to use all the instruments and equipment you've come across in class and can carry out all the techniques too. Here are some examples of equipment you should be able to use:

┌─ **Examples** ────────────────────────────

Measuring cylinders and graduated pipettes
These have a scale so you can measure specific volumes. Whichever one you use, make sure you read the volume from the bottom of the meniscus (the curved upper surface of the liquid) when it's at eye level — see Figure 1.

Water baths
Make sure you allow time for water baths to heat up before starting your experiment. Don't forget that your solutions will need time to get to the same temperature as the water before you start the experiment too. Also, remember to check the temperature of the water bath with a thermometer during the investigation to make sure it doesn't change.

Data loggers
Decide what you are measuring and what type of data logger you will need, e.g. temperature, pH. Connect an external sensor to the data logger if you need to. Decide how often you want the data logger to take readings depending on the length of the process that you are measuring.

You should also make sure you know how to do all the Required Practicals described in this book. You should be able to apply the techniques described in them to different contexts. For example, page 105 describes how to prepare serial dilutions in order to find out the water potential of potato cells. You could also use serial dilutions to prepare solutions of varying substrate concentration in order to investigate the effect of substrate concentration on enzyme activity.

Recording data

As you get your results, you need to record them. It's a good idea to draw a **table** to record the results of your experiment in. When you draw a table, make sure you include enough rows and columns to record all of the data you need to. You might also need to include a column for processing your data (e.g. working out the mean — see next page). Make sure each column has a heading so you know what's going to be recorded where. The units should be in the column heading only, not the table itself — see Figure 2.

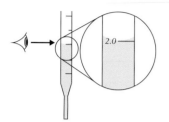

Figure 1: Measuring volume using the bottom of the meniscus.

Tip: A data logger (or data recorder) is an electronic device that can record data over time using a sensor. They can sometimes be connected to a computer.

Tip: If you're recording your data as decimals, make sure you do it to a consistent number of decimal places, e.g. when you're analysing your results, it makes sense to compare values that have been rounded to the same level of accuracy.

Figure 2: Table showing the number of different species and the length of hedgerows found on three farms.

Farm	Length of hedgerows (km)	Number of species
1	49	21
2	90	28
3	155	30

Using frequency tables

A **frequency table** is just a table that shows how many of each value there are. They usually have three columns. The first column just gives the values or names of the different pieces of data. The second column shows a mark for each piece of data — this is the **tally**. The third column is the **frequency**, which you get by adding up the tally marks.

You can draw a frequency table for data you've already collected, or to record the data straight into.

Tip: Frequency is just the number of times that something occurs.

┌─ Example ── **Maths Skills** ─────────────────────────

To record the number of individuals of different species of bird observed in a garden:

1. Draw a table with three columns. Give the columns the headings 'species', 'tally' and 'frequency'.

2. Record the data by drawing a tally mark in the correct row to represent each piece of data.

3. Add up the tally marks in each row when you've finished recording your data. This is the frequency.

species	tally	frequency
sparrow	IIII II	7
blue tit	IIII	4
goldfinch	II	2
blackbird	IIII IIII	10

Tip: To record 5 results you write IIII, not IIIII. This makes it easier to keep track of the numbers.

Anomalous results

When you look at all the data in your table, you may notice that you have a result that doesn't seem to fit in with the rest at all. These results are called **anomalous results**.

You should investigate anomalous results — if you can work out what happened (e.g. you measured something totally wrong) you can ignore them when processing your results. However, you can't just exclude a value just because you don't like the look of it.

Tip: Doing repeats makes it easier to spot anomalous results.

3. Processing Data

Processing data means taking raw data and doing some calculations with it, to make it more useful. This is where your maths skills really come in.

Exam Tip
At least 10% of your AS Biology marks will come from assessment of maths skills in the exams.

Summarising your data

Once you've collected all your data, it's useful to summarise it using a few handy-to-use figures — like the mean and the range.

Mean and range

When you've done repeats of an experiment you should always calculate a **mean** (a type of average). To do this add together all the data values and divide by the total number of values in the sample.

You might also need to calculate the **range** (how spread out the data is). To do this find the largest data value and subtract the smallest data value from it. You shouldn't include anomalous results when calculating the mean or the range.

Tip: When people talk about an <u>average</u>, they are usually referring to the <u>mean value</u>.

Example — Maths Skills

Compare the mean result and range for test tubes A and B in the table on the right.

Test tube	Repeat (g)		
	1	*2*	*3*
A	28	37	32
B	47	51	45

To calculate the means:

- Add up the three data values for A, then divide by three.
  A: (28 + 37 + 32) ÷ 3 = 97 ÷ 3 = **32 g** *(2 s.f.)*

- Do the same for B.
  B: (47 + 51 + 45) ÷ 3 = 143 ÷ 3 = **48 g** *(2 s.f.)* **B has the higher mean.**

To find the range of results for each test tube, subtract the smallest result from the largest result.
  A: 37 – 28 = **9 g**   *B: 51 – 45 =* **6 g**   **B has the smaller range.**

Tip: Averages and range values have the same units as the data used in the calculation.

Tip: S.f. stands for 'significant figures'. You can find out how many significant figures to use when rounding answers on page 8.

Standard deviation

Standard deviation can be more useful than the range because it tells you how values are spread about the mean rather than just the total spread of data. A small standard deviation means the repeated results are all similar and close to the mean, i.e. they are precise. There's more on standard deviation on pages 247-249.

Median and mode

Like the mean, the median and mode are both types of average.

To calculate the median, put all your data in numerical order. The median is the middle value in this list. If you have an even number of values, the median is halfway between the middle two values.

To calculate the mode, count how many times each value comes up. The mode is the number that appears most often. A set of data might not have a mode — or it might have more than one.

Tip: If all the values in your data are different, there won't be a mode at all.

Example — Maths Skills

The number of days survived without watering was recorded for a species of drought-resistant plant. The results were as follows:

        26   24   29   24   22   26   25   27   24   21   22   27

Calculate the median and mode of these results.

1. Put the data in numerical order:
     21   22   22   24   24   24   25   26   26   27   27   29

2. Find the middle value (the median):
   There are 12 values, so the median is between the 6th and 7th numbers. The 6th number is 24 and the 7th number is 25, so the median is **24.5**.

3. Count how many times each value comes up to find the mode:
   24 comes up three times. None of the other numbers come up more than twice. So the mode is **24**.

Tip: To find the value halfway between two numbers, add the two numbers together and then divide by two.
E.g. 24 + 25 = 49,
49 ÷ 2 = 24.5.

Calculating percentages

Calculating **percentages** helps you to compare amounts from samples of different sizes. To give the amount X as a percentage of sample Y, you need to divide X by Y, then multiply by 100.

Example — **Maths Skills**

A tissue sample containing 50 cells is viewed under the microscope. 22 are undergoing mitosis. What percentage of cells are undergoing mitosis?

1. Divide 22 by 50: $22 \div 50 = 0.44$
2. Multiply by 100. $0.44 \times 100 = $ **44%**

Calculating percentage change

Calculating **percentage change** helps to quantify how much something has changed, e.g. the percentage change in the growth rate of pea plants when a fertiliser is added. To calculate it you use this equation:

$$\text{Percentage change} = \frac{\text{final value} - \text{original value}}{\text{original value}} \times 100$$

Exam Tip
The examiners just love getting you to calculate percentage changes, including percentage increases and decreases, so make sure you learn this formula.

A positive value indicates an increase and a negative value indicates a decrease.

Example — **Maths Skills**

Three sets of potato chips were weighed, then each set was placed in a solution containing a different concentration of sucrose. After 24 hours the chips were removed from the solution, patted dry and weighed again. **Calculate the percentage change in mass for the chips in each solution.**

Concentration of sucrose (M)	0.0	0.2	0.4
Mass before (g)	7.7	9.8	8.6
Mass after (g)	9.4	10.2	7.1

Potato chips in 0.0 M sucrose solution:
$$\text{Percentage change} = \frac{(9.4 - 7.7)}{7.7} \times 100 = \frac{1.7}{7.7} \times 100 = \textbf{22\%}$$

Potato chips in 0.2 M sucrose solution:
$$\text{Percentage change} = \frac{(10.2 - 9.8)}{9.8} \times 100 = \frac{0.4}{9.8} \times 100 = \textbf{4.1\%}$$

Potato chips in 0.4 M sucrose solution:
$$\text{Percentage change} = \frac{(7.1 - 8.6)}{8.6} \times 100 = \frac{-1.5}{8.6} \times 100 = \textbf{--17\%}$$

Tip: Percentage <u>change</u> can be either positive or negative, depending on whether the value has gone up or down. However, percentage <u>increase</u> and percentage <u>decrease</u> are both written as positive numbers because the direction of the change has already been taken into account.

Using ratios

Ratios can be used to compare lots of different types of quantities. For example, an organism with a surface area to volume ratio of 2 : 1 would theoretically have a surface area twice as large as its volume.

Ratios are usually most useful in their simplest (smallest) form. To simplify a ratio, divide each side by the same number. It's in its simplest form when there's nothing left you can divide by. To get a ratio of X : Y in the form X : 1, divide both sides by Y.

Tip: If you're not sure what number to divide by to simplify a ratio, start by trying to divide both sides by a small number, e.g. 2 or 3, then check to see if you can simplify your answer further. E.g. you could simplify 28 : 36 by dividing each side by 2 to get 14 : 18. But you could simplify it further by dividing by 2 again to get 7 : 9. You can't simplify the ratio any further, so it's in its simplest form.

Examples — **Maths Skills**

▪ To simplify the ratio 28 : 36, divide both sides by 4. You get **7 : 9**.
▪ To write the ratio 28 : 36 in the form of X : 1, just divide both sides by 36:
$$28 \div 36 = 0.78 \qquad 36 \div 36 = 1$$
So the ratio is **0.78 : 1**.

Rounding to significant figures

The first **significant figure** of a number is the first digit that isn't a zero. The second, third and fourth significant figures follow on immediately after the first (even if they're zeros). When you're processing your data you may well want to round any really long numbers to a certain number of significant figures.

> **Example**
>
> 0.6874976 rounds to **0.69** to **2 s.f.** and to **0.687** to **3 s.f.**

When you're doing calculations using measurements given to a certain number of significant figures, you should give your answer to the lowest number of significant figures that was used in the calculation.

> **Example** — **Maths Skills**
>
> For the calculation: $1.2 \div 1.85 = 0.648648648...$
>
> 1.2 is given to 2 significant figures. 1.85 is given to 3 significant figures. So the answer should be given to 2 significant figures.
>
> Round the final significant figure (0.6$\underline{4}$8) up to 5: $1.2 \div 1.85 = \mathbf{0.65\ (2\ s.f.)}$

The lowest number of significant figures in the calculation is used because the fewer digits a measurement has, the less accurate it is. Your answer can only be as accurate as the least accurate measurement in the calculation.

Tip: You may also want to round measurements to a certain number of significant figures when you're recording your data, e.g. if you're using a data logger that records data to several decimal places.

Tip: When rounding a number, if the next digit after the last significant figure you're using is <u>less than 5</u> you should round it <u>down</u>, and if it's <u>5 or more</u> you should <u>round it up</u>.

Writing numbers in standard form

When you're processing data you might also want to change very big or very small numbers that have lots of zeros into something more manageable — this is called standard form.

> **Examples**
>
> 1 000 000 can be written 1×10^6. 0.017 can be written 1.7×10^{-2}.

To do this you just need to move the decimal point left or right. The number of places the decimal point moves is then represented by a power of 10 — this is positive for big numbers, and negative for numbers smaller than one.

> **Example** — **Maths Skills**
>
> **To write 16 500 in standard form:**
>
> 1. Move the decimal point to give the smallest number you can between 1 and 10.
>
> $16\ 500 \longrightarrow 1.6500$
>
> 2. Count the number of places the decimal point has moved.
>   *The decimal point has moved four places to the left.*
>
> 3. Write that number as the power of ten. If the decimal point has moved to the left, the power is positive. If the decimal point has moved to the right, the power is negative.
>
> $16\ 500 = \mathbf{1.65 \times 10^4}$

Tip: When you're writing a measurement in standard form, make sure you keep the same number of significant figures. E.g. $0.00400\ cm^3 = 4.00 \times 10^{-3}\ cm^3$. This'll make sure that you don't lose any accuracy.

Tip: Double check you've got it right by doing the multiplication — you should end up with the number you started with. So for this example, you'd check $1.65 \times 10^4 = 16\ 500$.

Converting between units

When processing your data, you need to have all the data in the correct units. Make sure you can convert between common units of time, length and volume.

Examples

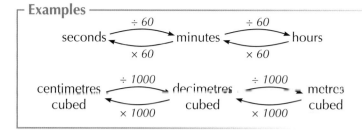

seconds $\xrightarrow{\div 60}$ minutes $\xrightarrow{\div 60}$ hours
$\xleftarrow{\times 60}$ $\xleftarrow{\times 60}$

centimetres cubed $\xrightarrow{\div 1000}$ decimetres cubed $\xrightarrow{\div 1000}$ metres cubed
$\xleftarrow{\times 1000}$ $\xleftarrow{\times 1000}$

Tip: One decimetre cubed (1 dm³) is the same as one litre (1 L).

Examples — Maths Skills

1. **The total lung capacity of a patient is 5430 cm³. What is the patient's lung capacity in dm³?**

   There are 1000 cm³ in one dm³, so you need to divide by 1000:
   5430 cm³ ÷ 1000 = **5.430 dm³**

2. **The volume of oxygen produced over time was measured for an enzyme-controlled reaction. The initial rate of reaction was found to be 8.4 cm³ min⁻¹. What is this rate in cm³ s⁻¹?**

   8.4 cm³ min⁻¹ means 8.4 cm³ oxygen was produced per minute. You want to find out the volume produced per second. There are 60 seconds in one minute, so you need to divide the volume by 60:
   8.4 cm³ min⁻¹ ÷ 60 = **0.14 cm³ s⁻¹**

Tip: Make sure your answer makes sense — if you're converting from a small unit (e.g. cm³) to a larger unit (e.g. dm³) you need to <u>divide</u> the value, so your answer should be <u>smaller</u> than the number you started with.

Statistical tests

Statistical tests are used to analyse data mathematically. You can be more confident in your **conclusions** (see page 18), if they're based on results that have been analysed using a statistical test.

Student's t-test

You can use the Student's t-test when you have two sets of data that you want to compare. It tests whether there is a significant difference in the means of the two data sets.

The value obtained is compared to a critical value, which helps you decide how likely it is that the results or 'differences in the means' were due to chance. If the value obtained from the t-test is greater than the critical value at a probability (**P value**) of 5% or less (≤ 0.05), then you can be 95% confident that the difference is significant and not due to chance. This is called a **95% confidence limit** — which is good enough for most biologists.

Tip: If the result of your statistical test is greater than (>) the critical value at a P value of less than 2% (< 0.02), or even 1%, you can be even more confident that the difference is significant.

Chi-squared test

You can use the Chi-squared test when you have categorical (grouped) data and you want to know whether your observed results are statistically different from your expected results. You compare your result to a critical value — if it's larger than the critical value at P = 0.05, you can be 95% certain the difference is significant.

Correlation coefficient

A correlation coefficient allows you to work out the degree to which two sets of data are correlated (see page 15 for more on correlation). It is given as a value between 1 and –1. A value of 1 indicates a strong positive correlation, 0 means there is no correlation and –1 is a strong negative correlation. You can then compare your result to a critical value to find out whether or not the correlation is significant. The **Spearman's rank correlation coefficient** is a type of correlation coefficient. See pages 254-255 for more on how to use it.

Exam Tip
When you're talking about the results of a statistical test and using the 95% confidence limit, make sure you refer to the probability as less than 0.05 or 5%, not 0.05%.

4. Presenting Data

Presenting your data can make it easier for you to understand your results and spot any trends. There are several different ways to do it though, and you need to be able to choose the best way for the data you've got.

Qualitative and discrete data

Qualitative data is non-numerical data, e.g. blood group, hair colour. **Discrete** data is numerical data that can only take certain values in a range, e.g. shoe size, number of patients. You can use **bar charts** or **pie charts** to present these types of data.

┌ **Example** ── **Maths Skills** ───────────────

The table shows the results of a survey into people's blood groups.

Blood group	Number of people
A	9
B	8
AB	2
O	17

To draw a bar chart from it:

1. **Space out each category evenly on the x-axis.**
   The blood groups are the categories so they go on the x-axis.
   The bars for different categories shouldn't touch each other.
   There should be equal spacing between each category.

2. **Choose a sensible scale for your y-axis.**
   The number of people (the thing that was measured in this survey) goes on the y-axis. The highest number of people is 17, so an axis running from 0 to 20 would work nicely.

3. **Draw a bar for each category.**

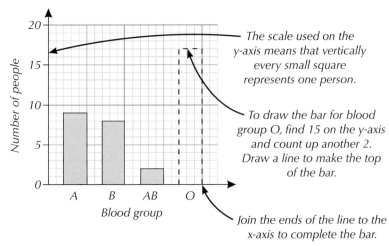

The scale used on the y-axis means that vertically every small square represents one person.

To draw the bar for blood group O, find 15 on the y-axis and count up another 2. Draw a line to make the top of the bar.

Join the ends of the line to the x-axis to complete the bar.

Tip: Qualitative data can also be called categorical data — all the data can be sorted into categories and values between categories don't exist.

Exam Tip
If you are asked to draw a graph or chart in your exam, don't forget to label the axes (including the quantity and units), choose a sensible scale and make sure that it covers at least half the graph paper.

Tip: Graph paper tends to be divided vertically and horizontally into groups of 10 squares. So axes that go up in 1s, 2s, 5s or 10s make data a lot easier to plot.

Tip: You can choose any width for the bars — just make sure they're all the same.

Continuous data

Continuous data is data that can take any value in a range, e.g. height or weight. You can use **line graphs** or **histograms** to present this type of data.

Line graphs

Line graphs often show how a variable changes over time.
The data on both axes is continuous.

Example

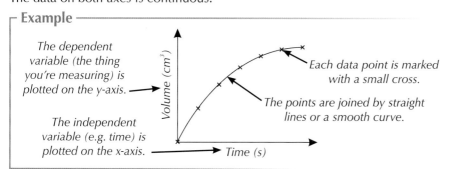

The dependent variable (the thing you're measuring) is plotted on the y-axis.

Each data point is marked with a small cross.

The points are joined by straight lines or a smooth curve.

The independent variable (e.g. time) is plotted on the x-axis.

Tip: The graph on the left is a line graph. Line graphs look a bit like scattergrams (see page 12), but the points on line graphs are joined together.

Histograms

Histograms are a useful way of displaying frequency data when the independent variable is continuous. They may look like bar charts, but it's the area of the bars that represents the frequency (rather than the height). The height of each bar is called the **frequency density**.

Example

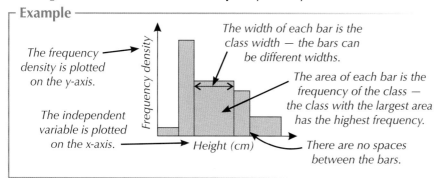

The frequency density is plotted on the y-axis.

The width of each bar is the class width — the bars can be different widths.

The area of each bar is the frequency of the class — the class with the largest area has the highest frequency.

The independent variable is plotted on the x-axis.

There are no spaces between the bars.

Tip: Don't be fooled by the height of the bars in a histogram — the tallest bar doesn't always belong to the class with the greatest frequency.

Tip: The data for a histogram is split into groups called classes, rather than categories. The class width is the range of the class.

Tip: If all the class widths are the same, you can just plot the frequency on the y-axis.

You calculate the frequency density using this formula:

$$\text{frequency density} = \text{frequency} \div \text{class width}$$

Example — **Maths Skills**

The table on the right shows the results of a study into variation in pea plant height. The heights of the plants were grouped into four classes.

Height of pea plant (cm)	Frequency
$0 \le x < 5$	5
$5 \le x < 10$	14
$10 \le x < 15$	11
$15 \le x < 30$	3

Tip: The continuous data here has been split into classes. $0 \le x < 5$ means the data in the class is more than or equal to 0 and less than 5.

1. To draw a histogram of the data, you first need to work out the width of each class. Write the class width in a new column.

Class width
$5 - 0 = \mathbf{5}$
$10 - 5 = \mathbf{5}$
$15 - 10 = \mathbf{5}$
$30 - 15 = \mathbf{15}$

2. Use the formula on the previous page to calculate the frequency density for each class and write it in another new column.

3. Work out a suitable scale for each axis, then plot the histogram. It should look something like this:

Frequency density
$5 \div 5 = \mathbf{1}$
$14 \div 5 = \mathbf{2.8}$
$11 \div 5 = \mathbf{2.2}$
$3 \div 15 = \mathbf{0.2}$

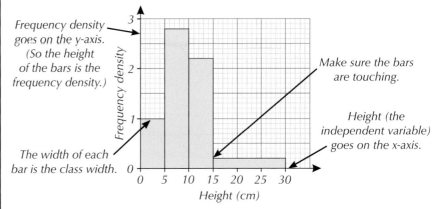

Frequency density goes on the y-axis. (So the height of the bars is the frequency density.)

Make sure the bars are touching.

The width of each bar is the class width.

Height (the independent variable) goes on the x-axis.

Scattergrams

When you want to show how two variables are related (or correlated, see page 15) you can use a **scattergram**. Both variables must be numbers.

— **Example** —

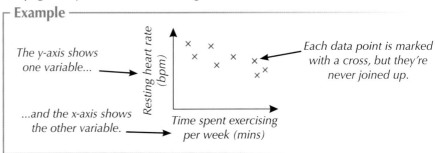

The y-axis shows one variable...

...and the x-axis shows the other variable.

Each data point is marked with a cross, but they're never joined up.

You can draw a **line** (or curve) **of best fit** on a scattergram to help show the trend in your results. To do so, draw the line through or as near to as many points as possible, ignoring any anomalous results.

— **Example** —

The number of organisms of one species on a rocky beach was recorded at different distances from the shore. The graph below shows the results, including a line of best fit.

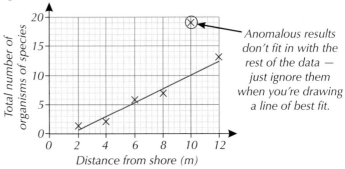

Anomalous results don't fit in with the rest of the data — just ignore them when you're drawing a line of best fit.

Finding the rate from a graph

Rate is a measure of how much something is changing over time.
Calculating a rate can be useful when analysing your data, e.g. you might want to the find the rate of a reaction. You can find the rate from a graph that shows a variable changing over time by finding the **gradient** (how steep it is):

Linear graphs

For a linear graph you can calculate the rate by finding the gradient of the line, using the equation:

$$\text{Gradient} = \frac{\text{Change in } y}{\text{Change in } x}$$

Change in y is the change in value on the y-axis and **change in x** is the change in value on the x-axis.

The equation of a straight line can always be written in the form $y = mx + c$, where m is the gradient and c is the y-intercept (this is the value of y when the line crosses the y-axis).

Tip: Linear graphs are graphs with a straight line.

Tip: When using this equation to find a rate, x should always be the time.

Example — Maths Skills

To find the rate at which oxygen is produced in the graph on the right:

1. Pick two points on the line that are easy to read and a good distance apart.

2. Draw a vertical line down from one point and a horizontal line across from the other to make a triangle.

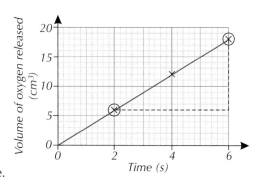

Tip: The graph on the left is a linear graph in which one variable increases in proportion with the other. The symbol for 'proportional to' is '$\propto$'. Here, you can say that volume of oxygen $\propto$ time.

3. Use the scales on the axes to work out the length of each line. The vertical side of the triangle is the change in y and the horizontal side of the triangle is the change in x.

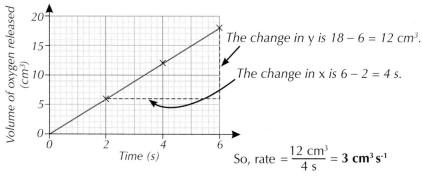

The change in y is $18 - 6 = 12$ cm³.

The change in x is $6 - 2 = 4$ s.

So, rate $= \dfrac{12 \text{ cm}^3}{4 \text{ s}} = \mathbf{3 \text{ cm}^3 \text{s}^{-1}}$

Tip: When drawing a triangle to calculate a gradient like this, the hypotenuse of the triangle should be at least half as long as the line of the graph itself.

To find the equation of the line you need the gradient (which is the same as the rate) and the y-intercept (where the line crosses the y-axis).

The gradient is 3 and the line crosses the y-axis where y is 0.

So the equation for the line is $y = 3x + 0$.

Since $c = 0$, the equation can be written as just $\mathbf{y = 3x}$.

Tip: The units for the gradient are the units for y divided by the units for x. Remember, cm³ s⁻¹ means the same as cm³/s (centimetres cubed per second).

Knowing the equation of the line allows you to estimate results not plotted on the graph:

For the reaction shown in the graph on the right, estimate the volume of oxygen released after 20 seconds.

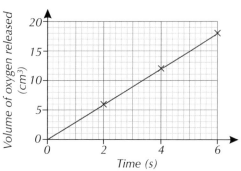

The equation for the line is $y = 3x$ (see previous page), where y is the volume of oxygen released (in cm^3) and x is the time (in seconds).

To find the value of y when x is 20 s, just replace x with 20 in the equation.

$$y = 3 \times 20 = \textbf{60 cm}^3$$

Tip: This is an estimate because you are assuming that the relationship between the two variables doesn't change after six seconds (so as time increases, the volume of oxygen released keeps increasing at the same rate).

Curved graphs

For a curved (non-linear) graph you can find the rate by drawing a **tangent**. A tangent is a straight line that touches a single point on the curve.

To find the rate of reaction when time = 30 seconds on the graph below:

1. Position a ruler on the graph at the point on the curve where you want to know the rate (so on this graph, find the point on the curve where $x = 30$).

2. Angle the ruler so there is equal space between the ruler and the curve on either side of the point.

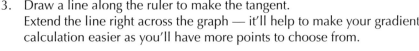

Tip: Look at the gaps on either side of the point — keep wiggling the ruler about until the two gaps look about the same size.

3. Draw a line along the ruler to make the tangent.
    Extend the line right across the graph — it'll help to make your gradient calculation easier as you'll have more points to choose from.

Tip: Always use a sharp pencil when drawing a tangent — you'll need to read points off the line in the next step, so make sure the line's nice and clear.

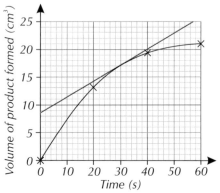

4. To find the rate, calculate the gradient of the tangent in the same way you would calculate the gradient of a straight line graph (see p. 13).

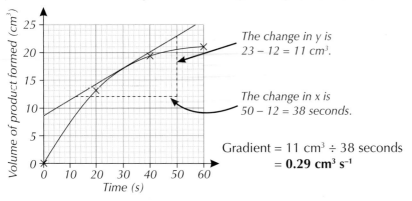

The change in y is
$23 - 12 = 11$ cm³.

The change in x is
$50 - 12 = 38$ seconds.

Gradient = 11 cm³ ÷ 38 seconds
= **0.29 cm³ s⁻¹**

Tip: Remember, gradient = change in y ÷ change in x.

Tip: Remember, the gradient of a tangent only tells you the rate at that particular point on the graph.

5. Drawing Conclusions and Evaluating

You need to be able to draw conclusions from your results and evaluate them. You also need to be able to draw conclusions from other people's data and evaluate them — which is what you're likely to be asked to do in your exams.

Drawing conclusions from data

Conclusions need to be **valid**. A conclusion can only be considered as valid if it uses valid data (see page 1).

Correlations and causal relationships

You can often draw conclusions by looking at the relationship (**correlation**) between two variables:

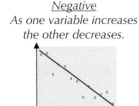
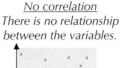

Positive	*Negative*	*No correlation*
As one variable increases the other increases.	As one variable increases the other decreases.	There is no relationship between the variables.

Tip: The closer the points are to the line of best fit, the stronger the correlation. You can calculate a correlation coefficient (see p. 9) to get a numerical value for how strong the correlation is.

You have to be very careful when drawing conclusions from data like this because a correlation between two variables doesn't always mean that a change in one variable causes a change in the other (the correlation could be due to chance or there could be a third variable having an effect).

If there's a relationship between two variables and a change in one variable does cause a change in the other it's called a **causal relationship**. It can be concluded that a correlation is a causal relationship if every other variable that could possibly affect the result is controlled.

Drawing specific conclusions

When you're making a conclusion you can't make broad generalisations from data — you have to be very specific. You can only conclude what the results show and no more.

Tip: In reality, concluding that a correlation is a causal relationship is very hard to do — correlations are generally accepted to be causal relationships if lots of studies have found the same thing, and scientists have figured out exactly how one factor causes the other.

Figure 1 shows the results from a study into the effect of penicillin dosage on the duration of fever in men.

What you can conclude from these results:
The only conclusion you can draw is that there's a negative correlation between penicillin dosage and duration of fever in men (as the dosage of penicillin increases, the duration of fever in men decreases).

What you <u>can't</u> conclude from these results:
You can't conclude that this is true for any other antibiotic, any other symptom or even for female patients — the results could be completely different. Without more information and the results from more studies, you can't conclude that the increasing penicillin dosage has caused the reduction in duration of fever either.

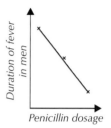

Figure 1: *The relationship between penicillin dosage and the duration of fever in men.*

Exam Tip
Being able to recognise correlations and causal relationships comes up a lot in Biology. It's really important that you learn how to do this and understand the difference between the two.

Uncertainty in data

When you draw a conclusion, it's often a good idea to talk about the uncertainty of your measurements. Uncertainty is the amount of error your measurements might have. The results you get from an experiment won't be completely perfect — there'll always be a degree of uncertainty in your measurements due to limits in the sensitivity of the apparatus you're using. A ± sign tells you the range in which the true value lies (usually to within a 95% confidence level). The range is called the **margin of error**.

Example

A 10 cm³ pipette has graduations to mark every 0.1 cm³. If you measure a volume with it, you are measuring to the nearest 0.1 cm³ — the real volume could be up to 0.05 cm³ less or 0.05 cm³ more. The uncertainty value of the pipette is ± 0.05 cm³, and so its margin of error is 0.1 cm³ (see Figure 2).

If you're combining measurements, you'll need to combine their uncertainties:

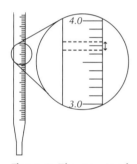

Figure 2: *The margin of error for a measurement of 3.7 cm³ using a 10 cm³ pipette.*

Example — **Maths Skills**

In a serial dilution, 5 cm³ of glucose solution is transferred using a pipette that measures to the nearest 0.5 cm³. It is added to 10 cm³ water that was measured in a graduated cylinder with graduations to mark every 1 cm³.

The uncertainty in the pipette is ± 0.25 cm³.
The uncertainty in the graduated cylinder is ± 0.5 cm³.

So the total uncertainty will be 0.25 cm³ + 0.5 cm³ = **± 0.75 cm³**.

Tip: The percentage error is the error as a <u>percentage</u> of the measured value, so you can use it to compare the uncertainty of two measurements (see next page).

Calculating percentage error

If you know the uncertainty value of your measurements, you can calculate the percentage error using:

$$\text{percentage error} = \frac{\text{uncertainty}}{\text{reading}} \times 100$$

Example — **Maths Skills**

50 cm³ of HCl is measured with an uncertainty value of ± 0.05 cm³.

The percentage error $= \frac{0.05}{50} \times 100 = \textbf{0.1}\%$

Minimising errors in data

One obvious way to reduce errors in your measurements is to buy the most sensitive equipment available. In real life there's not much you can do about this one — you're stuck with whatever your school or college has got. But there are other ways to lower the uncertainty in experiments.

Example — Measuring a greater amount of something

Using a 500 cm³ cylinder with an uncertainty value of ± 2.5 cm³ to measure 100 cm³ of liquid will give you a percentage error of: $\frac{2.5}{100} \times 100 = \textbf{2.5\%}$

But if you measure 200 cm³ in the same cylinder, the percentage error is: $\frac{2.5}{200} \times 100 = \textbf{1.25\%}$

Hey presto — you've just halved the uncertainty.

Tip: You can also minimise errors by using a <u>larger sample size</u>, as this reduces the chance of getting a freak result — see page 3.

Evaluating results

When you evaluate your results, you need to think about whether they were repeatable and reproducible and whether they were valid.

Repeatability
- Did you take enough repeat readings of the measurements?
- Would you do more repeats if you were to do the experiment again?
- Do you get similar data each time you carried out a repeat measurement?

If you didn't do any repeats, or enough repeats, you can't be sure your data is repeatable. Your repeated results need to be similar too. If you repeated a measurement three times and got a completely different result each time, your results aren't repeatable (or precise).

Reproducibility
Have you compared your results with other people's results and if so, were they similar? If not, you can't be sure your data is reproducible.

Validity
- Does your data answer the question you set out to investigate?
- Were all the variables controlled?

If you didn't control all the variables, you haven't answered the original question and your data isn't valid.

Exam Tip
If you're given data or a method to evaluate in the exam, you should be asking similar questions, e.g. were all the variables controlled? And if not, how should they have been controlled?

Example

You could only conclude from your results that the rate of activity of an enzyme is fastest at a particular temperature (see page 1) if you controlled all the other variables that could have affected enzyme activity in your experiment, e.g. pH, enzyme concentration, etc.

Tip: Think about whether other scientists could gain data showing the same relationships that are shown in your data.

Evaluating methods

When you evaluate your method, you need to think about how you could improve your experiment if you did it again. Here are some things to consider:

- Is there anything you could have done to make your results more precise or accurate?
- Were there any limitations in your method, e.g. should you have taken measurements more frequently?
- Was your sample size large enough?
- Were there any sources of error in your experiment?
- Could you have used more sensitive apparatus or equipment?

Tip: This is where you take the uncertainty of your measurements (see previous page) into account. Think about the size of the margin for error, and whether you could have reduced the uncertainty.

Having confidence in your conclusion

Once you've evaluated your results and method, you can decide how much confidence you have in your conclusion. For example, if your results are repeatable, reproducible and valid and they back up your conclusion then you can have a high degree of confidence in your conclusion.

You can also consider these points if you're asked to evaluate a conclusion in the exam.

Exam Tip
Data questions are fairly common in the exams. You might be given a conclusion for the data and asked to evaluate it — this just means you have to give reasons why it is (or isn't) a valid conclusion. You could also be asked how far data supports a conclusion — it requires a similar type of answer.

Example

A study examined the effect of farm hedgerow length on the number of species in a given area. The number of species present during a single week on 12 farms was counted by placing ground-level traps. All the farms were a similar size. The traps were left out every day, at 6 am for two hours and once again at 6 pm for two hours. The results are shown in Figure 3:

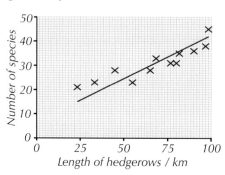

Figure 3: Scattergram to show relationship between number of species and length of hedgerows.

A journalist who read this study concluded that longer hedgerows cause the number of species in a given area to increase. Does the data support this conclusion? Explain your answer.

Yes — The data in the graph supports the conclusion as it shows that as the length of hedgerows increases, the number of species increases — the length of the hedgerows has a positive correlation with the number of species in that area.

No — You can't conclude that longer hedgerows cause the number of species to increase. Other factors may have been involved, for example, the number of predators in an area may have decreased or the farmers may have used less pesticide there.

Also, the study is quite small — they only used 12 farms. The trend shown by the data may not appear if 50 or 100 farms were studied, or if the farms were studied for a longer period of time.

The results are also limited by the method of trapping. Traps were placed on the ground, so species like birds weren't included, and they weren't left overnight, so nocturnal animals wouldn't get counted, etc. This could have affected the results.

Importantly, you're not told if all the other variables were controlled, e.g. you don't know if all the farms had a similar type of land, similar weather, the same crops growing, etc. This means you don't know how valid the study is — you can't be sure that the factor being investigated (hedgerows) is the only one affecting the thing being measured (number of species).

Overall — The limits of the study mean that the journalist's conclusion isn't well supported.

Tip: The method used to collect the data can bias the results. Bias is when someone intentionally or unintentionally favours a particular result — in the example on the right, the method of trapping gives results that are biased towards ground-dwelling species.

1. Molecules of Life

Learning Objectives:

- Understand that the variety of life, both past and present, is extensive, but the biochemical basis of life is similar for all living things.
- Know that polymers are molecules made from a large number of monomers joined together.
- Know that monomers are the smaller units from which larger molecules are made.
- Know that monosaccharides, amino acids and nucleotides are examples of monomers.
- Understand that a condensation reaction joins two molecules together with the formation of a chemical bond and the elimination of a molecule of water.
- Understand that a hydrolysis reaction breaks a chemical bond between two molecules and involves a molecule of water.

Specification Reference 3.1.1

There are loads of different types of biological molecules that make up all cells and organisms, such as carbohydrates, amino acids, proteins and lipids, etc. This topic (and Topic 1B) is all about these biological molecules...

Evidence for evolution

Evidence for evolution is information that supports the **theory of evolution** — the theory that all organisms on Earth are descended from one or a few common ancestors and that they have changed and diversified over time.

There is, and has been, a huge variety of different organisms on Earth but they all share some biochemistry. They all contain the same groups of carbon-based compounds that interact in similar ways — for example, they use the same nucleic acids (DNA and RNA) as genetic material and the same amino acids to build proteins.

These similarities suggest that animals and plants have a common ancestor, which provides indirect evidence for evolution.

Monomers and polymers

Most carbohydrates, proteins and nucleic acids are **polymers**. Polymers are large, complex molecules composed of long chains of **monomers** joined together.

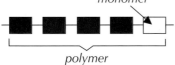

monomer

polymer

Figure 1: A polymer.

Monomers are small, basic molecular units that can form a polymer. Examples of monomers include monosaccharides, amino acids and nucleotides.

Making polymers

Most biological polymers are formed from their monomers by **condensation** reactions. A condensation reaction forms a chemical bond between monomers, releasing a molecule of water — see Figure 2.

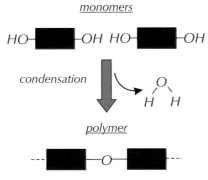

monomers

condensation

polymer

Figure 2: An example of the formation of a polymer.

Exam Tip
If you're asked to show a condensation reaction, don't forget to put the water molecule in as a product.

Breaking down polymers

Biological polymers can be broken down into monomers by **hydrolysis** reactions. A hydrolysis reaction breaks the chemical bond between monomers using a water molecule. It's basically the opposite of a condensation reaction.

Tip: A condensation reaction <u>removes</u> one molecule of water, but a hydrolysis reaction <u>adds</u> a molecule of water.

Tip: It's easy to remember what a hydrolysis reaction does as 'hydro' means water and 'lysis' means breaking down.

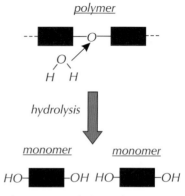

Figure 3: Hydrolysis of a polymer.

Practice Question — Application

Q1 Cytochrome c is a protein used in the reactions of respiration and is found across species of animals, plants and unicellular organisms. Suggest why the widespread occurrence of cytochrome c is considered to be evidence for evolution.

Practice Questions — Fact Recall

Q1 What is a polymer?

Q2 What is a monomer?

Q3 Give two examples of monomers.

Q4 Explain what happens in a condensation reaction between two monomers.

Q5 What type of reaction involves the breakage of a chemical bond between two monomers using water?

2. Sugars

Sugar is a general term for monosaccharides and disaccharides. Monosaccharides are the simplest sugars, and are the building blocks of carbohydrates.

Monosaccharides

All carbohydrates contain the elements C, H and O. The monomers that carbohydrates are made from are **monosaccharides**, e.g. glucose, fructose and galactose.

Glucose is a hexose sugar — a monosaccharide with six carbon atoms in each molecule. There are two types of glucose, alpha (α) and beta (β) glucose — they're isomers (molecules with the same molecular formula as each other, but with the atoms connected in a different way).

You need to learn the structures of both types of glucose for your exams — see Figure 1.

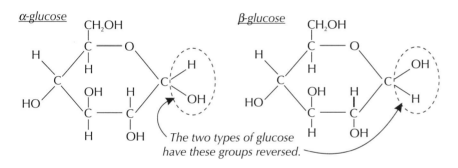

α-glucose   *β-glucose*

The two types of glucose have these groups reversed.

Figure 1: *Glucose isomers.*

Disaccharide formation

A disaccharide is formed when two monosaccharides join together. Monosaccharides are joined together by **condensation** reactions (see page 19) — a **glycosidic bond** forms between the two monosaccharides as a molecule of water is released.

--- Example ---

Two α-glucose molecules are joined together by a glycosidic bond to form maltose.

α-glucose   *α-glucose*   *maltose*

$+ H_2O$

H_2O is removed   glycosidic bond

Sucrose is a disaccharide formed from a condensation reaction between a glucose molecule and a fructose molecule. Lactose is another disaccharide, formed from a glucose molecule and a galactose molecule.

Learning Objectives:

- Understand that monosaccharides are the monomers from which larger carbohydrates are made.

- Know that glucose, galactose and fructose are common monosaccharides.

- Know that glucose has two isomers, α-glucose and β-glucose, and recall their structures.

- Know that a condensation reaction between two monosaccharides forms a glycosidic bond.

- Understand that disaccharides are formed from two monosaccharides by condensation reactions:

  - maltose is a disaccharide formed by condensation of two glucose molecules,

  - sucrose is a disaccharide formed by condensation of a glucose molecule and a fructose molecule,

  - lactose is a disaccharide formed by condensation of a glucose molecule and a galactose molecule.

- Recall the Benedict's test for reducing and non-reducing sugars.

  Specification Reference 3.1.2

The Benedict's test for sugars

All sugars can be classified as **reducing sugars** or **non-reducing sugars**. To test for sugars you use the Benedict's test. The test differs depending on the type of sugar you're testing for.

Reducing sugars

Reducing sugars include all monosaccharides and some disaccharides, e.g. maltose and lactose. You add Benedict's reagent (which is blue) to a sample and heat it in a water bath that's been brought to the boil. If the test's positive it will form a coloured precipitate — solid particles suspended in the solution. The colour of the precipitate changes as shown in Figure 2.

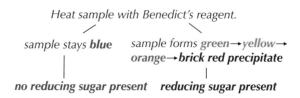

Heat sample with Benedict's reagent.

sample stays **blue**   sample forms **green**→**yellow**→ **orange**→**brick red precipitate**

no reducing sugar present   reducing sugar present

Figure 2: Benedict's test for reducing sugars.

The higher the concentration of reducing sugar, the further the colour change goes — you can use this to compare the amount of reducing sugar in different solutions. A more accurate way of doing this is to filter the solution and weigh the precipitate, or to remove the precipitate and use a **colorimeter** (see p. 98) to measure the absorbance of the remaining Benedict's reagent.

Non-reducing sugars

If the result of the reducing sugars test is negative, there could still be a non-reducing sugar present. To test for non-reducing sugars, like sucrose, first you have to break them down into monosaccharides. You do this by getting a new sample of the test solution (i.e. not the same one you've already added Benedict's reagent to), adding dilute hydrochloric acid and carefully heating it in a water bath that's been brought to the boil. Then you neutralise it by adding sodium hydrogencarbonate. Finally just carry out the Benedict's test as you would for a reducing sugar — see Figure 5.

Figure 3: A brick red colour indicates a positive Benedict's test result.

Figure 4: A blue colour indicates a negative Benedict's test result.

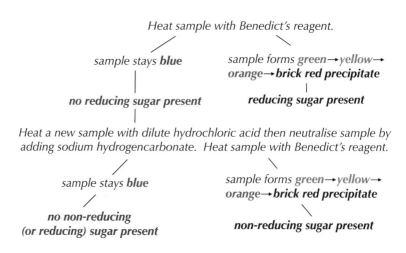

Heat sample with Benedict's reagent.

sample stays **blue**   sample forms **green**→**yellow**→ **orange**→**brick red precipitate**

no reducing sugar present   reducing sugar present

Heat a new sample with dilute hydrochloric acid then neutralise sample by adding sodium hydrogencarbonate. Heat sample with Benedict's reagent.

sample stays **blue**   sample forms **green**→**yellow**→ **orange**→**brick red precipitate**

no non-reducing (or reducing) sugar present   **non-reducing sugar present**

Figure 5: Benedict's test for non-reducing sugars.

Practice Questions — Application

Q1 Look at the following monosaccharides.

α-glucose   galactose   fructose

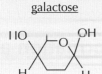

Draw the disaccharide that would be formed from a condensation reaction between:

a) α-glucose and galactose

b) α-glucose and fructose

Q2 The table shows data from four different Benedict's tests. What conclusions can you draw from each test?

Test	Procedure	Result
1	Sample heated with Benedict's reagent.	Blue
2	Sample heated with Benedict's reagent, (remained blue), then heated with hydrochloric acid and neutralised. Finally heated with Benedict's reagent.	Red
3	Sample heated with Benedict's reagent, (remained blue), then heat with hydrochloric acid and neutralised. Finally heated with Benedict's reagent.	Blue
4	Sample heated with Benedict's reagent.	Red

Tip: Structures aren't always drawn with everything on them, e.g. when you get a line with nothing on the end, like this

it just means there's a carbon there, with other elements (like hydrogen) attached to it.

Tip: Remember, the samples are heated in a <u>boiling</u> water bath.

Practice Questions — Fact Recall

Q1 Draw the structure of β-glucose.

Q2 What is the name of the bond that forms between two monosaccharides?

Q3 What molecule is released during a condensation reaction between two monosaccharides?

Q4 Which monosaccharides make up the disaccharides:

a) maltose?

b) sucrose?

c) lactose?

Q5 Describe how to test for reducing sugars and say what a positive and a negative result would look like.

- Understand that
  polysaccharides can
  be formed by the
  condensation of many
  glucose units.
- Know that glycogen
  and starch are formed
  by the condensation
  of α-glucose.
- Know that cellulose
  is formed by the
  condensation of
  β-glucose.
- Recall the basic
  structure and
  functions of glycogen,
  starch and cellulose
  and the relationship of
  structure to function
  of these substances in
  animal cells and plant
  cells.
- Recall the
  biochemical test for
  starch using iodine/
  potassium iodide.

**Specification
Reference 3.1.2**

3. Polysaccharides

Polysaccharides are carbohydrates. Polysaccharide molecules are made from large numbers of their monomers (monosaccharides).

Polysaccharide formation and break down

A **polysaccharide** is formed when more than two monosaccharides are joined together by condensation reactions.

─ **Example** ──────────────────────

Lots of α-glucose molecules are joined together by glycosidic bonds to form amylose.

glycosidic bonds

Polysaccharides can be broken down into their constituent monosaccharides by hydrolysis reactions.

─ **Example** ──────────────────────

Amylose is hydrolysed into α-glucose molecules.

amylose   *α-glucose*

$+ H_2O$ ➡

glycosidic bonds

Exam Tip
All you need to
remember for questions
like Q2 is to split them
at the glycosidic bond
and add a 'H' to either
side.

Practice Questions — Application

Q1 The structure of α-glucose is shown on the right. Draw a polysaccharide made of three α-glucose molecules.

Q2 Draw the monosaccharides produced from hydrolysis of the polysaccharides shown below.

a)

b)

Functions of polysaccharides

You need to know about the relationship between the structure and function of three polysaccharides — starch, glycogen and cellulose.

Starch

Cells get energy from glucose. Plants store excess glucose as starch (when a plant needs more glucose for energy, it breaks down starch to release the glucose). Starch is a mixture of two polysaccharides of alpha-glucose — amylose and amylopectin:

- **Amylose** is a long, unbranched chain of α-glucose. The angles of the glycosidic bonds give it a coiled structure, almost like a cylinder. This makes it compact, so it's really good for storage because you can fit more in to a small space.

- **Amylopectin** is a long, branched chain of α-glucose. Its side branches allow the enzymes that break down the molecule to get at the glycosidic bonds easily. This means that the glucose can be released quickly.

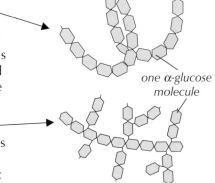

one α-glucose molecule

Figure 1: The structures of amylose (top) and amylopectin (bottom).

Starch is insoluble in water and doesn't affect water potential (see page 104), so it doesn't cause water to enter cells by osmosis, which would make them swell. This makes it good for storage.

Glycogen

Animal cells get energy from glucose too. But animals store excess glucose as glycogen — another polysaccharide of alpha-glucose. Its structure is very similar to amylopectin, except that it has loads more side branches coming off it — see Figure 2. Loads of branches means that stored glucose can be released quickly, which is important for energy release in animals. It's also a very compact molecule, so it's good for storage.

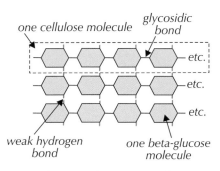

Figure 2: The structure of glycogen.

Cellulose

Cellulose is made of long, unbranched chains of beta-glucose. When beta-glucose molecules bond, they form straight cellulose chains. The cellulose chains are linked together by **hydrogen bonds** to form strong fibres called **microfibrils** — see Figure 3. The strong fibres mean cellulose provides structural support for cells (e.g. in plant cell walls).

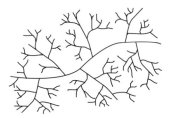

one cellulose molecule glycosidic bond

etc.

etc.

etc.

weak hydrogen bond

one beta-glucose molecule

Figure 3: The structure of a cellulose microfibril.

Figure 4: Coloured scanning electron micrograph (SEM) of cellulose microfibrils in a plant cell wall.

Tip: You can test for the presence of starch using the iodine test (see next page).

Tip: Hydrogen bonds between α-glucose molecules help to hold amylose in its helical structure.

Exam Tip
When you're describing the structure of these polysaccharides, always specify whether you're talking about α-glucose or β-glucose — you won't get a mark for only saying glucose.

Tip: Starch is a large molecule, so it can't leave the cell — this is another reason why it's a good storage molecule.

Exam Tip
If you're asked about the function of glycogen in the exam, make sure you say it acts as an energy store or reserve — you won't get marks just for saying it 'contains energy'.

The iodine test for starch

Exam Tip
Make sure you always talk about <u>iodine in potassium iodide solution</u>, not just iodine.

If you want to test for the presence of starch in a sample, you'll need to do the iodine test.

Just add iodine dissolved in potassium iodide solution to the test sample. If there is starch present, the sample changes from browny-orange to a dark, blue-black colour — see Figure 5.

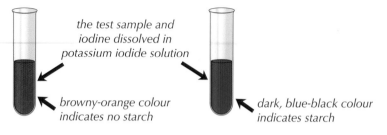

the test sample and iodine dissolved in potassium iodide solution

browny-orange colour indicates no starch

dark, blue-black colour indicates starch

Figure 5: *A negative (left) and positive (right) iodine test result.*

Figure 6: *A dark blue-black colour indicates the presence of starch in an iodine test.*

Practice Questions — Fact Recall

Q1 Name the type of monomer that makes up polysaccharides.

Q2 What is the main energy storage material in:
a) plants,   b) animals?

Q3 a) Is starch soluble or insoluble?
b) Use your answer to a) to describe why starch is good for storage.

Q4 a) Name the structures shown below:

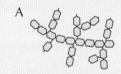 

A   B

b) Explain an advantage of structure A that makes it suitable for energy storage.

Q5 a) Which polysaccharide is the major component of plant cell walls?
b) Describe the structure of this polysaccharide, and explain how its structure makes it suited to its function in cell walls.

Q6 Sketch and label a diagram of a microfibril.

Q7 Describe the method you would use to test for the presence of starch, and say what a positive and a negative result would look like.

Exam Tip
Don't panic if you're asked to draw a diagram in the exam — you don't have to be the best artist in the world, but make sure you add labels to point out all the important bits.

4. Lipids

Lipids are commonly known as fats or oils. They're found all cells, and have a variety of different properties.

What are lipids made from?

Lipids are different from proteins (see pages 31-33) and carbohydrates (see pages 24-25) because they're not polymers formed from long chains of monomers. Lipids are made from a variety of different components, but they all contain **hydrocarbons** (molecules that contain only hydrogen and carbon atoms). The components they're made from relates to the lipid's function. There are two types of lipid you need to know about — triglycerides and phospholipids.

Triglycerides

Triglycerides have one molecule of glycerol with three fatty acids attached to it. Fatty acid molecules have long 'tails' made of hydrocarbons. The tails are 'hydrophobic' (they repel water molecules). These tails make lipids insoluble in water.

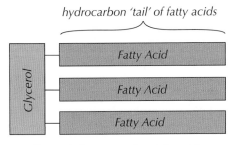

Figure 1: *Structure of a triglyceride.*

Fatty acids

All fatty acids consist of the same basic structure, but the hydrocarbon tail varies — see Figure 2. There are two kinds of fatty acids — saturated and unsaturated. The difference is in their hydrocarbon tails (R groups):

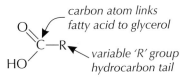

Figure 2: *Structure of a fatty acid.*

- **Saturated fatty acids** don't have any double bonds between their carbon atoms. The fatty acid is 'saturated' with hydrogen.

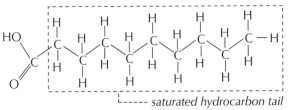

Figure 3: *Saturated fatty acid.*

- **Unsaturated fatty acids** do have double bonds between carbon atoms, which cause the chain to kink.

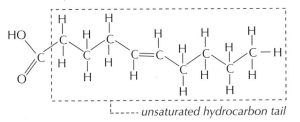

Figure 4: *Unsaturated fatty acid.*

Triglyceride formation

Tip: There's more about condensation reactions on page 19.

Triglycerides are formed by condensation reactions. Figure 5 shows a fatty acid joining to a glycerol molecule. An **ester bond** forms between the two molecules, releasing a molecule of water — this is a condensation reaction. This process happens twice more to form a triglyceride.

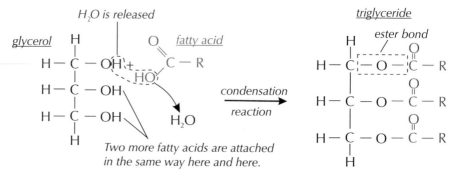

Tip: You can pretty much ignore the 'R' group on the fatty acid — it never gets involved in the reaction.

Figure 5: Triglyceride formation.

Phospholipids

The lipids found in cell membranes aren't triglycerides — they're phospholipids. Phospholipids are pretty similar to triglycerides except one of the fatty acid molecules is replaced by a phosphate group. The phosphate group is hydrophilic (attracts water). The fatty acid tails are hydrophobic (repel water). This is important in the cell membrane (see next page to find out why).

Tip: Remember, a <u>phospho</u>lipid has a <u>phosph</u>ate group.

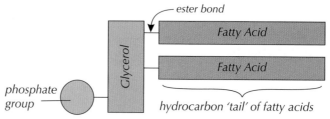

Figure 6: Structure of a phospholipid.

Properties of lipids

Tip: Lipids have many uses, including as certain hormones, such as testosterone, and as respiratory substrates (molecules used in respiration to release energy).

You need to know how the structures of triglycerides and phospholipids are related to their properties:

Triglycerides

Triglycerides are mainly used as energy storage molecules. They're good for this because the long hydrocarbon tails of the fatty acids contain lots of chemical energy — a load of energy is released when they're broken down. Because of these tails, lipids contain about twice as much energy per gram as carbohydrates.

Tip: Storage molecules also need to be insoluble because otherwise they'd just dissolve (and release whatever they were storing) whenever they came into contact with water.

Also, they're insoluble in water, so they don't affect the water potential (see p. 104) of the cell and cause water to enter the cells by osmosis (which would make them swell). The triglycerides bundle together as insoluble droplets in cells because the fatty acid tails are hydrophobic (water-repelling) — the tails face inwards, shielding themselves from water with their glycerol heads — see Figure 7.

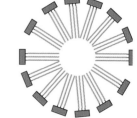

Figure 7: Diagram showing an insoluble triglyceride droplet.

Phospholipids

Phospholipids make up the bilayer of cell membranes (see p. 95).
Cell membranes control what enters and leaves a cell.

Phospholipid heads are hydrophilic and their tails are hydrophobic, so they form a double layer with their heads facing out towards the water on either side. The centre of the bilayer is hydrophobic, so water-soluble substances can't easily pass through it — the membrane acts as a barrier to those substances.

Tip: There's more about the role of phospholipids in cell membranes on page 96.

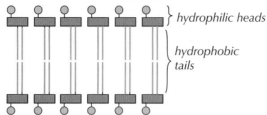

Figure 8:
A phospholipid bilayer.

hydrophilic heads

hydrophobic tails

The emulsion test for lipids

If you wanted to test for the presence of lipids in a sample, you'll need to do the **emulsion test**:

- Shake the test substance with ethanol for about a minute, then pour the solution into water.
- Any lipid will show up as a milky emulsion — see Figures 9 and 10.
- The more lipid there is, the more noticeable the milky colour will be.

Tip: Ethanol is flammable, so make sure you do this test away from any open flames.

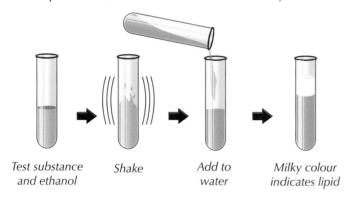

Test substance and ethanol   Shake   Add to water   Milky colour indicates lipid

Figure 9: The emulsion test for lipids.

Figure 10: A positive result using the emulsion test.

Practice Questions — Application

Q1 A triglyceride is shown on the right. Draw one molecule of the fatty acid that makes up the hydrocarbon tail.

Q2 The table below shows the structures of four fatty acids.

Name:	Structure:
Propanoic acid	CH_3CH_2COOH
Palmitic acid	$CH_3(CH_2)_{14}COOH$
Stearic acid	$CH_3(CH_2)_{16}COOH$
Oleic acid	$CH_3(CH_2)_7CH=CH(CH_2)_7COOH$

Tip: For Q2 b), think about which part of the fatty acid molecule reacts with glycerol.

a) Identify the 'R' groups in each of the fatty acids in the table.

b) Draw the triglyceride that would be formed from condensation reactions between a molecule of glycerol and three molecules of propanoic acid.

c) Unsaturated fatty acids will decolourise iodine solution. Which of the fatty acids in the table above will produce a positive result when added to iodine solution?

Practice Questions — Fact Recall

Q1 What are the components of a triglyceride?

Q2 Explain the difference between a saturated fatty acid and an unsaturated fatty acid.

Q3 Name the structures A-D in the diagram of a phospholipid below.

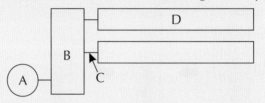

Q4 Give two reasons why triglycerides are used as energy storage molecules.

Q5 Explain how the structure of phospholipids makes them able to form the bilayer of cell membranes.

Q6 A student carries out an emulsion test on a food sample.

a) What is the student testing for?

b) Describe how the student should carry out the test and what he should expect to see if the result is positive.

5. Proteins

Proteins come in all shapes and sizes and have a huge variety of functions in all living organisms.

What are proteins made from?

The monomers of proteins are amino acids. A **dipeptide** is formed when two amino acids join together. A **polypeptide** is formed when more than two amino acids join together. Proteins are made up of one or more polypeptides.

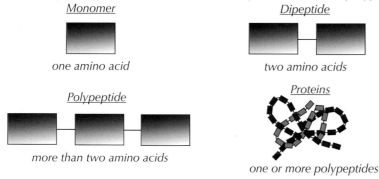

Monomer

one amino acid

Dipeptide

two amino acids

Polypeptide

more than two amino acids

Proteins

one or more polypeptides

Figure 1: *Amino acids join together to form peptides and proteins.*

Amino acid structure

Amino acids have the same general structure — a carboxyl group (-COOH), an amine or amino group ($-NH_2$) and a carbon-containing R group (also known as a variable side group) attached to a carbon atom. (The only exception to this rule is glycine — its R group consists of just one hydrogen atom.)

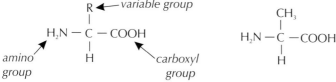

variable group

amino group   carboxyl group

Figure 2: *The general structure of an amino acid (left) and the structure of alanine (right).*

All living things share a bank of only 20 amino acids. The only difference between them is what makes up their carbon-containing R group.

Dipeptide and polypeptide formation

Amino acids are linked together by **condensation reactions** (see page 19) to form dipeptides and polypeptides. A molecule of water is released during the reaction. The bonds formed between amino acids are called **peptide bonds**. The reverse reaction (hydrolysis) happens when dipeptides and polypeptides are broken down.

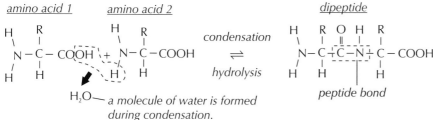

amino acid 1   *amino acid 2*   *dipeptide*

condensation ⇌ hydrolysis

H_2O — a molecule of water is formed during condensation.

peptide bond

Figure 3: *Dipeptide formation.*

Learning Objectives:

- Know that amino acids are the monomers from which proteins are made.
- Know that dipeptides are formed by the condensation of two amino acids, and polypeptides by the condensation of many amino acids.
- Know that a functional protein may contain one or more polypeptides.
- Know the general structure of an amino acid.
- Understand that the twenty amino acids that are common in all organisms differ only in their side group.
- Understand that a condensation reaction between two amino acids forms a peptide bond.
- Recall the role of hydrogen bonds, ionic bonds and disulfide bridges in the structure of proteins.
- Understand the relationship between primary, secondary, tertiary and quaternary protein structure, and protein function.
- Know that proteins have a variety of functions within all living organisms.
- Be able to relate the structure of proteins to the properties of proteins named throughout the specification.
- Recall the biuret test for proteins.

Specification Reference 3.1.4.1

Protein structure

Proteins are big, complicated molecules. They're much easier to explain if you describe their structure in four 'levels'. These levels are a protein's primary, secondary, tertiary and quaternary structures.

Tip: Remember, proteins are polymers of amino acids (see page 19).

Primary structure

This is the sequence of amino acids in the polypeptide chain.

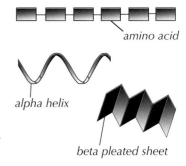

amino acid

Secondary structure

The polypeptide chain doesn't remain flat and straight. Hydrogen bonds form between the amino acids in the chain. This makes it automatically coil into an alpha (α) helix or fold into a beta (β) pleated sheet — this is the secondary structure.

alpha helix

beta pleated sheet

Tip: A hydrogen bond is a relatively weak bond formed between hydrogen atoms and other atoms, e.g. nitrogen or oxygen.

Tertiary structure

The coiled or folded chain of amino acids is often coiled and folded further. More bonds form between different parts of the polypeptide chain, including **hydrogen bonds** and **ionic bonds** (attractions between negative and positive charges on different parts of the molecule). **Disulfide bridges** also form whenever two molecules of the amino acid cysteine come close together — the sulfur atom in one cysteine bonds to the sulfur atom in the other. For proteins made from a single polypeptide chain, the tertiary structure forms their final 3D structure.

one long polypeptide chain

Tip: Think of the tertiary structure like a big, tangled-up spring.

Tip: Disulfide bridges are <u>covalent</u> bonds between sulfur atoms. They're a lot stronger than the ionic and hydrogen bonds in proteins.

Quaternary structure

Some proteins are made of several different polypeptide chains held together by bonds. The quaternary structure is the way these polypeptide chains are assembled together. For proteins made from more than one polypeptide chain (e.g. haemoglobin, insulin, collagen), the quaternary structure is the protein's final 3D structure.

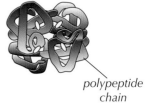

polypeptide chain

Tip: Not all proteins have a quaternary structure — some are made of only <u>one</u> polypeptide chain.

Protein shape and function

A protein's shape determines its function — e.g. haemoglobin is a compact, soluble protein, which makes it easy to transport. This makes it great for carrying oxygen around the body (see p. 168). There are loads of different proteins found in living organisms. They've all got different structures and shapes, which makes them specialised to carry out particular jobs.

Examples

Enzymes — They're usually roughly spherical in shape due to the tight folding of the polypeptide chains. They're soluble and often have roles in metabolism, e.g. some enzymes break down large food molecules (digestive enzymes, see pages 164-166) and other enzymes help to synthesise (make) large molecules.

Antibodies — Antibodies are involved in the immune response and are found in the blood. They're made up of two light (short) polypeptide chains and two heavy (long) polypeptide chains bonded together. Antibodies have variable regions (see p. 117) — the amino acid sequences in these regions vary greatly.

Transport proteins — E.g. channel proteins are present in cell membranes (page 101). Channel proteins contain hydrophobic (water hating) and hydrophilic (water loving) amino acids, which cause the protein to fold up and form a channel (see Figure 5). These proteins transport molecules and ions across membranes.

Structural proteins — Structural proteins are physically strong. They consist of long polypeptide chains lying parallel to each other with cross-links between them. Structural proteins include keratin (found in hair and nails) and collagen (found in connective tissue). Collagen has three polypeptide chains tightly coiled together, which makes it strong. This makes it a great supportive tissue in animals.

Exam Tip
You need to be able to relate the structure of a protein to its function for any protein you're given.

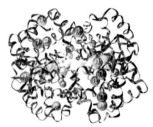

Figure 4: A molecular model of haemoglobin.

Tip: Proteins are also used as chemical messengers in the body, e.g. as hormones like insulin.

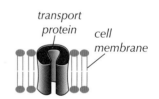

Figure 5: A transport protein in a cell membrane.

The biuret test for proteins

If you needed to find out if a substance, e.g. a food sample, contained protein you'd use the biuret test. There are two stages to this test.

1. The test solution needs to be alkaline, so first you add a few drops of sodium hydroxide solution.
2. Then you add some copper(II) sulfate solution.

If protein is present, the solution turns purple. If there's no protein, the solution will stay blue — see Figure 7. The colours can be fairly pale, so you might need to look carefully.

Figure 6: A molecular model of collagen.

Tip: Remember to assess any hazards before doing tests like these. For example, if you're using dilute sodium hydroxide you'll need to wear safety goggles as it's an irritant.

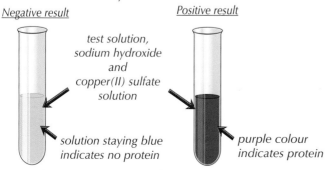

Negative result   _Positive result_

test solution, sodium hydroxide and copper(II) sulfate solution

solution staying blue indicates no protein

purple colour indicates protein

Figure 7: A negative and positive biuret test result.

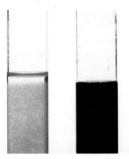

Figure 8: *A negative (left) and positive (right) biuret test result.*

Practice Questions — Application

A biuret test was carried out to determine which liquids contained protein. The results of the experiment are shown in the table below.

Liquid	Result
De-ionised water	Blue
Cow's milk	Blue
Orange juice	Purple
Orange squash	Blue
Goat's milk	Purple

Q1 Which of the liquids in the table gave a positive test result?

Q2 Suggest why the scientist tested de-ionised water.

Q3 The scientist measured the pH of each liquid after the test. The pH of the cow's milk was below 7, so the scientist marked the test result as void.

　　a) Why did they mark the result as void?

　　b) Suggest what mistake the scientist might have made during the experiment.

Practice Questions — Fact Recall

Q1 What are the monomers of proteins?

Q2 What is a polypeptide?

Q3 Draw the general structure of an amino acid.

Q4 What sort of reaction links amino acids together?

Q5 What is the name of the bond that forms between amino acids?

Q6 Name three bonds that may be formed between the amino acids in a polypeptide chain to form the tertiary structure of a protein.

Q7 Explain how the shape of structural proteins make them specialised for their function.

Q8 The biuret test is used to test for proteins.

　　a) What is added to the test solution to make it alkaline?

　　b) What is added next to the solution?

　　c) What would a positive test result look like?

6. Enzymes

Enzymes are proteins that speed up the rate of chemical reactions.

Enzymes as biological catalysts

Enzymes speed up chemical reactions by acting as biological catalysts. They catalyse metabolic reactions — both at a cellular level (e.g. respiration) and for the organism as a whole (e.g. digestion in mammals). Enzymes can affect structures in an organism (e.g. enzymes are involved in the production of collagen, an important protein in the connective tissues of animals) as well as functions (like respiration). Enzyme action can be intracellular — within cells, or extracellular — outside cells.

Enzymes are proteins (see page 33). Enzymes have an **active site**, which has a specific shape. The active site is the part of the enzyme where the substrate molecules (the substance that the enzyme interacts with) bind to. Enzymes are highly specific due to their tertiary structure (see page 32).

How enzymes speed up reactions

In a chemical reaction, a certain amount of energy needs to be supplied to the chemicals before the reaction will start. This is called the **activation energy** — it's often provided as heat. Enzymes lower the amount of activation energy that's needed, often making reactions happen at a lower temperature than they could without an enzyme. This speeds up the rate of reaction.

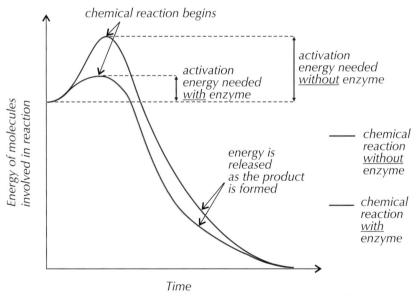

Figure 1: A graph to show the activation energy needed for a reaction with and without an enzyme.

When a substrate fits into the enzyme's active site it forms an **enzyme-substrate complex** — it's this that lowers the activation energy. Here are two reasons why:

- If two substrate molecules need to be joined, being attached to the enzyme holds them close together, reducing any repulsion between the molecules so they can bond more easily.

- If the enzyme is catalysing a breakdown reaction, fitting into the active site puts a strain on bonds in the substrate, so the substrate molecule breaks up more easily.

Learning Objectives:

- Be able to appreciate that enzymes catalyse a wide range of intracellular and extracellular reactions that determine structures and functions from cellular to whole-organism level.

- Know that each enzyme lowers the activation energy of the reaction it catalyses.

- Be able to appreciate how models of enzyme action have changed over time.

- Recall the induced-fit model of enzyme action.

- Understand the specificity of enzymes.

- Know how the properties of an enzyme relate to the tertiary structure of its active site and its ability to combine with complementary substrate(s) to form an enzyme-substrate complex.

Specification Reference 3.1.4.2

Tip: A catalyst is a substance that speeds up a chemical reaction without being used up in the reaction itself.

Models of enzyme action

Scientists now have a pretty good understanding of how enzymes work. As with most scientific theories, this understanding has changed over time.

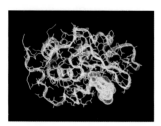

Figure 2: Computer model of an enzyme-substrate complex. The substrate (yellow) has bound to the enzyme's active site.

The 'lock and key' model

Enzymes are a bit picky — they only work with substrates that fit their active site. Early scientists studying the action of enzymes came up with the 'lock and key' model. This is where the substrate fits into the enzyme in the same way that a key fits into a lock — the active site and the substrate have a complementary shape.

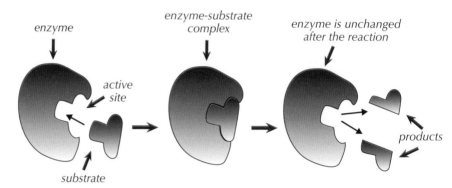

Figure 3: The 'lock and key' model.

Exam Tip
When describing enzyme action you need to say the active site and the substrate have a <u>complementary</u> shape, rather than the <u>same</u> shape.

Scientists soon realised that the lock and key model didn't give the full story. The enzyme and substrate do have to fit together in the first place, but new evidence showed that the enzyme-substrate complex changed shape slightly to complete the fit. This locks the substrate even more tightly to the enzyme. Scientists modified the old lock and key model and came up with the 'induced fit' model.

The 'induced fit' model

The 'induced fit' model helps to explain why enzymes are so specific and only bond to one particular substrate. The substrate doesn't only have to be the right shape to fit the active site, it has to make the active site change shape in the right way as well. This is a prime example of how a widely accepted theory can change when new evidence comes along. The 'induced fit' model is still widely accepted — for now, anyway.

Tip: The diagrams on this page show how enzymes break substrates down (e.g. one substrate molecule goes into the active site and two products come out). Enzymes can also catalyse <u>synthesis</u> reactions (e.g. two substrate molecules go into the active site, bind together and one product comes out).

Tip: After the products are released, the active site returns to its original shape and can bind to the next substrate molecule.

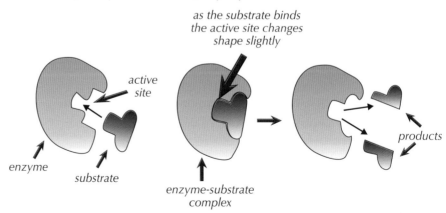

Figure 4: The 'induced fit' model.

Enzyme properties

Enzyme properties are related to their tertiary structure. Enzymes are very specific — they usually only catalyse one reaction, e.g. maltase only breaks down maltose, sucrase only breaks down sucrose. This is because only one complementary substrate will fit into the active site. The active site's shape is determined by the enzyme's tertiary structure (which is determined by the enzyme's primary structure). Each different enzyme has a different tertiary structure and so a different shaped active site. If the substrate shape doesn't match the active site, an enzyme-substrate complex won't be formed and the reaction won't be catalysed — see Figure 5.

Tip: See page 32 for more on the primary and tertiary structure of proteins.

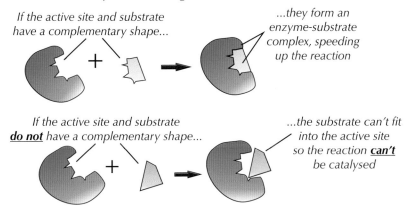

If the active site and substrate have a complementary shape...

...they form an enzyme-substrate complex, speeding up the reaction

*If the active site and substrate **do not** have a complementary shape...*

*...the substrate can't fit into the active site so the reaction **can't** be catalysed*

Figure 5: *An enzyme's active site has a complementary shape to the substrate.*

If the tertiary structure of a protein is altered in any way, the shape of the active site will change. This means the substrate won't fit into the active site, an enzyme-substrate complex won't be formed and the enzyme will no longer be able to carry out its function. The tertiary structure of an enzyme may be altered by changes in pH or temperature (see pages 38-39).

The primary structure (amino acid sequence) of a protein is determined by a gene. If a mutation occurs in that gene, it could change the tertiary structure of the enzyme produced.

Tip: See page 221 for more on mutations.

Practice Questions — Fact Recall

Q1 What term is used to describe an enzyme that acts outside cells?

Q2 Look at the graph on the right.
   a) Which line shows a reaction with the presence of an enzyme?
   b) What does the line labelled X represent?

Q3 Explain, in terms of activation energy, why an enzyme enables reactions to happen at lower temperatures than they could without an enzyme.

Q4 What is the main difference between the lock and key model and the induced fit model?

Q5 What determines the shape of an enzyme's active site?

Q6 Why will an enzyme only bind with one substrate?

Tip: If you're having problems getting your head around activation energy, just imagine you have to get to the top of a mountain to start a chemical reaction. It would take a lot of energy to get to the top. An enzyme effectively reduces the height of the mountain, so it doesn't take as much energy to start the reaction.

▪ Be able to describe
and explain the
effects of enzyme
concentration,
substrate
concentration,
concentration of
competitive and of
non-competitive
inhibitors, pH and
temperature on
the rate of enzyme
controlled reactions.
**Specification
Reference 3.1.4.2**

7. Factors Affecting Enzyme Activity

Enzymes are great at speeding up reactions, but there are several factors that affect how fast they work.

Measuring enzyme activity

Measuring the rate of a reaction can be done in two ways:

1. How fast the product is made

There are different molecules present at the end of a chemical reaction than there are at the beginning. By measuring the amount of end product present at different times during the experiment the reaction rate can be calculated.

2. How fast the substrate is broken down

To produce the end products in a reaction, substrate molecules have to be used up. By measuring the amount of substrate molecules left at different times during the experiment the reaction rate can be calculated.

Temperature

Like any chemical reaction, the rate of an enzyme-controlled reaction increases when the temperature's increased. More heat means more kinetic energy, so molecules move faster. This makes the substrate molecules more likely to collide with the enzymes' active sites. The energy of these collisions also increases, which means each collision is more likely to result in a reaction.

But, if the temperature gets too high, the reaction stops. The rise in temperature makes the enzyme's molecules vibrate more. If the temperature goes above a certain level, this vibration breaks some of the bonds that hold the enzyme in shape. The active site changes shape and the enzyme and substrate no longer fit together. At this point, the enzyme is **denatured** — it no longer functions as a catalyst — see Figure 1.

Tip: In most cases, denaturation <u>permanently</u> changes an enzymes's shape, i.e. it won't go back to normal when the temperature decreases again.

Exam Tip
Make sure you don't say the enzyme's killed by high temperatures — it's <u>denatured</u>.

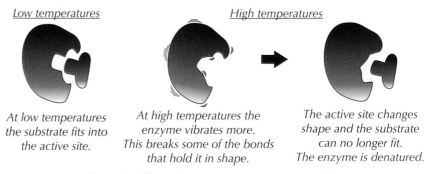

Low temperatures   *High temperatures*

At low temperatures the substrate fits into the active site.

At high temperatures the enzyme vibrates more. This breaks some of the bonds that hold it in shape.

The active site changes shape and the substrate can no longer fit. The enzyme is denatured.

Figure 1: Effect of temperature on enzyme activity.

Exam Tip
You need to understand that different enzymes can have different optimum temperatures, but you don't have to learn any specific optimum temperature values.

Every enzyme has an optimum temperature. For most human enzymes it's around 37 °C, but some enzymes, like those used in biological washing powders, can work well at 60 °C.

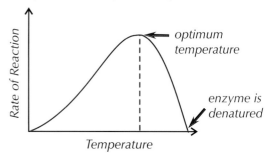

Figure 2: Effect of temperature on the rate of an enzyme-controlled reaction.

pH

All enzymes have an optimum pH value. Most human enzymes work best at pH 7 (neutral), but there are exceptions. Pepsin, for example, works best at pH 2 (acidic), which is useful because it's found in the stomach. Above and below the optimum pH, the H⁺ and OH⁻ ions found in acids and alkalis can disrupt the ionic bonds and hydrogen bonds that hold the enzyme's tertiary structure in place. The enzyme becomes denatured, and the active site changes shape.

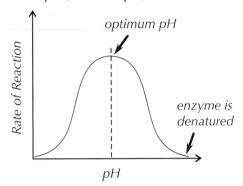

Figure 3: Effect of pH on the rate of an enzyme-controlled reaction.

Tip: Ionic bonds are attractions between negative and positive charges on different parts of the molecule (see p. 32).

Exam Tip
Don't forget — both a pH that's too high and one that's too low will denature an enzyme, not just one that's too high.

Substrate concentration

The higher the substrate concentration, the faster the reaction — more substrate molecules means a collision between substrate and enzyme is more likely and so more active sites will be occupied. This is only true up until a 'saturation' point though. After that, there are so many substrate molecules that the enzymes have about as much as they can cope with (all the active sites are full), and adding more makes no difference — see Figures 4 and 5.

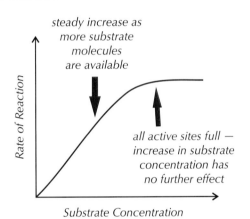

Figure 4: A graph to show the rate of an enzyme-controlled reaction against substrate concentration.

Tip: These graphs show the rate of reaction (i.e. the speed of the reaction). When the line on the graph plateaus it doesn't mean the reaction has stopped, just that it isn't going any faster.

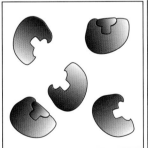

Low substrate concentration — not all active sites are occupied.

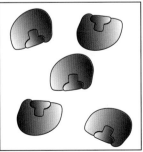

Saturation point — all active sites are occupied.

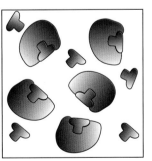

Beyond saturation point — all active sites are occupied and there are spare substrate molecules.

Figure 5: Effect of substrate concentration on occupation of active sites.

Exam Tip
Don't ever say that the enzymes are used up — say that all the active sites are occupied.

Enzyme concentration

Tip: The enzyme concentration and substrate concentration graphs initially show a <u>linear</u> (straight line) relationship between the concentration and the rate of reaction. This means you can use the gradient of the line to work out how fast the rate is changing — see p. 13 for more.

The more enzyme molecules there are in a solution, the more likely a substrate molecule is to collide with one and form an enzyme-substrate complex. So increasing the concentration of the enzyme increases the rate of reaction.

But, if the amount of substrate is limited, there comes a point when there's more than enough enzyme molecules to deal with all the available substrate, so adding more enzyme has no further effect.

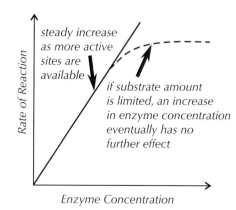

steady increase as more active sites are available

if substrate amount is limited, an increase in enzyme concentration eventually has no further effect

Figure 6: *A graph to show the rate of an enzyme-controlled reaction against enzyme concentration.*

Interpreting line graphs

You might be asked to interpret the graph of an enzyme-controlled reaction in the exam.

Tip: The graph on the right shows the release of a product over time.

Exam Tip
The graph in your exam could be based on any variable — e.g. pH, temperature, enzyme concentration or substrate concentration. You'll have to use your knowledge of enzymes to explain what's going on.

— Example —

You might be asked a question like this in the exam:
'Describe and explain the differences between the three curves shown on the graph below.'

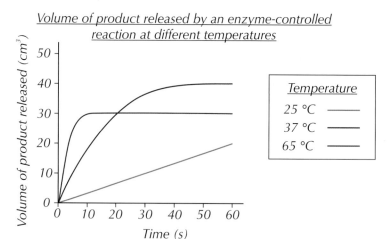

Volume of product released by an enzyme-controlled reaction at different temperatures

Temperature	
25 °C	———
37 °C	———
65 °C	———

Here's how to answer it:

1. **Compare the rates of reaction at the start of the graph.**

   E.g. in the graph above, the rate of reaction at the start was fastest at 65 °C. This is because the molecules have more kinetic energy at 65 °C, so they are moving faster, meaning the substrate is more likely to collide with an enzyme's active site and more enzyme-substrate complexes are formed. More energy also means collisions are more likely to result in a reaction.

Exam Tip
You might have to work out the initial rate of reaction in the exam — see page 46 for how to do this.

2. **Look at the rest of the graph and compare the different temperatures.**

At 37 °C the graph has plateaued (flattened out) after 40 s because all the substrate has been used up. At 65 °C the graph has plateaued earlier than at 37 °C (at about 10 s), because the high temperature caused the enzyme to denature, so the reaction stopped sooner. Not as much product was made because not all the substrate was converted to product before the enzyme was denatured, so there is still substrate left. At 25 °C the rate of reaction is remaining constant and the volume of product is continuing to increase because not all of the substrate has been used up.

Practice Questions — Application

Q1 Hyperthermophilic bacteria are found in hot springs where temperatures reach 80 °C. Psychrotrophic bacteria are found in very cold environments. The graph on the right shows the rate of reaction for an enzyme from three different bacteria.

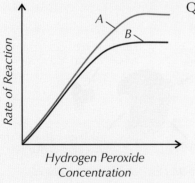

a) Explain which curve on the graph shows the enzyme from:

i) hyperthermophilic bacteria.

ii) psychrotrophic bacteria.

b) Explain what would happen to enzyme activity for each type of bacteria shown on the graph if they were put into an environment with a temperature range of 60-75 °C.

Exam Tip
When you're asked to answer questions about a graph, use specific values in your answer where you can.

Q2 The graph on the left shows the rate of reaction for the enzyme catalase under two different conditions. Catalase is found in the liver.

a) Explain which curve on the graph represents the reaction with the greatest concentration of catalase.

b) Both of the curves flatten out. Explain why this is.

Tip: Catalase catalyses the breakdown of hydrogen peroxide.

Q3 A group of students were investigating the effect of pH on the efficiency of enzyme A. They measured the volume of product released from the enzyme-controlled reaction at two different pH values. Their results are shown in the graph on the right.

Describe and explain the differences between the curves.

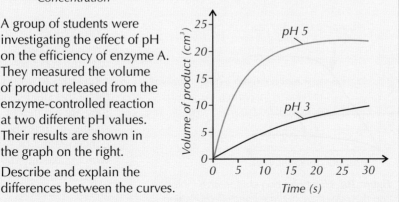

Enzyme inhibitors

Enzyme activity can be prevented by enzyme inhibitors — molecules that bind to the enzyme that they inhibit. Inhibition can be competitive or non-competitive.

Competitive inhibitors

Exam Tip
Don't say that the inhibitor molecule and the substrate have the same shape — they have a <u>similar</u> shape.

Competitive inhibitor molecules have a similar shape to that of substrate molecules. They compete with the substrate molecules to bind to the active site, but no reaction takes place. Instead they block the active site, so no substrate molecules can fit in it — see Figure 7.

How much the enzyme is inhibited depends on the relative concentrations of the inhibitor and substrate. If there's a high concentration of the inhibitor, it'll take up nearly all the active sites and hardly any of the substrate will get to the enzyme. But if there's a higher concentration of substrate, then the substrate's chances of getting to an active site before the inhibitor increase. So increasing the concentration of substrate will increase the rate of reaction (up to a point).

Tip: If you have a competitive inhibitor, increasing the concentration of substrate will reverse its effects — the substrate will out-compete the inhibitor for the active site.

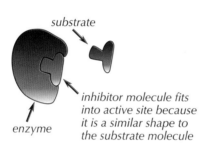

Figure 7: Competitive inhibition.

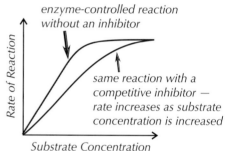

Figure 8: Effect of a competitive inhibitor on the rate of an enzyme-controlled reaction.

Non-competitive inhibitors

Exam Tip
When you're talking about shape change, always refer to the <u>active site</u> — don't just say the enzyme's changed shape.

Non-competitive inhibitor molecules bind to the enzyme away from its active site. This causes the active site to change shape so the substrate molecules can no longer bind to it — see Figure 9.

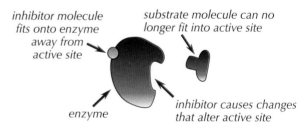

Figure 9: Non-competitive inhibition.

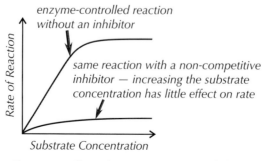

Figure 10: Effect of a non-competitive inhibitor on the rate of an enzyme-controlled reaction.

Non-competitive inhibitor molecules don't compete with the substrate molecules to bind to the active site because they are a different shape. Increasing the concentration of substrate won't make any difference — enzyme activity will still be inhibited.

Practice Questions — Application

Methanol is broken down in the body into formaldehyde. The build up of formaldehyde can cause death. The enzyme that hydrolyses the reaction is alcohol dehydrogenase. The enzyme-substrate complex formed is shown on the right.

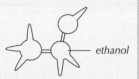

Q1 A diagram of ethanol is shown on the right. If someone had been poisoned with methanol, they could be helped by being given ethanol as soon as possible. Explain why.

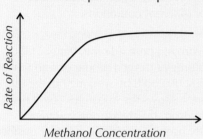

Q2 The graph shows the rate of the reaction with no ethanol present. Sketch a graph with the same axes showing the rate of reaction with the presence of ethanol.

Exam Tip
This is exactly the kind of question you could get in the exam — enzyme-inhibition is a favourite with examiners, so make sure you know it inside out.

Practice Questions — Fact Recall

Q1 Explain why an increase in temperature increases the rate of enzyme activity.

Q2 Explain how a very high temperature can stop an enzyme from working.

Q3 What happens to an enzyme's shape and function when it is denatured?

Q4 Give a factor other than temperature that can denature an enzyme.

Q5 What is meant by the 'saturation point' in an enzyme controlled reaction?

Q6 Explain what happens to the rate of an enzyme-controlled reaction when the substrate concentration is increased after the saturation point.

Q7 Explain the effect of increasing the enzyme concentration on the rate of an enzyme-controlled reaction.

Q8 Where do the following molecules bind to an enzyme:
   a) a non-competitive inhibitor?
   b) a competitive inhibitor?

Q9 Explain how non-competitive inhibition prevents enzyme activity.

Exam Tip
Don't get confused when talking about the active site — it's always on the enzyme, not on the substrate.

Tip: There are lots of similar sounding words here — look back through the section if you're struggling to remember the difference between them.

Learning Objective:

- Be able to investigate the effect of a named variable on the rate of an enzyme-controlled reaction (Required Practical 1).

Specification Reference 3.1.4.2

8. Enzyme-Controlled Reactions

You need to know how to measure the effect of any of the variables described on pages 38-40 on the rate of an enzyme-controlled reaction.

Measuring the rate of an enzyme-controlled reaction

REQUIRED PRACTICAL **1**

You know from page 38 that there are two ways of measuring the rate of an enzyme-controlled reaction, so here are some more details about both of those ways:

1. You can measure how fast the product of the reaction appears and use this to compare the rate of reaction under different conditions.

Tip: If you're measuring the rate of a reaction, you need to find out how much the amount of reactant or product is changing over time.

─ **Example** ─────────

Catalase catalyses the breakdown of hydrogen peroxide into water and oxygen. It's easy to measure the volume of oxygen produced and to work out how fast it's given off. In this experiment, you'll be working out the rate of reaction at different temperatures. Figure 1 shows the apparatus you'll need. The oxygen released displaces the water from the measuring cylinder. (A stand and clamp would also be pretty useful to hold the cylinder upside down, as would a stopwatch and a water bath.)

Tip: Don't forget to do a risk assessment before you do either this experiment or the one on the next page. You should always take basic safety precautions like wearing goggles and a lab coat.

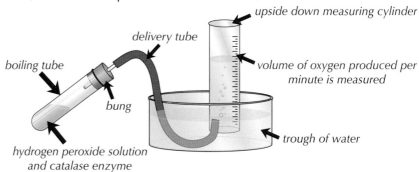

Figure 1: *Apparatus needed for investigating the breakdown of hydrogen peroxide.*

Here's how to carry out the experiment:

Tip: Enzymes can irritate the skin and may cause an allergic reaction, so they need to be handled with care.

1. Set up boiling tubes containing the same volume and concentration of hydrogen peroxide. To keep the pH constant, add equal volumes of a suitable buffer solution to each boiling tube.

2. Set up the rest of the apparatus as shown in the diagram.

Tip: A buffer solution is able to resist changes in pH when small amounts of acid or alkali are added.

3. Put each boiling tube in a water bath set to a different temperature (e.g. 10 °C, 20 °C, 30 °C and 40 °C) along with another tube containing catalase. Wait 5 minutes before moving onto the next step so the enzyme gets up to temperature.

4. Use a pipette to add the same volume and concentration of catalase to each boiling tube. Then quickly attach the bung and delivery tube.

5. Record how much oxygen is produced in the first minute (60 s) of the reaction. Use a stopwatch to measure the time.

Tip: A negative control reaction, i.e. a boiling tube containing hydrogen peroxide but no catalase, should also be carried out at each temperature.

6. Repeat the experiment at each temperature three times, and use the results to find the mean volume of oxygen produced.

7. Calculate the mean rate of reaction at each temperature by dividing the volume of oxygen produced by the time taken (i.e. 60 s). The units will be cm^3 s^{-1}.

2. You can measure how fast the substrate is broken down and use this to compare the rate of reaction under different conditions.

Tip: Which method you use to measure the rate of a reaction will normally depend on whether the product or the substrate is easier to test for.

Example

The enzyme amylase catalyses the breakdown of starch to maltose. You can test for the presence of starch in a solution using iodine in potassium iodide solution — in this experiment, you're using this to work out the rate of reaction at different concentrations of enzyme. Figure 2 shows how the experiment can be set up. You'll need the apparatus shown in Figure 2 as well as a stopwatch.

mixture sampled every ten seconds

dropping pipette

test tube

drop of iodine in potassium iodide

starch solution and amylase enzyme

spotting tile

Figure 2: *Apparatus needed for investigating the breakdown of starch.*

1. Put a drop of iodine in potassium iodide solution into each well on a spotting tile. Label the wells to help you read your results.

2. Mix together a known concentration and volume of amylase and starch in a test tube.

3. Use a dropping pipette to put a drop of this mixture into one of the wells containing the iodine solution at regular intervals (e.g. every 10 seconds).

4. Observe the resulting colour. The iodine solution goes dark blue-black when starch is present but remains its normal browny-orange colour when there's no starch around.

5. You can see how fast amylase is working by recording how long it takes for the iodine solution to no longer turn blue-black when the starch/amylase mixture is added.

Exam Tip
You might have learnt different methods for measuring the rate of an enzyme-controlled reaction to those shown here and on the previous page — it doesn't matter which ones you revise, so long as you know them well enough to describe in the exam.

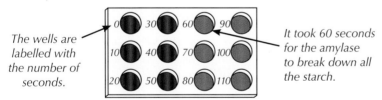

The wells are labelled with the number of seconds.

It took 60 seconds for the amylase to break down all the starch.

Tip: This experiment uses the starch test — see page 26.

Figure 3: *Example results from investigating the breakdown of starch.*

6. Repeat the experiment using different concentrations of amylase.

7. Make sure that you also repeat the experiment three times at each amylase concentration and use your results to find the mean time taken.

Variables

The experiments above and on the previous page show you how you can investigate the effects of temperature and enzyme concentration on the rate of enzyme-controlled reactions.

You can also alter these experiments to investigate the effect of a different variable, such as pH (by adding a buffer solution with a different pH to each test tube or boiling tube) or substrate concentration (you could use serial dilutions to make substrate solutions with different concentrations). The key to experiments like this is to remember to only change one variable — everything else should stay the same.

Tip: There's more about controlling variables on page 1.

Tip: You can read all about how to make serial dilutions on page 105.

Estimating the initial rate of reaction

You can use a **tangent** to estimate the initial rate of reaction from a graph. The initial rate of reaction is the rate of reaction right at the start of the reaction, close to time equals zero (t = 0) on the graph. To work out the initial rate of reaction, carry out the following steps:

Tip: For more details on how to draw a tangent, see pages 14-15.

1. Draw a tangent to the curve at t = 0, using a ruler. Do this by positioning the ruler so it's an equal distance from the curve at both sides of where it's touching it. Here you'll have to estimate where the curve would continue if it carried on below zero. Then draw a line along the ruler.

2. Calculate the **gradient** of the tangent — this is the initial rate of reaction. The equation for the gradient of a straight line is: Gradient = change in y axis ÷ change in x axis.

Tip: When you're working out a rate, the variable on the x axis should always be time.

3. Finally, you need to work out the units of the rate. The units will vary depending on what was measured in the experiment. To work out the units of rate from a graph, divide the units of the y axis by the units of the x axis.

Tip: If you're comparing the initial rate of reaction for two different reactions, you can work out the ratio of the rates to give you a quick and easy comparison. E.g. if the initial rate of a reaction at 30 °C is 1.2 cm³ s⁻¹ and the initial rate at 60 °C is 3.0 cm³ s⁻¹, you could write the ratio of the initial rates of reaction at 30 °C : 60 °C as 1 : 2.5. There's more about working out ratios on page 7.

Example — Maths Skills

The graph below shows the volume of product released by an enzyme-controlled reaction at 37 °C.

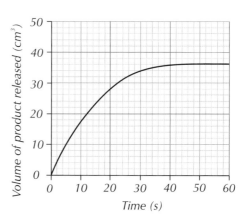

To work out the initial rate of reaction:

1. **Draw a tangent at t = 0.** (See the red line on the graph on the right.)

2. **Calculate the gradient of the tangent.** The gradient at t = 0 is: change in y ÷ change in x = 50 ÷ 18 = 2.8

3. **Work out the units.** units of y ÷ units of x = cm³ ÷ s = cm³ s⁻¹

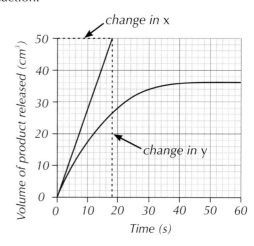

So the initial rate of reaction is **2.8 cm³ s⁻¹**.

Practice Questions — Application

Q1 The graph below shows the increase in the concentration of product from an enzyme-catalysed reaction at 25 °C.

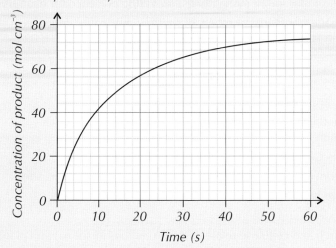

Use this graph to calculate the initial rate of reaction.

Tip: Use a pencil to draw your tangents — then if you make a mistake or aren't happy with your line, you can just erase it and start again.

Q2 A group of students were investigating the effect of hydrogen peroxide concentration on the rate of breakdown of hydrogen peroxide by the enzyme catalase. They measured the volume of oxygen released by the reaction. Their results are shown in the graph below.

Exam Tip
Don't forget to add the correct units to your answer, or you may miss out on some easy marks.

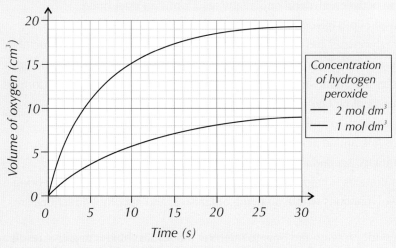

a) Name two variables that the students should keep the same during this investigation.

b) Calculate the ratio of the initial rates of reaction at 2 mol dm³ : 1 mol dm³ hydrogen peroxide. Write your answer in the form X : 1.

Practice Question — Fact Recall

Q1 Describe how you could measure the rate of the breakdown of hydrogen peroxide by catalase at different temperatures, including the equipment you would use.

Section Summary

Make sure you know...

- That the biochemical basis of life is similar for all living things, providing evidence for evolution.
- That polymers are big molecules made from large numbers of smaller units called monomers.
- That monosaccharides, amino acids and nucleotides are examples of monomers.
- What is meant by a condensation reaction and a hydrolysis reaction, and how they work.
- That the monomers of carbohydrates are monosaccharides, e.g. glucose, galactose and fructose.
- The structure of α-glucose and the structure of β-glucose.
- That disaccharides are formed from the condensation reaction of two monosaccharides (forming glycosidic bonds) and which monosaccharides make up maltose, sucrose and lactose.
- How the Benedict's test for sugars is carried out and how to interpret the results.
- That polysaccharides are formed from the condensation of more than two monosaccharides.
- That starch and glycogen are formed by the condensation of α-glucose units.
- That cellulose is formed by the condensation of β-glucose units.
- How the structures of glycogen, starch and cellulose relate to their functions in animal and plant cells.
- How the iodine test for starch is carried out and how to interpret the results (blue-black = positive).
- That triglycerides and phospholipids are two groups of lipid.
- The basic structure of triglycerides (glycerol and three fatty acids) and how they're formed.
- The basic structure of fatty acids, including if they're saturated or unsaturated, and be able to recognise them.
- That a condensation reaction between glycerol and a fatty acid forms an ester bond.
- The basic structure of a phospholipid (glycerol, two fatty acids and a phosphate group).
- The different properties of triglycerides and phospholipids, and how they relate to their structures.
- How to carry out an emulsion test — shake sample with ethanol, add to water, milky = lipid present.
- That the monomers of proteins are amino acids, and how dipeptides and polypeptides are formed.
- That a functional protein may contain one or more polypeptides.
- The general structure of an amino acid and that they differ only in their side (R) group.
- How condensation reactions link amino acids together with peptide bonds.
- The relationship between primary, secondary, tertiary and quaternary protein structure.
- That the tertiary structure of proteins is held by hydrogen bonds, ionic bonds and disulfide bridges.
- That proteins have a variety of functions within all living organisms, and how their functions are related to their shape.
- How to carry out a biuret test for proteins and how to interpret the results (blue = negative result and purple = positive result).
- That enzymes catalyse a wide range of intracellular and extracellular reactions that determine structures and functions from cellular to whole-organism level.
- How enzymes catalyse reactions by lowering the activation energy of reactions.
- What the induced fit model of enzyme action is and how models of enzyme action have changed over time (from the lock and key model).
- Why enzymes are very specific and how the properties of enzymes relate to their tertiary structure (and their ability to form enzyme-substrate complexes).
- How temperature, pH, substrate concentration, enzyme concentration, and competitive and non-competitive inhibitors affect enzyme activity, and how to investigate these variables (Required Practical 1).
- How to draw a tangent to a graph and use it to work out the initial rate of a reaction.

Exam-style Questions

1 Disaccharides and polysaccharides are made from monosaccharides.
Figure 1 shows the disaccharide molecule sucrose.

Figure 1

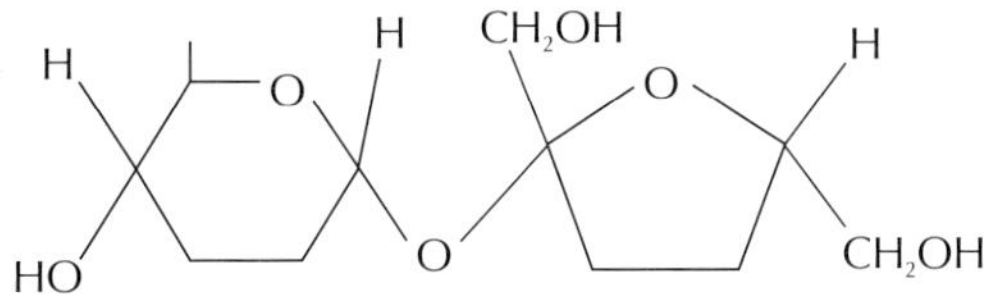

1.1 Describe the structure of sucrose and explain how it's formed.

(4 marks)

1.2 Draw the **two** monosaccharides that join together to form sucrose.

(2 marks)

1.3 Sucrose is a non-reducing sugar.

Describe a biochemical test you could use to identify the presence of a non-reducing sugar.

(5 marks)

1.4 Glycogen is a polysaccharide.

Describe the structure of glycogen and explain how its structure makes it suited to its function.

(4 marks)

2 Proteins are important biological molecules.

2.1 The biuret test can be used to test for the presence of protein in a sample.
Describe how this test would be carried out, including what observations would indicate positive and negative results.

(4 marks)

Enzymes are proteins. Pepsin is an enzyme released in the stomach to break down other proteins into smaller polypeptides.
Figure 2 shows a simplified diagram of the action of pepsin.

Figure 2

protein

A

pepsin

2.2 Name the type of monomer represented by the letter **A** in **Figure 2** and draw its general structure.

(2 marks)

2.3 Describe the process by which pepsin breaks down a protein.

(3 marks)

2.4 Describe an enzyme's tertiary structure and how it relates to its properties.

(5 marks)

3   Triglycerides are a type of fat found in foods. In the stomach, gastric lipase acts as a catalyst to break triglycerides down into diglycerides and fatty acids.

gastric
lipase

triglyceride ⟶ diglyceride + fatty acid

Figure 3 shows the rate of reaction for gastric lipase at different pH values.

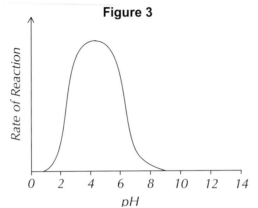

Figure 3

3.1 What is the optimum pH of gastric lipase?

(1 mark)

3.2 At what pH value(s) is gastric lipase denatured? Give a reason for your answer.

(2 marks)

3.3   Explain what happens when an enzyme is denatured.

(2 marks)

3.4   Suggest **two** variables you would control if you were investigating the activity of gastric lipase at different pH values.

(2 marks)

The weight-loss drug, orlistat, stops triglycerides from being broken down. Orlistat is a competitive inhibitor of gastric lipase.

Figure 4 shows the reaction with and without orlistat present.

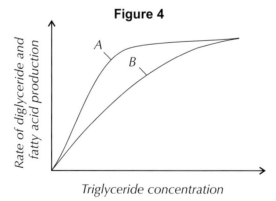

Figure 4

3.5   Which curve on the graph shows the reaction without the presence of orlistat? Give a reason for your answer.

(1 mark)

3.6   Explain the action of orlistat in this reaction.

(3 marks)

1. DNA and RNA

DNA and RNA are both essential for the function of living organisms...

DNA and RNA function

DNA and RNA are both types of nucleic acid. They're found in all living cells and they both carry information.

Your **DNA** (**deoxyribonucleic acid**) is used to store your genetic information — that's all the instructions needed to grow and develop from a fertilised egg to a fully grown adult. There's more on the role of DNA on p. 202.

RNA (**ribonucleic acid**) is similar in structure to DNA. One of its main functions is to transfer genetic information from the DNA to the ribosomes. Ribosomes are the body's 'protein factories' — they read the RNA to make polypeptides (proteins) in a process called translation (see pages 207-208). Ribosomes themselves are made from RNA and proteins.

Nucleotide structure

Molecules of DNA and RNA are polymers of nucleotides. A nucleotide is a type of biological molecule which is made from three different components: a pentose sugar (that's a sugar with 5 carbon atoms), a nitrogen-containing organic base (organic means that it contains carbon), and a phosphate group — see Figure 1.

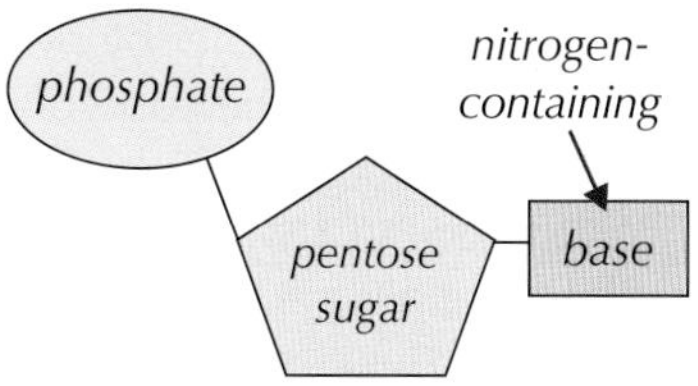

Figure 1: *A nucleotide.*

Nucleotides are really important. For a start they're the monomers (see p. 19) that make up DNA and RNA.

Polynucleotide structure

Many nucleotides join together to form polynucleotide strands (or chains). The nucleotides join up via a condensation reaction (see p. 19) between the phosphate group of one nucleotide and the sugar of another. This forms a phosphodiester bond (consisting of the phosphate group and two ester bonds). The chain of phosphates and sugars is known as the **sugar-phosphate backbone** — see Figure 2.

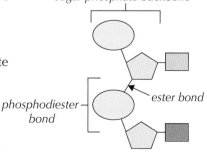

Figure 2: *Structure of a single polynucleotide strand.*

Learning Objectives:

- Understand that deoxyribonucleic acid (DNA) and ribonucleic acid (RNA) are important information-carrying molecules. In all living cells, DNA holds genetic information and RNA transfers genetic information from DNA to the ribosomes.

- Know that ribosomes are formed from RNA and proteins.

- Know that both DNA and RNA are polymers of nucleotides.

- Know the components of a nucleotide, and how they differ in DNA and RNA nucleotides.

- Know that a condensation reaction between two nucleotides forms a phosphodiester bond.

- Recall that a DNA molecule is a double helix with two polynucleotide chains held together by hydrogen bonds between specific complementary base pairs.

- Know that an RNA molecule is a relatively short polynucleotide chain.

- Appreciate that the relative simplicity of DNA led many scientists to doubt that it carried the genetic code.

Specification Reference 3.1.5.1

DNA structure

DNA has a **double helix** structure. This means that a DNA molecule is formed from two separate strands which wind around each other to form a spiral (see Figure 3). The strands are polynucleotides. They're made up of lots of nucleotides joined together in a long chain — see previous page.

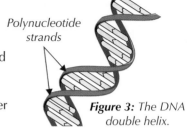

Polynucleotide strands

Figure 3: *The DNA double helix.*

DNA molecules are really long and are coiled up very tightly, so a lot of genetic information can fit into a small space in the cell nucleus.

DNA nucleotide structure

A DNA nucleotide is made from a phosphate group, the pentose sugar **deoxyribose** and a nitrogen-containing organic **base**.

Each DNA nucleotide has the same sugar and phosphate. The base on each nucleotide can vary though. There are four possible bases — adenine (A), thymine (T), cytosine (C) and guanine (G). The structure of a DNA nucleotide is illustrated in Figure 4.

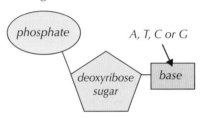

Figure 4: *A DNA nucleotide.*

Complementary base pairing

Tip: If you're struggling to remember which base pairs with which, just think — you eat <u>A</u>pple <u>T</u>urnover with <u>G</u>loopy <u>C</u>ustard.

Two DNA polynucleotide strands join together by hydrogen bonds between the bases. Each base can only join with one particular partner — this is called complementary base pairing (or specific base pairing). Adenine always pairs with thymine (A - T) and guanine always pairs with cytosine (G - C) — see Figure 5. This means there are always equal amounts of adenine and thymine in a DNA molecule and equal amounts of cytosine and guanine. Two hydrogen bonds form between A and T, and three hydrogen bonds form between C and G.

Tip: The two ends of a polynucleotide strand are different — one end has a phosphate group and the other has a hydroxyl (OH) group attached to the sugar. That's how you can tell which direction a strand is running in.

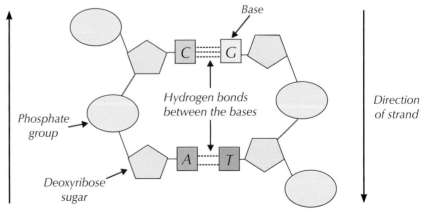

Figure 5: *Complementary base pairing in DNA molecules.*

The two polynucleotide strands are antiparallel — they run in opposite directions. Two antiparallel strands twist to form a DNA double helix.

Summary of a DNA molecule

If you tie all this information together, you end up with a DNA molecule that looks like the one in Figure 6.

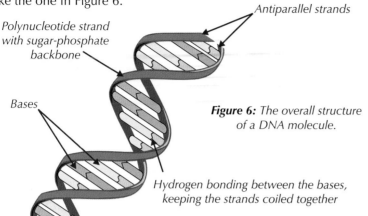

Polynucleotide strand with sugar-phosphate backbone

Antiparallel strands

Bases

Figure 6: *The overall structure of a DNA molecule.*

Hydrogen bonding between the bases, keeping the strands coiled together

Figure 7: *X-ray diffraction picture of DNA. The cross of bands shows that the molecule is a helix.*

Tip: The structure of a nucleotide and the arrangement of the DNA double helix is the same in all living organisms.

Practice Questions — Application

Q1 Here are the base sequences of two short stretches of DNA. For each one, write down the sequence of bases they would pair up with:

a) ACTGTCGTAGTCGATGCTA   b) TGCACCATGTGGTAAATCG

Q2 Scientists analysed a section of double stranded DNA. There were 68 bases in total (34 base pairs) and 22 of the bases were adenine. How many of the bases were:

a) thymine?   b) cytosine?   c) guanine?

RNA structure

Like DNA, RNA is made of nucleotides that contain a sugar, a phosphate group and one of four different bases. The nucleotides also form a polynucleotide strand with a sugar-phosphate backbone. But the structure of RNA differs from DNA in four main ways:

- The sugar in RNA nucleotides is a **ribose** sugar (not deoxyribose). It's still a pentose sugar though.
- **Uracil** (U, a pyrimidine) replaces thymine as a base. Uracil always pairs with adenine in RNA.
- The nucleotides form a single polynucleotide strand (not a double one).
- RNA strands are much **shorter** than most DNA polynucleotides.

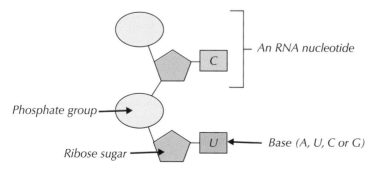

An RNA nucleotide

Phosphate group

Ribose sugar

Base (A, U, C or G)

Figure 8: *Structure of an RNA strand.*

DNA and RNA comparison

Questions asking you to compare the structure of DNA and RNA are a regular feature in the exam. Luckily for you, the main points are summarised in the table below:

	DNA	RNA
Shape	Double-stranded — twisted into a double helix and held together by hydrogen bonds	Single-stranded
Pentose sugar	Deoxyribose sugar	Ribose sugar
Bases	A, T, C, G	A, U, C, G
Size	Long	Relatively short

DNA as the carrier of the genetic code

DNA was first observed in the 1800s, but lots of scientists at the time doubted that it could carry the genetic code because it has a relatively simple chemical composition. Some argued that genetic information must be carried by proteins — which are much more chemically varied.

By 1953, experiments had shown that DNA was the carrier of the genetic code. This was also the year in which the double helix structure, which helps DNA to carry out its function, was determined by scientists James Watson and Francis Crick (see Figure 9).

Figure 9: *Watson and Crick, two of the scientists who discovered the structure of DNA, and their model of the DNA double helix.*

Practice Questions — Fact Recall

Q1 What is the function of DNA?

Q2 What are ribosomes made up of?

Q3 Name the monomer of DNA and RNA.

Q4 The diagram below shows the structure of a nucleotide.

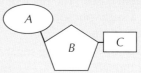

Name parts A, B and C.

Q5 Describe the structure of a DNA nucleotide.

Q6 Name the four possible bases in DNA.

Q7 What type of bond, present in a polynucleotide chain, consists of two ester bonds and a phosphate group?

Q8 Describe how a DNA double helix is formed from two polynucleotide strands.

Q9 Name the sugar in RNA.

Q10 Name the four possible bases in RNA.

Q11 Describe three differences between DNA and RNA.

Q12 What caused many scientists to doubt that DNA carried the genetic code?

2. DNA Replication

DNA is able to replicate itself and it does so on a regular basis. Clever thing.

Why does DNA replicate?

DNA copies itself before cell division (see p. 84) so that each new cell has the full amount of DNA. The method is called semi-conservative replication because half of the strands in each new DNA molecule are from the original DNA molecule. This means that there's genetic continuity between generations of cells (i.e. the cells produced by cell division inherit their genes from their parent cells).

How is DNA replicated?

A DNA molecule has a paired base structure (see page 52), which makes it easy for DNA to copy itself. Here's how it works:

1 The enzyme **DNA helicase** breaks the hydrogen bonds between bases on the two polynucleotide DNA strands. This makes the helix unwind to form two single strands.	**2** Each original single strand acts as a template for a new strand. Complementary base pairing means that free-floating DNA nucleotides are attracted to their complementary exposed bases on each original template strand — A with T and C with G.
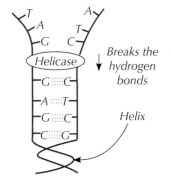	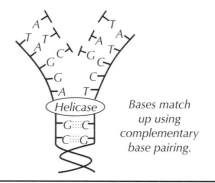

3 Condensation reactions join the nucleotides of the new strand together — catalysed by the enzyme **DNA polymerase**. Hydrogen bonds form between the bases on the original and new strands.

Each new DNA molecule contains one strand from the original DNA molecule and one new strand.

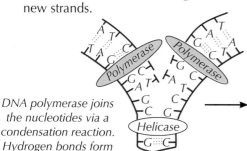

DNA polymerase joins the nucleotides via a condensation reaction. Hydrogen bonds form between strands.

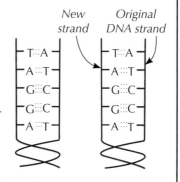

Learning Objectives:

- Understand that the semi-conservative replication of DNA ensures genetic continuity between generations of cells.

- Understand the process of semi-conservative replication of DNA in terms of:
  - unwinding of the double helix,
  - the breakage of hydrogen bonds between complementary bases in the polynucleotide strands,
  - the role of DNA helicase in unwinding DNA and breaking its hydrogen bonds,
  - attraction of new DNA nucleotides to exposed bases on template strands and base pairing,
  - the role of DNA polymerase in the condensation reaction that joins adjacent nucleotides.

- Be able to evaluate the work of scientists in validating the Watson-Crick model of DNA replication.

    Specification Reference 3.1.5.2

Exam Tip
If you're asked to describe the process of semi-conservative replication in the exam, you need to make sure you do it in the <u>correct order</u> or you won't get all the marks.

The action of DNA polymerase

Each end of a DNA strand is slightly different in its structure. One end is called the 3' (pronounced 'three prime') end and one end is called the 5' (five prime) end.

During DNA replication the active site of DNA polymerase is only complementary to the 3' end of the newly forming DNA strand — so the enzyme can only add nucleotides to the new strand at the 3' end. This means that the new strand is made in a 5' to 3' direction and that DNA polymerase moves down the template strand in a 3' to 5' direction — see Figure 1.

Tip: The 3' and 5' ends of a DNA strand are different. At the 3' end is a hydroxyl group (OH) that is attached to the pentose sugar of the nucleotide. At the 5' end there is a phosphate group. Take a look back at page 52 for a reminder of the structure of DNA.

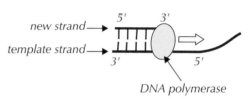

***Figure 1:** Detail of DNA polymerase action.*

Because the strands in the double helix are antiparallel, the DNA polymerase working on one of the template strands moves in the opposite direction to the DNA polymerase working on the other template strand — see Figure 2.

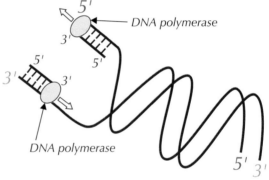

***Figure 2:** DNA polymerase working on a double stranded DNA molecule.*

Practice Questions — Application

Tip: Have a look back at page 52 if you're struggling to remember which bases pair up with each other.

Q1 The diagram below shows a molecule of DNA.

Draw the original and replicated strands after semi-conservative replication.

Q2 The diagram below shows a template strand of DNA. Give the sequence of the new strand that would be synthesised by the action of DNA polymerase. Write the sequence in the order that the bases would be added to the strand.

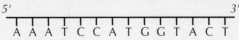

Evidence for semi-conservative replication

You might remember from page 54 that Watson and Crick determined the structure of DNA. They also came up with the theory of semi-conservative DNA replication.

However, it wasn't until Meselson and Stahl's experiment a few years later that this theory was validated. Before that, people were unsure whether DNA replication was semi-conservative or conservative. If the method was conservative, the original DNA strands would stay together and the new DNA molecules would contain two new strands.

Meselson and Stahl's experiment

Meselson and Stahl showed DNA is replicated using the semi-conservative method. Their experiment used two isotopes of nitrogen (DNA contains nitrogen) — heavy nitrogen (^{15}N) and light nitrogen (^{14}N).

Tip: Isotopes are different forms of the same element.

1. Two samples of bacteria were grown for many generations — one in a nutrient broth containing light nitrogen, and one in a broth with heavy nitrogen. As the bacteria reproduced, they took up nitrogen from the broth to help make nucleotides for new DNA. So the nitrogen gradually became part of the bacteria's DNA.

Tip: There's more on how centrifuges work on page 82.

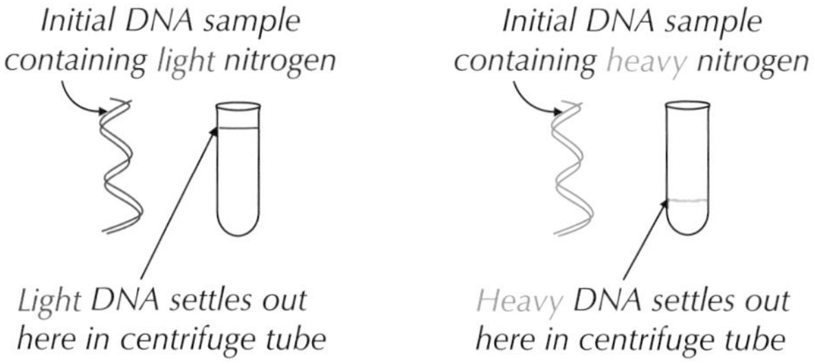

2. A sample of DNA was taken from each batch of bacteria, and spun in a centrifuge. The DNA from the heavy nitrogen bacteria settled lower down the centrifuge tube than the DNA from the light nitrogen bacteria — because it's heavier (see Figure 3).

Initial DNA sample containing light nitrogen

Initial DNA sample containing heavy nitrogen

Light DNA settles out here in centrifuge tube

Heavy DNA settles out here in centrifuge tube

Figure 3: *Diagram to show the results of steps 1 and 2 of the Meselson and Stahl experiment.*

3. Then the bacteria grown in the heavy nitrogen broth were taken out and put in a broth containing only light nitrogen. The bacteria were left for one round of DNA replication, and then another DNA sample was taken out and spun in the centrifuge — see Figure 5.

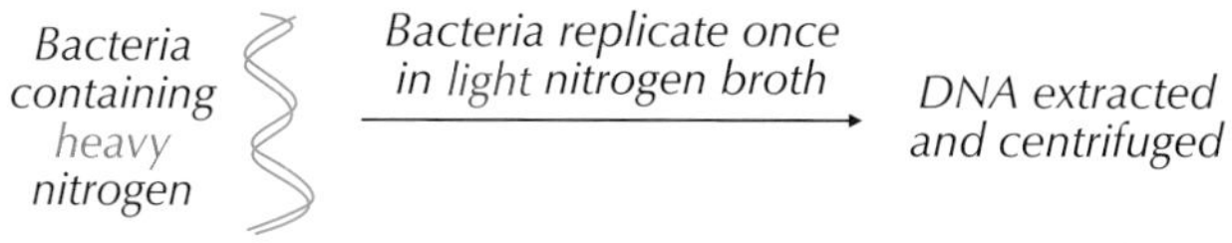

Bacteria containing heavy nitrogen

Bacteria replicate once in light nitrogen broth

DNA extracted and centrifuged

Figure 5: *Diagram to show step 3 of the Meselson and Stahl experiment.*

4. If replication was conservative, the original heavy DNA, which would still be together, would settle at the bottom and the new light DNA would settle at the top — see Figure 6.

5. If replication was semi-conservative, the new bacterial DNA molecules would contain one strand of the old DNA containing heavy nitrogen and one strand of new DNA containing light nitrogen. So the DNA would settle out between where the light nitrogen DNA settled out and where the heavy nitrogen DNA settled out — see Figure 6.

Figure 4: *Liquid growth medium or broth before bacteria are added.*

Exam Tip
Remember, in the exam you might be asked about an experiment you're not familiar with. Don't panic though, just read it through and make sure you understand it before applying your knowledge to answer the questions on it.

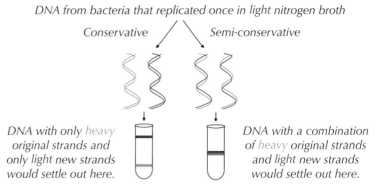

DNA from bacteria that replicated once in light nitrogen broth

Conservative / \ Semi-conservative

DNA with only *heavy* original strands and only light new strands would settle out here.

DNA with a combination of *heavy* original strands and light new strands would settle out here.

Figure 6: *Diagram to show the possible results of step 3 of the Meselson and Stahl experiment.*

6. As it turned out, the DNA settled out in the middle, showing that the DNA molecules contained a mixture of heavy and light nitrogen. The bacterial DNA had replicated semi-conservatively in the light nitrogen.

Once Meselson and Stahl had confirmed that DNA replication in bacteria was semi-conservative, other scientists carried out experiments to show that it was the universal method for DNA replication in all living things.

Practice Question — Application

Q1 A scientist performed an experiment to demonstrate that DNA replicates in a semi-conservative way. As shown in the diagram, the scientist grew *E. coli* in nutrient broths containing either $^{15}NH_4^+$ (a source of heavy nitrogen) or $^{14}NH_4^+$ (a source of light nitrogen). At each stage of the experiment a DNA sample was extracted from the bacterial populations and spun in a centrifuge. The results are shown in the tubes on the diagram.

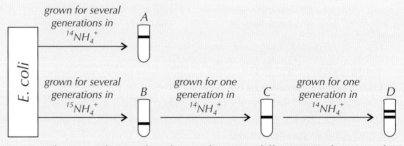

a) Why were the results of centrifugation different in tubes A and B?
b) Describe and explain the results seen in tube C.
c) Describe and suggest reasons for the results seen in tube D.

Practice Questions — Fact Recall

Q1 DNA is copied by semi-conservative replication of DNA. What is meant by this?

Q2 Name the two enzymes involved in DNA replication.

Q3 Describe the first stage of DNA replication, in which two strands of DNA are separated.

Q4 Describe the second stage of DNA replication, where the single strands of DNA act as templates.

3. ATP

Energy is required for all life processes. This means that being able to store and release energy is really important for plants and animals.

Why Is energy Important?

Plant and animal cells need energy for biological processes to occur.

Examples

- Plants need energy for things like active transport (e.g. to transport solutes from their leaves — see p. 194), DNA replication (see p. 55), cell division (see p. 84) and protein synthesis (see p. 204).

- Animals need energy for things like active transport (e.g. to absorb glucose from the ileum epithelium into the bloodstream — see p. 109), DNA replication, cell division and protein synthesis.

Adenosine triphosphate (ATP)

Plant and animal cells release energy from glucose — this process is called respiration. A cell can't get its energy directly from glucose. So, in respiration, the energy released from glucose is used to make ATP (adenosine triphosphate).

ATP is made from the nucleotide base adenine, combined with a ribose sugar and three phosphate groups (see Figure 1). It's what's known as a nucleotide derivative because it's a modified form of a nucleotide.

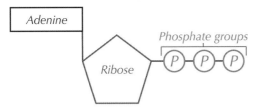

Figure 1: *The structure of ATP.*

Once made, ATP diffuses to the part of the cell that needs energy. The energy in ATP is stored in high energy bonds between the phosphate groups. It's released via hydrolysis reactions (see below).

Making and using ATP

When energy is needed by a cell, ATP is broken down into ADP (adenosine diphosphate) and P_i (inorganic phosphate). This is a **hydrolysis** reaction. A phosphate bond is broken and energy is released. The reaction is catalysed by the enzyme **ATP hydrolase** (see Figure 2).

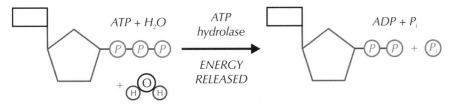

Figure 2: *The breakdown of ATP — a hydrolysis reaction.*

Learning Objectives:

- Understand that a single molecule of adenosine triphosphate (ATP) is a nucleotide derivative and is formed from a molecule of ribose, a molecule of adenine and three phosphate groups.

- Know that the hydrolysis of ATP to adenosine diphosphate (ADP) and an inorganic phosphate group (P_i) is catalysed by the enzyme ATP hydrolase.

- Understand that the hydrolysis of ATP can be coupled to energy-requiring reactions within cells.

- Know that the inorganic phosphate released during the hydrolysis of ATP can be used to phosphorylate other compounds, often making them more reactive.

- Know that ATP is resynthesised by the condensation of ADP and P_i.

- Understand that this reaction is catalysed by the enzyme ATP synthase during photosynthesis, or during respiration.

Specification Reference 3.1.6

Tip: Take a look at page 51 for a reminder about nucleotide structure.

Tip: Inorganic phosphate (P_i) is just the fancy name for a single phosphate.

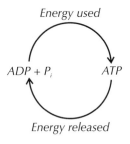
ATP hydrolysis can be 'coupled' to other energy-requiring reactions in the cell — this means the energy released can be used directly to make the coupled reaction happen, rather than being lost as heat.

The released inorganic phosphate can also be put to use — it can be added to another compound (this is known as **phosphorylation**), which often makes the compound more reactive.

ATP can be resynthesised in a condensation reaction between ADP and P_i. This happens during both respiration and photosynthesis, and is catalysed by the enzyme **ATP synthase** (see Figure 3).

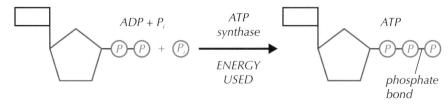

Figure 3: The synthesis of ATP — a condensation reaction.

Practice Questions — Application

Q1 In addition to ADP and ATP, cells can also contain a molecule called AMP (adenosine monophosphate). Suggest what the structure of this molecule is.

Q2 The movement of calcium ions across a cell membrane can occur via the energy-requiring process of active transport. This movement of calcium ions is coupled to the breakdown of ATP. Suggest why.

Practice Questions — Fact Recall

Q1 What does 'ATP' stand for?

Q2 Describe the structure of a molecule of ATP.

Q3 a) What is ATP broken down into?

b) By what type of reaction is ATP broken down?

c) What enzyme catalyses the breakdown of ATP?

Q4 a) How can inorganic phosphate (released by the breakdown of ATP) be used?

b) Give the abbreviation that can be used for inorganic phosphate.

Q5 ATP can be reformed by the addition of an inorganic phosphate to ADP.

a) What type of reaction is this?

b) Give an example of a process during which this reaction takes place.

4. Water

Water is essential for life. The next few pages will show you what it is about water that makes it so important.

The importance of water

Water is vital to living organisms. It makes up about 80% of a cell's contents and has loads of important functions, inside and outside cells:

- Water is a metabolite in loads of important metabolic reactions, including condensation and hydrolysis reactions (see pages 19-20).

- Water is a solvent, which means some substances dissolve in it. Most metabolic reactions take place in solution (e.g. in the cytoplasm of eukaryotic and prokaryotic cells) so water's pretty essential.

- Water helps with temperature control because it has a high latent heat of vaporisation and a high specific heat capacity (see p. 63).

- Water molecules are very cohesive (they stick together), which helps water transport in plants (see p. 189) as well as transport in other organisms.

Structure of water

To understand the structure of water, you need to know a bit about the chemistry involved in holding water molecules together.

Polarity of water

A molecule of water (H_2O) is one atom of oxygen (O) joined to two atoms of hydrogen (H_2) by shared electrons — see Figure 1.

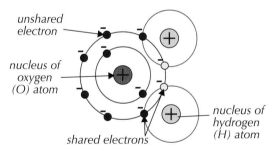

unshared electron

nucleus of oxygen (O) atom

shared electrons

nucleus of hydrogen (H) atom

Figure 1: *The structure of a water molecule.*

Because the shared negative hydrogen electrons are pulled towards the oxygen atom, the other side of each hydrogen atom is left with a slight positive charge ($\delta+$). The unshared negative electrons on the oxygen atom give it a slight negative charge ($\delta-$). This makes water a polar molecule — it has a slight (partial) negative charge on one side and a slight (partial) positive charge on the other (see Figure 2).

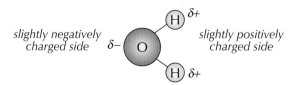

slightly negatively charged side $\delta-$ $\delta+$ *slightly positively charged side*

Figure 2: *The slight charges on a water molecule.*

Learning Objectives:

- Understand that water is a major component of cells. It has several properties that are important in biology. In particular, water:

  - is a metabolite in many metabolic reactions, including condensation and hydrolysis reactions,

  - is an important solvent in which metabolic reactions occur,

  - has a relatively large latent heat of vaporisation, providing a cooling effect with little loss of water through evaporation,

  - has a relatively high heat capacity, buffering changes in temperature,

  - has strong cohesion between water molecules; this supports columns of water in the tube-like transport cells of plants and produces surface tension where water meets air.

Specification Reference 3.1.7

Tip: We know that water, as the most common component of cells, is really important to living organisms. That's why our search for other life in the universe involves searching for liquid water.

Tip: '$\delta+$' is pronounced 'delta positive' and '$\delta-$' is 'delta negative'.

Hydrogen bonding

Hydrogen bonds are weak bonds between a slightly positively charged hydrogen atom in one molecule and a slightly negatively charged atom in another molecule. Hydrogen bonds form between water molecules because the slightly negatively charged oxygen atoms of water attract the slightly positively charged hydrogen atoms of other water molecules. This hydrogen bonding gives water some of its useful properties.

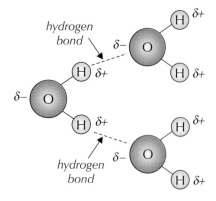

Figure 3: Diagram showing how hydrogen bonds hold water molecules together.

Exam Tip
If you're asked to draw water molecules in the exam, make sure you draw the hydrogen bonds as dashed lines and include the partial charges ($\delta+$ or $\delta-$) on all the atoms.

Properties of water

Here's a bit more about each of the useful properties of water that you need to learn for your exam.

Important metabolite

Many metabolic reactions involve a condensation or hydrolysis reaction. A hydrolysis reaction requires a molecule of water to break a bond. A condensation reaction releases a molecule of water as a new bond is formed. For example, amino acids are joined together to make polypeptides (proteins) by condensation reactions (see page 31). Energy from ATP is released through a hydrolysis reaction (see page 59).

Tip: A metabolic reaction is a chemical reaction that happens in a living organism to keep the organism alive. A metabolite is a substance involved in a metabolic reaction.

Good solvent

A lot of important substances in biological reactions are ionic (like salt, for example). This means they're made from one positively charged atom or molecule and one negatively charged atom or molecule (e.g. salt is made from a positive sodium ion and a negative chloride ion).

Tip: Most biological reactions take place in solution, so water's pretty essential.

Because water is polar, the slightly positively charged end of a water molecule will be attracted to the negative ion, and the slightly negatively charged end of a water molecule will be attracted to the positive ion. This means the ions will get totally surrounded by water molecules — in other words, they'll dissolve (see Figure 4). So water's polarity makes it useful as a solvent (a substance capable of dissolving another substance). This means living organisms can take up useful substances (e.g. mineral ions) dissolved in water and these dissolved substances can be transported around the organism's body.

Tip: Remember — a molecule is polar if it has a slightly negatively charged side and a slightly positively charged side.

Tip: Polar molecules, such as glucose, dissolve in water because hydrogen bonds form between them and the water molecules.

Exam Tip
If you're asked about how a particular ion dissolves in water, don't get put off by the ion itself — just figure out if it's positively charged or negatively charged.

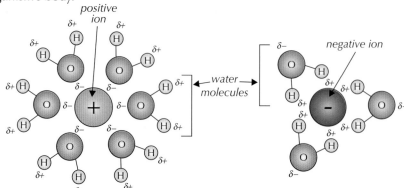

Figure 4: A positive ion (left) and a negative ion (right) dissolved in water.

High latent heat of vaporisation

Water evaporates (vaporises) when the hydrogen bonds holding water molecules together are broken. This allows the water molecules on the surface of the water to escape into the air as a gas. It takes a lot of energy (heat) to break the hydrogen bonds between water molecules, so a lot of energy is used up when water evaporates. This means water has a high latent heat of vaporisation — lots of heat is used to change it from a liquid to a gas.

This is useful for living organisms because it means they can use water loss through evaporation to cool down without losing too much water. When water evaporates it carries away heat energy from a surface, which cools the surface and helps to lower the temperature (e.g. when humans sweat to cool down).

Tip: Latent heat is the heat energy that's needed to change a substance from one state to another, e.g. from a liquid to a gas.

Can buffer (resist) changes in temperature

Hydrogen bonds give water a high **specific heat capacity** — this is the energy needed to raise the temperature of 1 gram of a substance by 1 °C. When water is heated, a lot of the heat energy is used to break the hydrogen bonds between the water molecules. This means there is less heat energy available to actually increase the temperature of the water. So water has a high specific heat capacity — it takes a lot of energy to heat it up.

This is useful for living organisms because it means that water doesn't experience rapid temperature changes. This makes water a good habitat because the temperature under water is likely to be more stable than on land. The water inside organisms also remains at a fairly stable temperature — helping them to maintain a constant internal body temperature.

Tip: Enzyme activity is affected by temperature (see page 38). Some important biological processes need enzymes to work (e.g. digestion and respiration) — these may not work properly if the organism's temperature is not kept fairly stable.

Very cohesive

Cohesion is the attraction between molecules of the same type (e.g. two water molecules). Water molecules are very cohesive (they tend to stick together) because they're polar. Strong cohesion helps water to flow, making it great for transporting substances. For example, it's how water travels in columns up the xylem (tube-like transport cells) in plants (see p. 189). Strong cohesion also means that water has a high surface tension when it comes into contact with air. This is the reason why sweat forms droplets, which evaporate from the skin to cool an organism down. It's also the reason that pond skaters, and some other insects, can 'walk' on the surface of a pond.

Practice Questions — Fact Recall

Q1 Name two reactions that water is involved in.

Q2 Why is water classed as a polar molecule?

Q3 Label this diagram of a water molecule showing the name and charge on each atom.

Q4 What is a hydrogen bond?

Q5 What is a metabolite?

Q6 What makes water useful as a solvent?

Q7 Water has a high latent heat of vaporisation. What does this mean?

Q8 Explain why water has a high specific heat capacity.

Q9 a) What is cohesion?

   b) Why is cohesion between water molecules important in plants?

- Know that inorganic ions occur in solution in the cytoplasm and body fluids of organisms, some in high concentrations and others in very low concentrations.

- Understand that each type of ion has a specific role, depending on its properties.

- Be able to recognise the role of ions in the following topics:

    - iron ions as a component of haemoglobin,

    - hydrogen ions and pH,

    - sodium ions in the co-transport of glucose and amino acids,

    - phosphate ions as components of DNA and of ATP.

  Specification Reference 3.1.8

5. Inorganic Ions

Ions might not be the first thing you think about when you think of biological molecules but they have some very important roles in organisms.

What are ions?

An **ion** is an atom (or group of atoms) that has an electric charge. An ion with a positive charge is called a cation.

--- Examples ---

Na^+ — this is a sodium ion, it has a charge of +1.

Ca^{2+} — this is a calcium ion, it has a charge of +2.

An ion with a negative charge is called an anion.

--- Examples ---

Cl^- — this is a chlorine ion, it has a charge of –1.

PO_4^{3-} — this is a phosphate ion, it has a charge of –3.

Inorganic ions

An inorganic ion is one which doesn't contain carbon (although there are a few exceptions to this rule). There are inorganic ions, in solution, in the cytoplasm of cells and in the body fluids of organisms. Each ion has a specific role, depending on its properties. An ion's role determines whether it is found in high or low concentrations.

--- Examples ---

Iron ions in haemoglobin

Haemoglobin is a large protein that carries oxygen around the body, in the red blood cells. It's made up of four different polypeptide chains, each with an iron ion (Fe^{2+}) in the centre. It's the Fe^{2+} that actually binds to the oxygen in haemoglobin — so it's a pretty key component. When oxygen is bound, the Fe^{2+} ion temporarily becomes an Fe^{3+} ion, until oxygen is released.

Hydrogen ions

pH is calculated based on the concentration of hydrogen ions (H^+) in the environment. The more H^+ present, the lower the pH (and the more acidic the environment). Enzyme-controlled reactions are all affected by pH.

Sodium ions

Glucose and amino acids need a bit of help crossing cell membranes. A molecule of glucose or an amino acid can be transported into a cell (across the cell-surface membrane) alongside sodium ions (Na^+). This is known as co-transport (see pages 108 and 109 for more).

Phosphate ions

When a phosphate ion (PO_4^{3-}) is attached to another molecule, it's known as a phosphate group. DNA, RNA and ATP all contain phosphate groups. It's the bonds between phosphate groups that store energy in ATP (see page 59). The phosphate groups in DNA and RNA allow nucleotides to join up to form the polynucleotides (see p. 51).

Figure 1: A computer model of a haemoglobin molecule. There's an iron atom (the yellow sphere) in each of the four polypeptide chains.

Q1 What is an inorganic ion?

Q2 Where do inorganic ions occur?

Q3 What determines an ion's specific role?

Q4 a) What ions are part of haemoglobin molecules?

    b) What is the role of these ions in haemoglobin?

Q5 Name the ion that is linked to pH.

Q6 a) Which type of ion is involved in moving glucose and amino acids across cell membranes?

    b) What is the name of this process?

Section Summary

Make sure you know:

- How DNA and RNA are important molecules that carry information.
- That ribosomes are formed from RNA and proteins.
- The general structure of a nucleotide, and how the structure of DNA and RNA nucleotides differ.
- That DNA and RNA are both nucleotide polymers that contain phosphodiester bonds between nucleotides as a result of condensation reactions.
- That there are differences between the overall DNA and RNA molecule structures — DNA forms a double helix with hydrogen bonds between two polynucleotide strands as a result of complementary base pairing, whereas molecules of RNA form single polynucleotide strands and are short in length compared to DNA.
- Why, in the past, scientists doubted that DNA was capable of carrying the genetic code.
- Why DNA replication is semi-conservative and how the process takes place — the hydrogen bonds between the bases on polynucleotide strands are broken by DNA helicase, free DNA nucleotides are attracted to their complementary exposed bases, and the nucleotides are joined together by DNA polymerase to form a DNA molecule with one new strand and one original strand.
- How to evaluate the work of scientists in validating the Watson-Crick model of DNA replication, e.g. Meselson and Stahl's experiment (to show semi-conservative replication in DNA).
- That ATP is a modified nucleotide composed of adenine, a ribose sugar and three phosphate groups.
- That ATP is hydrolysed to ADP and an inorganic phosphate group (P_i) by the enzyme ATP hydrolase and that the energy released from this hydrolysis reaction can be used directly in a coupled reaction.
- That the P_i released from ATP hydrolysis can be added to another compound (by phosphorylation) which often makes the compound more reactive.
- That ATP can be resynthesised from ADP and P_i in a condensation reaction that's catalysed by ATP synthase — this reaction occurs during photosynthesis and respiration.
- That water makes up 80% of a cell's contents and has lots of important properties such as: it functions as a metabolite, it's a good solvent, it has a large latent heat of vaporisation allowing organisms to lose heat through evaporation, it has a high specific heat capacity and so can buffer changes in temperature, and it's a very cohesive substance.
- That inorganic ions are ions that don't contain carbon and that they occur, in solution, in the cytoplasms of cells and in the body fluids of organisms.
- That inorganic ions have specific roles depending on their properties and that you know the roles of iron, hydrogen, sodium and phosphate ions in the body.

Exam-style Questions

1   Inside the cell, the mitochondrion produces ATP.
Molecules of ATP contain three phosphate groups.

1.1   Describe the rest of the structure of ATP.

(2 marks)

1.2   Name the enzyme that catalyses the formation of ATP.

(1 mark)

1.3   Name **one** other molecule that contains a phosphate ion.

(1 mark)

ATP hydrolysis is coupled to the action of DNA helicases in
unwinding a DNA molecule during DNA replication.

1.4   Describe the reaction of ATP hydrolysis.

(3 marks)

1.5   Suggest why ATP hydrolysis is coupled to the action of DNA helicase.

(2 marks)

2   When humans exercise vigorously they lose water from their bodies in sweat.

2.1   Name the property of water that enables sweating to have a cooling effect
on the body during exercise and explain how it has this effect.

(3 marks)

Sweat contains ions, such as sodium ions (Na^+), dissolved in water.

2.2   Describe how sodium ions dissolve in water.

(3 marks)

2.3   Give **one** use of sodium ions in the body.

(1 mark)

Figure 1 shows the amount of
sweat lost by a person over the
course of one hour of exercise.

2.4   How much sweat had the person
lost after 14 minutes?

(1 mark)

2.5   Calculate the person's sweat rate
at 20 minutes.

(2 marks)

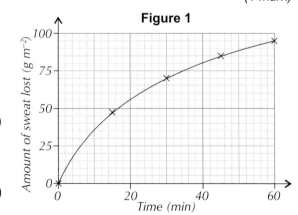

Figure 1

3   DNA replication is the process by which DNA copies itself. The process can be divided into a number of stages which are listed in **Table 1** below.

Table 1

Stage	Description
A	Adjacent DNA nucleotides on each new DNA strand are joined together by an enzyme. Hydrogen bonds form between the bases on the original and new strands.
B	DNA helicase attaches to the DNA molecule and breaks the hydrogen bonds between the bases on the two polynucleotide strands. The DNA unwinds to form two strands.
C	Free-floating DNA nucleotides are attracted to exposed bases on each template strand.
D	Two DNA molecules are produced. Each one contains one strand from the original DNA molecule (the template strand) and one new strand.

3.1   The stages shown above are not listed in the correct order.
List the stages in the correct order

(1 mark)

3.2   Name the enzyme involved in Stage **A**.

(1 mark)

3.3   In Stage **A**, name the type of reaction that joins adjacent DNA nucleotides together.

(1 mark)

3.4   In Stage **C**, free-floating nucleotides are attracted to exposed bases on the template strand via complementary base pairing. Explain what happens in complementary base pairing.

(2 marks)

4   DNA and RNA are both polynucleotides but have different functions.

4.1   Describe the difference between the functions of the two molecules.

(1 mark)

Figure 2 below shows a general nucleotide structure.

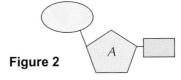

Figure 2

4.2   How is part **A** different in a DNA nucleotide compared to an RNA nucleotide?

(1 mark)

4.3   Describe **two** other differences between the structures of the polynucleotides DNA and RNA.

(2 marks)

1. Eukaryotic Cells and Organelles

Learning Objectives:

- Know the structure of eukaryotic cells, restricted to the structure and function of:
  - the cell-surface membrane
  - the nucleus (containing chromosomes consisting of protein-bound linear DNA and one or more nucleoli)
  - mitochondria
  - chloroplasts
  - Golgi apparatus and Golgi vesicles
  - lysosomes (a Golgi vesicle containing lysozymes)
  - ribosomes
  - rough endoplasmic reticulum and smooth endoplasmic reticulum
  - the cell wall
  - the cell vacuole (of plant cells only).
- Understand that in complex multicellular organisms, eukaryotic cells become specialised for specific functions.
- Be able to apply your knowledge of these features in explaining adaptations of eukaryotic cells.
- Know that specialised cells are organised into tissues, tissues into organs and organs into systems.

Specification Reference 3.2.1.1

No doubt you learnt about cell structure at GCSE, but there's a lot more to it at this level — as you're about to find out...

Eukaryotes and prokaryotes

All living organisms are made of cells, which have the same basic features in common. This suggests that all living things evolved from the same common ancestor (see page 19 for more).

There are two main types of organism — eukaryotes and prokaryotes. Prokaryotic organisms are **prokaryotic cells** (i.e. they're single-celled organisms). Eukaryotic organisms are made up of **eukaryotic cells**. Both types of cells contain organelles (see below). Eukaryotic cells are complex. Prokaryotic cells are smaller and simpler. There's more on prokaryotic cells on page 75.

Organelles

Organelles are parts of cells. Each one has a specific function. If you examine a cell through an electron microscope (see page 80) you can see its organelles and the internal structure of most of them. Everything you need to know about eukaryotic cell organelles is covered over the next few pages.

Eukaryotic cells

Eukaryotic cells are generally a bit more complicated than prokaryotic cells and have more organelles. Animal, plant, algal and fungal cells are all eukaryotic. You've probably been looking at animal and plant cell diagrams for years, so hopefully you'll be familiar with some of the bits and pieces...

Animal cells

Figure 1 shows the organelles found in a typical animal cell. You can compare these to the ones found in a typical plant cell on the next page.

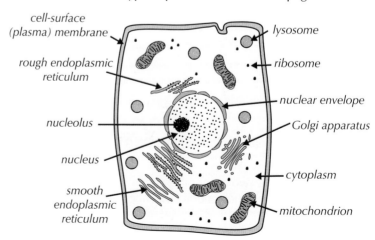

Figure 1: *The structure of a typical animal cell.*

Plant cells

Plant cells have the same organelles as animal cells,
but with a few added extras:

- a cellulose cell wall with plasmodesmata ('channels' for exchanging substances between adjacent cells),

- a vacuole (fluid-filled compartment),

- and of course good old chloroplasts (the organelles involved in photosynthesis).

These organelles are all shown in Figure 2.

Exam Tip
In the exam, you might
be shown electron
micrographs of different
types of cell, as well
as diagrams like the
ones here. Make
sure you know all the
distinguishing features
for each cell type.

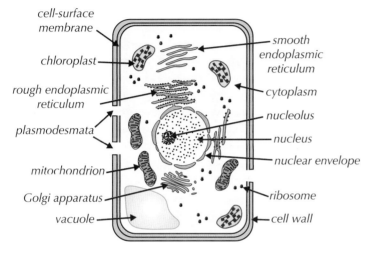

Figure 2: The structure of a typical plant cell.

Tip: You might also see
starch grains in plant
cells, although they're
not organelles. Plants
use starch grains to store
excess sugars.

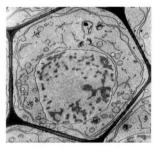

Figure 3: An electron
micrograph of a plant cell.
The cell walls appear
red/brown and the nucleus
appears blue.

Algal cells

Algae carry out photosynthesis, like plants, but unlike plants they can be
unicellular (e.g. *Chlorella*) or multicellular (e.g. seaweed). Figure 4 shows
some of the features of an algal cell.

Algal cells are a lot like plant cells — they have all the same
organelles, including a cellulose cell wall and chloroplasts. However,
the chloroplasts in many algal cells are a different shape and size to plant
chloroplasts. For example, some algae have one large chloroplast rather than
several smaller chloroplasts.

Tip: There are lots
of different types of
animal, plant, algal and
fungal cells and they
won't all look exactly
like the ones shown
here or have exactly
the same organelles
(e.g. not all plant cells
contain chloroplasts).

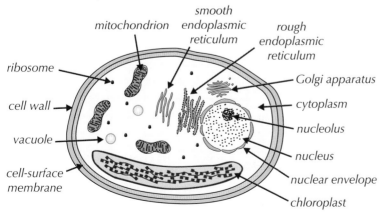

Figure 4: Structural features of an algal cell.

Fungal cells

Fungi can also be multicellular (e.g. mushrooms) or unicellular (e.g. yeast). Fungal cells (Figure 5) are also a lot like plant cells, but with two key differences:

- their cell walls are made of chitin, not cellulose.
- they don't have chloroplasts (because they don't photosynthesise).

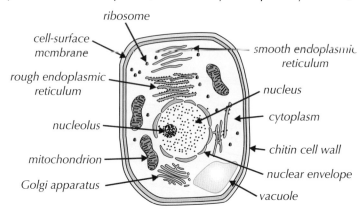

Figure 5: *Structural features of a fungal cell.*

Functions of organelles

Here's a big list of organelles — you need to know the structure and function of them all. Sorry.

Cell-surface membrane (Also called the plasma membrane)

Description

The membrane found on the surface of animal cells and just inside the cell wall of other cells. It's made mainly of lipids and protein.

Function

Regulates the movement of substances into and out of the cell. It also has receptor molecules on it, which allow it to respond to chemicals like hormones. See pages 95-96 for more.

Nucleus

Description

A large organelle surrounded by a nuclear envelope (double membrane), which contains many pores. The nucleus contains **chromosomes** (which are made from protein-bound linear DNA — see page 201) and one or more structure(s) called a **nucleolus**.

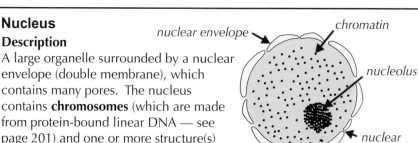

Function

The nucleus controls the cell's activities (by controlling the transcription of DNA — see pages 205-206). DNA contains instructions to make proteins. The pores allow substances (e.g. RNA) to move between the nucleus and the cytoplasm. The nucleolus makes ribosomes (see page 72).

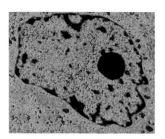

Figure 6: *An electron micrograph of a nucleus, showing the nucleolus and nuclear envelope.*

Tip: The plural of nucleus is nuclei and the plural of nucleolus is nucleoli. Weird.

Mitochondrion

Description

They're usually oval-shaped. They have a double membrane — the inner one is folded to form structures called cristae. Inside is the matrix, which contains enzymes involved in respiration.

Function

The site of aerobic respiration. Aerobic respiration produces ATP — a common energy source in the cell. Mitochondria are found in large numbers in cells that are very active and require a lot of energy.

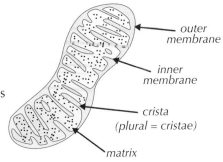

outer membrane

inner membrane

crista (plural = cristae)

matrix

Tip: The plural of mitochondrion is mitochondria.

Chloroplast

Description

A small, flattened structure found in plant cells and algal cells. It's surrounded by a double membrane, and also has membranes inside called thylakoid membranes. These membranes are stacked up in some parts of the chloroplast to form grana. Grana are linked together by lamellae — thin, flat pieces of thylakoid membrane.

Function

The site where photosynthesis takes place. Some parts of photosynthesis happen in the grana, and other parts happen in the stroma (a thick fluid found in chloroplasts).

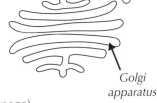

stroma

two membranes

granum (plural = grana)

lamella (plural = lamellae)

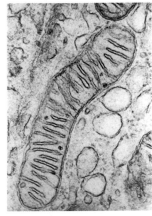

Figure 7: *An electron micrograph of a mitochondrion.*

Golgi apparatus

Description

A group of fluid-filled membrane-bound flattened sacs. Vesicles (see below) are often seen at the edges of the sacs.

Function

It processes and packages new lipids and proteins. It also makes lysosomes (see next page).

Golgi apparatus

Figure 8: *An electron micrograph of a chloroplast.*

Golgi vesicle

Description

A small fluid-filled sac in the cytoplasm, surrounded by a membrane and produced by the Golgi apparatus.

Function

Stores lipids and proteins made by the Golgi apparatus and transports them out of the cell (via the cell-surface membrane).

Golgi vesicle

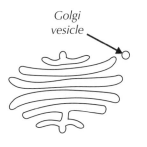

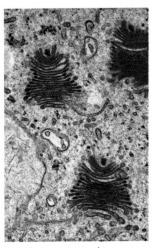

Figure 9: *An electron micrograph of Golgi apparatus.*

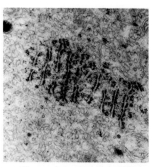

Figure 10: An electron micrograph showing SER (red-brown) and RER (blue).

Lysosome

Description
A round organelle surrounded by a membrane, with no clear internal structure. It's a type of Golgi vesicle.

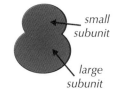

Function
Contains digestive enzymes called lysozymes. These are kept separate from the cytoplasm by the surrounding membrane, and can be used to digest invading cells or to break down worn out components of the cell.

Ribosome

Description
A very small organelle that floats free in the cytoplasm or is attached to the rough endoplasmic reticulum. It's made up of proteins and RNA (see page 53). It's not surrounded by a membrane.

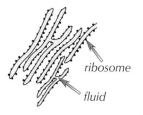

small subunit

large subunit

Function
The site where proteins are made.

Rough endoplasmic reticulum (RER)

Description
A system of membranes enclosing a fluid-filled space. The surface is covered with ribosomes.

Function
Folds and processes proteins that have been made at the ribosomes.

ribosome

fluid

Smooth endoplasmic reticulum (SER)

Description
Similar to rough endoplasmic reticulum, but with no ribosomes.

Function
Synthesises and processes lipids.

Cell wall

Description
A rigid structure that surrounds cells in plants, algae and fungi. In plants and algae it's made mainly of the carbohydrate cellulose. In fungi, it's made of chitin.

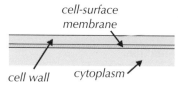

cell-surface membrane

cell wall   *cytoplasm*

Function
Supports cells and prevents them from changing shape.

Cell vacuole (plants)

Description
A membrane-bound organelle found in the cytoplasm. It contains cell sap — a weak solution of sugar and salts. The surrounding membrane is called the tonoplast.

tonoplast

Function
Helps to maintain pressure inside the cell and keep the cell rigid. This stops plants wilting. It's also involved in the isolation of unwanted chemicals inside the cell.

Cell function and organelles

In multicellular eukaryotic organisms, cells become specialised to carry out specific functions.

A cell's structure (i.e. its shape and the organelles it contains) helps it to carry out its function — so depending on what job it does, a specialised cell can look very different to the cells you saw on pages 68-70.

In the exam, you might get a question where you need to apply your knowledge of organelles to explain why a specialised cell is particularly suited to its function. You'll need to think about what organelles the cell needs to do its job — e.g. if the cell uses a lot of energy, it'll need lots of mitochondria. If it makes a lot of proteins it'll need a lot of ribosomes.

Examples

Epithelial cells

Epithelial cells in the small intestine are adapted to absorb food efficiently:

- The walls of the small intestine have lots of finger-like projections called villi. These increase surface area for absorption.

- The epithelial cells on the surface of the villi have folds in their cell-surface membranes, called **microvilli**. Microvilli increase surface area even more.

- They also have lots of mitochondria — to provide energy for the transport of digested food molecules into the cell.

microvilli increase surface area

nucleus

cytoplasm

mitochondrion

Red blood cells

Red blood cells are adapted to carry oxygen around the body. They have no nucleus to make more room for the oxygen-carrying compound haemoglobin.

Sperm cells

Sperm cells contain a lot of mitochondria to provide the large amounts of energy they need to propel themselves towards an egg.

Cell organisation

In multicellular eukaryotic organisms, specialised cells are grouped together to form **tissues**. A tissue is a group of cells working together to perform a particular function. Different tissues work together to form **organs**. Different organs make up an **organ system**.

Example

Epithelial cells make up epithelial tissue. Epithelial tissue, muscular tissue and glandular tissue (which secretes chemicals) all work together to form the stomach — an organ. The stomach is part of the digestive system — this is an organ system made up of all the organs involved in the digestion and absorption of food (including the small intestine, large intestine and liver).

Q1 Figure 11 below shows a mitochondrion.
    Name the parts labelled A-C.

Q2 Identify the organelle shown in Figure 12.

Tip: The mitochondrion here appears round rather than elongated like the one on page 71 because of the way the specimen was cut for the electron micrograph.

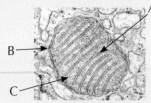

Figure 11

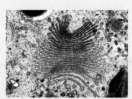

Figure 12

Q3 Below is a list of cell types and their function.

Cell type	Function
Cardiac muscle cells	Contraction of the heart.
Alveolar macrophage cells	To ingest and digest pathogens invading the lungs.
Beta cells in islets of Langerhans	To produce insulin (a protein).
Proximal tubule epithelial cells	To reabsorb useful molecules filtered out of the blood by the kidneys.

a) Name one organelle you would expect to find a lot of in cardiac muscle cells. Give a reason for your answer.

b) Suggest how alveolar macrophage cells are adapted to their function in terms of the organelles they contain.

c) Name three organelles you would expect to find a lot of in beta cells in the islets of Langerhans.

d) Suggest how proximal tubule epithelial cells are adapted to their function in terms of the organelles they contain.

Q1 Give two functions of the cell-surface membrane.

Q2 The diagram on the right is of a cell nucleus.
    Name the structures labelled A-D.

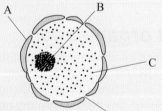

Q3 Describe the function of the nucleus.

Q4 Describe the appearance of the Golgi apparatus.

Q5 Give one function of a lysosome.

Q6 What is the function of the smooth endoplasmic reticulum?

Q7 Explain the difference between a tissue and an organ.

Q8 What is an organ system?

2. Prokaryotic Cells and Viruses

Prokaryotic cells and viruses are different from eukaryotic cells — in fact, viruses aren't even cells. And you can't get much more different than that. You need to learn their structures and how they replicate.

Prokaryotic cell structure

Prokaryotes are single-celled organisms.
Bacteria (like *E. coli*) are examples of prokaryotes.

You need to know the structure of a prokaryotic cell and what all the different organelles inside are for — see Figure 1. Prokaryotic cells are much smaller and simpler than eukaryotic cells — and they don't have any membrane-bound organelles (like a nucleus) in their cytoplasm.

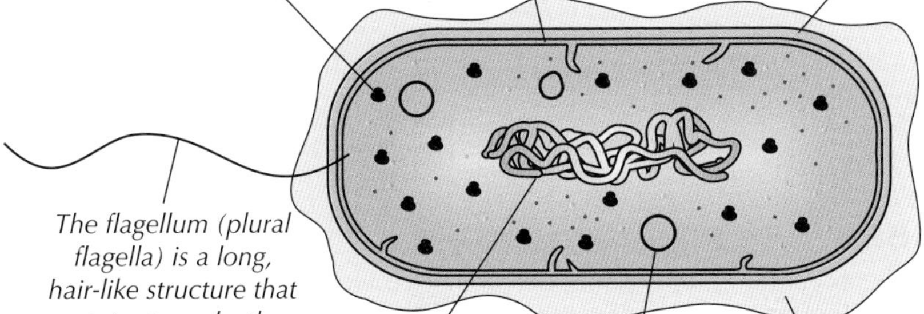

Just like in a eukaryotic cell, the cell-surface membrane is mainly made of lipids and proteins. It controls the movement of substances into and out of the cell.

The cell wall supports the cell and prevents it from changing shape. It's made of a polymer called murein. Murein is a glycoprotein (a protein with a carbohydrate attached).

Cytoplasm contains ribosomes — but they're smaller than those in a eukaryotic cell.

The flagellum (plural flagella) is a long, hair-like structure that rotates to make the prokaryotic cell move. Not all prokaryotes have a flagellum. Some have more than one.

Some prokaryotes (e.g. bacteria) also have a capsule made up of secreted slime. It helps to protect the bacteria from attack by cells of the immune system.

Unlike a eukaryotic cell, a prokaryotic cell doesn't have a nucleus. Instead, the DNA floats free in the cytoplasm. It's circular DNA, present as one long coiled-up strand. It's not attached to any histone proteins (see p. 201).

Plasmids are small loops of DNA that aren't part of the main circular DNA molecule. Plasmids contain genes for things like antibiotic resistance, and can be passed between prokaryotes. Plasmids are not always present in prokaryotic cells. Some prokaryotic cells have several.

Figure 1: *The structure of a prokaryotic cell.*

Prokaryotic cells are extremely small — less than 2 μm in diameter (that's two millionths of a metre or 0.002 mm). Eukaryotic cells can be up to 50 times bigger (although that's still only around 0.1 mm).

Learning Objectives:

- Know that prokaryotic cells are much smaller than eukaryotic cells and differ from eukaryotic cells in having:
  - cytoplasm that lacks membrane-bound organelles
  - smaller ribosomes
  - no nucleus (instead they have a single circular DNA molecule that is free in the cytoplasm and is not associated with proteins)
  - a cell wall that contains murein (a glycoprotein).
- Know that prokaryotic cells may also have one or more plasmids, a capsule surrounding the cell and one or more flagella.
- Know that binary fission in prokaryotic cells involves replication of the circular DNA and plasmids and division of the cytoplasm to produce two daughter cells (each with a single copy of the circular DNA and a variable number of copies of plasmids).
- Recall that viruses are acellular and non-living.
- Know the structure of virus particles.
- Know that viruses do not undergo cell division. Following injection of their nucleic acid, the infected host cell replicates virus particles.

Specification Reference 3.2.1.2 and 3.2.2

Figure 2: An electron micrograph of the bacteria that cause cholera. The long 'tails' are flagella.

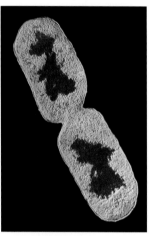

Figure 4: E.coli bacteria replicating by binary fission. The red blobs are DNA.

Tip: DNA and RNA are nucleic acids — see pages 51-53 for more.

Tip: There are lots of different viruses and they can look very different from each other. Some viruses (e.g. HIV) also have an envelope, which surrounds the capsid.

Prokaryotic cell replication

Prokaryotic cells replicate by a process called **binary fission**. In binary fission, the cell replicates (makes copies of) its genetic material, before physically splitting into two daughter cells.

The process of binary fission

Step 1

The circular DNA and plasmid(s) replicate. The main DNA loop is only replicated once, but plasmids can be replicated loads of times.

Step 2

The cell gets bigger and the DNA loops move to opposite 'poles' (ends) of the cell.

Step 3

The cytoplasm begins to divide (and new cell walls begin to form).

Step 4

The cytoplasm divides and two daughter cells are produced. Each daughter cell has one copy of the circular DNA, but can have a variable number of copies of the plasmid(s).

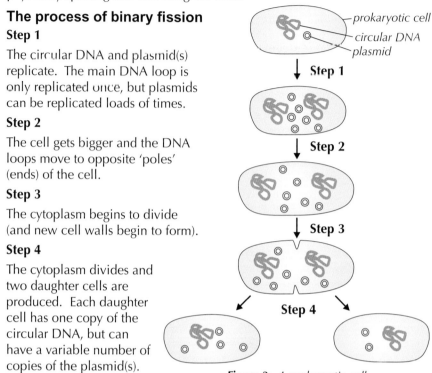

Figure 3: A prokaryotic cell undergoing binary fission.

Viruses

Viruses are **acellular** — they're not cells. In fact, viruses are just nucleic acids surrounded by protein — they're not even alive. Examples of viruses include HIV (which causes AIDS — see p. 130), influenza (which causes the flu) and rhinoviruses (which cause colds). All viruses invade and reproduce inside the cells of other organisms (see next page). These cells are known as **host cells**.

You need to learn the basic structure of a virus — see Figure 5. Unlike bacteria, viruses have no cell-surface membrane, no cytoplasm and no ribosomes. They do have a protein coat, called a **capsid**, with **attachment proteins** sticking out from it. The attachment proteins let the virus cling onto a suitable host cell. Viruses are even smaller than bacteria — e.g. HIV is about 0.1 μm across.

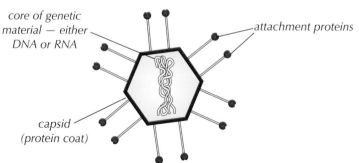

Figure 5: The general structure of a virus.

Viral replication

Because they're not alive, viruses don't undergo cell division. Instead, they inject their DNA or RNA into the host cell — this hijacked cell then uses its own 'machinery' (e.g. enzymes, ribosomes) to do the virus's dirty work and replicate the viral particles. The overall process is shown in Figure 6.

In order to inject their DNA or RNA, viruses first have to attach to the host cell surface. To do this they use their attachment proteins to bind to complementary receptor proteins on the cell-surface membrane of the host cells. Different viruses have different attachment proteins and therefore require different receptor proteins on host cells. As a result, some viruses can only infect one type of cell (e.g. some viruses can only infect one species of bacteria), while others can infect lots of different cells (e.g. influenza).

Tip: The receptor proteins on the host cells aren't just there to let viruses attach. They're actually proteins that play a role in the normal workings of the cell. Viruses have just evolved to exploit them.

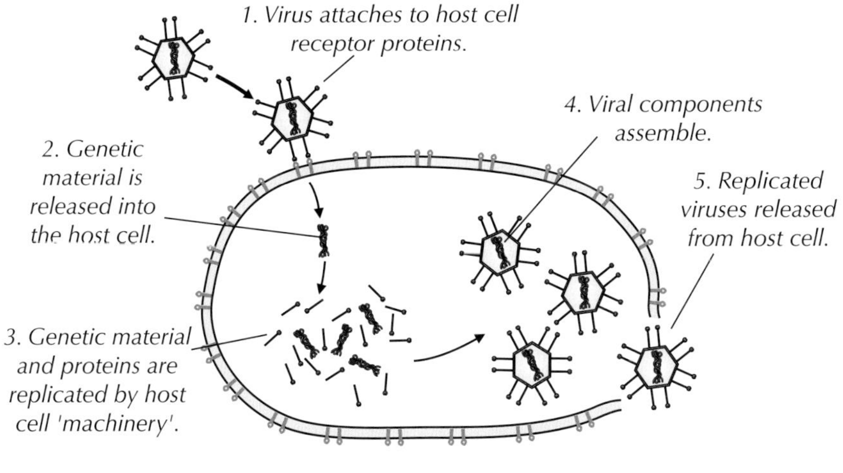

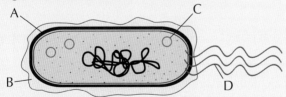

1. Virus attaches to host cell receptor proteins.

4. Viral components assemble.

2. Genetic material is released into the host cell.

5. Replicated viruses released from host cell.

3. Genetic material and proteins are replicated by host cell 'machinery'.

Figure 6: Example of viral replication by the host cell.

Tip: Different viruses enter and leave the host cell in different ways and are replicated by the host cell in slightly different ways. E.g. HIV releases its capsid into the cell as well as its genetic material — see page 131. Figure 6 just shows the basic concept.

Practice Questions — Application

A scientist investigating the cause of an outbreak of food poisoning has found a type of bacterium in a faeces sample that he thinks is causing the illness. A diagram of the bacterium is shown below:

A   C

B   D

Q1 Name the features labelled A-D.

Q2 Suggest why features B and D make this bacterium well adapted to living in the gut.

Q3 Describe how the genetic material is arranged in this cell.

Practice Questions — Fact Recall

Q1 Where is murein used in prokaryotic cells?

Q2 Name and describe the process by which prokaryotic cells reproduce.

Q3 What is a capsid?

Q4 What is the role of viral attachment proteins?

- Be able to use this
  formula to calculate
  magnification:

  $$\frac{\text{size of image}}{\text{size of real object}}$$

- Know the
  difference between
  magnification and
  resolution.

- Know the principles
  and limitations of
  optical microscopes
  and transmission and
  scanning electron
  microscopes.

- Appreciate that there
  was a considerable
  period of time
  during which the
  scientific community
  distinguished between
  artefacts and cell
  organelles.

- Understand how cell
  fractionation and
  ultracentrifugation are
  used to separate cell
  components.

**Specification
Reference 3.2.1.3**

3. Analysis of Cell Components

Investigating cells, and what's in them, involves digging out your microscope.

Magnification and resolution of microscopes

We all know that microscopes produce a magnified image of a sample,
but resolution is just as important...

Magnification

Magnification is how much bigger the image is than the specimen (the sample
you're looking at). It's calculated using this formula:

$$\text{magnification} = \frac{\text{size of image}}{\text{size of real object}}$$

Examples — Maths Skills

Calculating magnification

If you have a magnified image that's 5 mm
wide and your specimen is 0.05 mm wide the
magnification is:

$$\text{magnification} = \frac{\text{size of image}}{\text{size of real object}}$$

$$= \frac{5}{0.05} = \times\,100$$

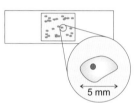
5 mm

Calculating size of image

If your specimen is 0.1 mm wide and the magnification of the microscope
is × 20, then the size of the image is:

$$\text{size of image} = \text{magnification} \times \text{size of real object}$$
$$= 20 \times 0.1 = \mathbf{2\ mm}$$

Calculating size of real object

If you have a magnified image that's 5 mm wide and the magnification is
× 50, then the size of the real object (i.e. the size of the specimen you're
looking at) is:

$$\text{size of real object} = \frac{\text{size of image}}{\text{magnification}} = \frac{5}{50} = \mathbf{0.1\ mm}$$

When you're calculating magnification you need to make sure that all lengths
are in the same unit, e.g. all in millimetres. When dealing with microscopes
these units can get pretty tiny. The table below shows common units:

Exam Tip
If you find rearranging
formulas hard you can
use a formula triangle
to help:

All you do is put your
finger over the one you
want and read off the
formula. E.g. if you
want the size of the real
object, you put your
finger over that and it
leaves behind size of
image ÷ magnification.

To convert	Unit	How many millimetres it is:	To convert
× 1000	Millimetre (mm)	1 mm	÷ 1000
× 1000	Micrometre (µm)	0.001 mm	÷ 1000
	Nanometre (nm)	0.000001 mm	

Example — Maths Skills

To convert from a smaller unit to a bigger unit you divide by 1000.
So to convert 6 micrometres to millimetres you divide 6 by 1000
= 0.006 mm. To go from a bigger unit to a smaller unit you times by 1000.

Resolution

Resolution is how detailed the image is. More specifically, it's how well a microscope distinguishes between two points that are close together. If a microscope lens can't separate two objects, then increasing the magnification won't help.

Tip: A microscope can't distinguish between objects that are smaller than its maximum resolution.

┌ **Example** ─────────────────────────────

When you look at a car in the dark that's a long way away you see the two headlights as one light. This is because your eyes can't distinguish between the two points at that distance — your eyes produce a low resolution image. When the car gets a bit closer you can see both headlights — a higher resolution image.

Practice Questions — Application

Q1 Image A shows a cartilage cell under a × 3150 microscope.

Image A

a) What is the diameter of the nucleus (labelled A) in millimetres?

b) What is the diameter of the cell (labelled B) in millimetres?

Q2 A researcher is examining some ribosomes under a microscope. Ribosomes are around 0.00002 mm long. How long will the image appear through a × 40 microscope? Give your answer in standard form.

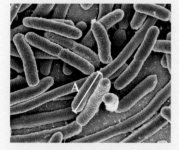

Image B

Q3 Image B shows some bacteria. It was taken using a × 7000 microscope. How long is the bacterium labelled A, in micrometres?

Q4 Rhinovirus particles are around 0.023 μm in diameter. What will the diameter of the image be through a × 1500 microscope? Give your answer in millimetres.

Image C

Q5 Image C shows a blood clot in an artery (labelled A). The clot is 2 mm in diameter.

a) What is the magnification of the microscope?

b) The diameter of the artery is 3 mm. If the same specimen was examined under a × 50 microscope, what would the diameter of the artery in the image be?

Q6 A mitochondrion is 10 μm long. In a microscope image it is 10 mm. What is the magnification of the microscope?

Exam Tip
You might have to use standard form in your exam. It's when numbers are written to the power of 10, e.g. 2×10^{-5} instead of 0.00002 mm. See p. 8.

Exam Tip
Don't forget that the units need to be the same, e.g. all in millimetres, or all in micrometres.

Exam Tip
In the exam, you could be given a micrograph with a scale bar drawn on it. E.g. ├─┤ 10 μm . If so, you can use this bar to work out the size of the real object. E.g. if the specimen is 4 bars long, it would measure:
$4 \times 10 = 40$ μm.

Types of microscope

Optical (light) microscopes

They use light to form an image. They have a maximum resolution of about 0.2 micrometres (μm). This means you can't use an optical microscope to view organelles smaller than 0.2 μm. That includes ribosomes, the endoplasmic reticulum and lysosomes. You may be able to make out mitochondria — but not in perfect detail. You can also see the nucleus. The maximum useful magnification of an optical microscope is about × 1500.

Electron microscopes

They use electrons to form an image. They have a higher resolution than optical microscopes, so give a more detailed image (and can be used to look at more organelles). They have a maximum resolution of about 0.0002 micrometres (μm). (About 1000 times higher than optical microscopes.) The maximum useful magnification of an electron microscope is about × 1 500 000. Electron microscopes produce black and white images, but these are often coloured by a computer.

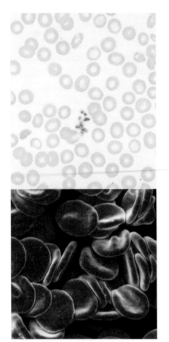

Figure 1: *Red blood cells seen under an optical microscope (top) and an electron microscope (bottom).*

	Optical microscope	Electron microscope
Magnification	Lower (maximum of × 1500)	Higher (maximum of × 1 500 000)
Resolution	Lower (maximum of 0.2 μm)	Higher (maximum of 0.0002 μm)

Figure 2: *Comparison table of optical and electron microscope features.*

Types of electron microscope

Transmission electron microscopes (TEMs)

TEMs use electromagnets to focus a beam of electrons, which is then transmitted through the specimen. Denser parts of the specimen absorb more electrons, which makes them look darker on the image you end up with. TEMs are good because they give high resolution images, so you see the internal structure of organelles like chloroplasts. But you've got to view the specimen in a vacuum, so they're no good for looking at living organisms. They can also only be used on thin specimens.

Scanning electron microscopes (SEMs)

SEMs scan a beam of electrons across the specimen. This knocks off electrons from the specimen, which are gathered in a cathode ray tube to form an image. The images you end up with show the surface of the specimen and they can be 3-D. SEMs are good because they can be used on thick specimens, but they give lower resolution images than TEMs.

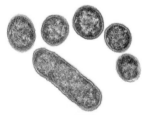

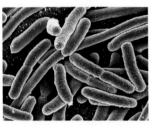

Figure 3: *A TEM (top), and SEM (bottom) of E.coli bacteria.*

	TEMs	SEMs
Advantages	Give high resolution images, so shows small objects.	Can be used on thick specimens. Can be 3-D.
Disadvantages	Can only be used on thin specimens. Can only be used on non-living specimens.	Give lower resolution images than TEMs. Can only be used on non-living specimens.

Figure 4: *Comparison table of TEM and SEM features.*

Preparing microscope slides

If you want to look at a specimen with an optical microscope, you'll need to put it on a microscope slide (strip of clear glass or plastic) first. This is often done using a **temporary mount** (also known as a wet mount). This is where the specimen is suspended in a drop of liquid (e.g. water, oil) on the slide.

1. Start by pipetting a small drop of water onto the centre of the slide.

2. Then use tweezers to place a thin section of your specimen on top of the water drop. (Your specimen needs to let light through it for you to be able to see it clearly under the microscope — so if you've got quite a thick specimen, you'll need to take a thin slice to use on your slide).

3. Add a drop of a stain. Stains are used to highlight objects in a cell.

   - **Examples**
     - Eosin is used to make the cytoplasm show up.
     - Iodine in potassium iodide solution (see page 26) is used to stain starch grains in plant cells.

4. Finally, add the cover slip (a square of clear glass or plastic that protects the specimen). To do so, stand the slip upright on the slide, next to the water droplet. Then carefully tilt and lower it so it covers the specimen. Try not to get any air bubbles under there (see below) — they'll obstruct your view of the specimen. These steps are shown in Figure 5.

Tip: You can also get dry mounts, where the specimen is put on the slide without being suspended in liquid.

Tip: Make sure that you're aware of any hazards, particularly for any stains you're using, before you start preparing your slide.

Tip: Temporary mounts can't be stored for very long — that's why they're temporary. They're good for looking at organisms that live in water though, e.g. algae.

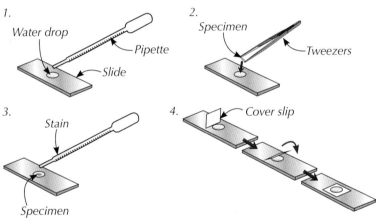

Figure 5: Preparation of a temporary mount microscope slide.

Figure 6: *A scientist adding a drop of stain during the preparation of a temporary mount microscope slide.*

Microscope artefacts

Artefacts are things that you can see down the microscope that aren't part of the cell or specimen that you're looking at. They can be anything from bits of dust, air bubbles and fingerprints, to inaccuracies caused by squashing and staining your sample. Artefacts are usually made during the preparation of your specimen and shouldn't really be there at all.

Artefacts are especially common in electron micrographs because specimens need a lot of preparation before you can view them under an electron microscope.

The first scientists to use electron microscopes could only distinguish between artefacts and organelles by repeatedly preparing specimens in different ways. If an object could be seen with one preparation technique, but not another, it was more likely to be an artefact than an organelle.

Figure 7: *A close up of a bee's eye, taken with an electron microscope, showing artefacts (purple and brown circles) caused by incorrect preparation of the specimen.*

Cell fractionation

Suppose you wanted to look at some organelles under an electron microscope. First you'd need to separate them from the rest of the cell — you can do this by cell fractionation. There are three steps to this technique:

1. Homogenisation — breaking up the cells

Homogenisation can be done in several different ways, e.g. by vibrating the cells or by grinding the cells up in a blender. This breaks up the plasma membrane and releases the organelles into solution.

The solution must be kept ice-cold, to reduce the activity of enzymes that break down organelles. The solution should also be isotonic — this means it should have the same concentration of chemicals as the cells being broken down, to prevent damage to the organelles through osmosis. A buffer solution should be added to maintain the pH.

2. Filtration — getting rid of the big bits

Next, the homogenised cell solution is filtered through a gauze to separate any large cell debris or tissue debris, like connective tissue, from the organelles. The organelles are much smaller than the debris, so they pass through the gauze.

3. Ultracentrifugation — separating the organelles

After filtration, you're left with a solution containing a mixture of organelles. To separate a particular organelle from all the others you use ultracentrifugation:

- The cell fragments are poured into a tube. The tube is put into a centrifuge (a machine that separates material by spinning) and is spun at a low speed. The heaviest organelles, like nuclei, get flung to the bottom of the tube by the centrifuge. They form a thick sediment at the bottom — the pellet. The rest of the organelles stay suspended in the fluid above the sediment — the supernatant.

- The supernatant is drained off, poured into another tube, and spun in the centrifuge at a higher speed. Again, the heaviest organelles form a pellet at the bottom of the tube. The supernatant containing the rest of the organelles is drained off and spun in the centrifuge at an even higher speed.

- This process is repeated at higher and higher speeds, until all the organelles are separated out — see Figure 9. Each time, the pellet at the bottom of the tube is made up of lighter and lighter organelles.

The organelles are separated in order of mass (from heaviest to lightest) — this order is usually: nuclei, then mitochondria, then lysosomes, then endoplasmic reticulum, and finally ribosomes. In plant cells, the chloroplasts come out after the nuclei, but before the mitochondria.

Tip: There's loads more about osmosis on pages 104-105.

Tip: Filtration separates cell debris from the organelles, it doesn't separate out the different organelles (that's the job of ultracentrifugation).

Figure 8: *A centrifuge.*

Exam Tip
You can remember the order the organelles separate out in (Nuclei, Chloroplasts, Mitochondria, Lysosomes, ER, Ribosomes) using "Naughty Clever Monkeys Like Eating Red Raspberries".

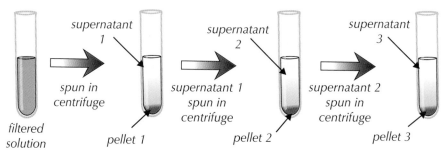

Figure 9: *Ultracentrifugation.*

Practice Questions — Application

Q1 Suggest what type of microscope you would use in each of the following scenarios. Give a reason for each answer.

a) Studying how *E.coli* bacteria replicate.

b) Studying the 3-D structure of red blood cells.

c) Studying virus particles that are 0.1 μm in diameter.

Tip: For Q1, you need to think about the advantages and disadvantages of each type of microscope.

Q2 The diagram below shows the first few steps in the ultracentrifugation of animal tissue.

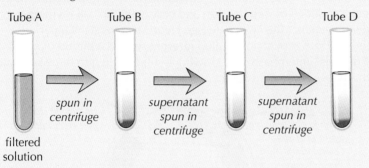

Which organelles would you expect to find in:

a) Tube A

b) The pellet in Tube B

c) The supernatant in Tube D

Practice Questions — Fact Recall

Q1 What is the formula for calculating the magnification of a microscope?

Q2 What's the difference between the magnification of a microscope and its resolution?

Q3 What is the maximum resolution for:

a) An optical microscope?

b) An electron microscope?

Q4 Which has a higher maximum magnification, an optical microscope or an electron microscope?

Q5 What type of microscope would you use to study lysosomes?

Q6 How do transmission electron microscopes work?

Q7 How do scanning electron microscopes work?

Q8 Give one advantage and one disadvantage of TEMs.

Q9 Give one advantage of SEMs over TEMs.

Q10 What is a temporary mount microscope slide?

Q11 What is a microscope artefact?

Q12 How did the first scientists to use electron microscopes distinguish between artefacts and organelles?

Q13 Give two ways homogenisation for cell fractionation is done.

Q14 Describe what happens at the filtration step of cell fractionation and explain why it is carried out.

- Know that within multicellular organisms, not all cells retain the ability to divide — cells that do show a cell cycle.
- Know that DNA replication occurs during interphase of the cell cycle.
- Know that mitosis is the part of the cell cycle in which a eukaryotic cell divides to produce two daughter cells, each with the identical copies of DNA produced by the parent cell during DNA replication.
- Recall the behaviour of chromosomes in interphase and at each stage of mitosis.
- Know the role of spindle fibres attached to centromeres in the separation of chromatids.
- Know that division of the cytoplasm (cytokinesis) usually occurs, producing two new cells.
- Be able to recognise the stages of the cell cycle.
- Be able to explain the appearance of cells at each stage of mitosis.
- Know that mitosis is a controlled process and that uncontrolled cell division can lead to the formation of tumours and of cancers.
- Know that many cancer treatments are directed at controlling the rate of cell division.

Specification Reference 3.2.2

4. Cell Division — Mitosis

We need new cells for growth and to replace damaged tissue, so our body cells need to be able to make more of themselves. They do this during the cell cycle, which includes mitosis.

The cell cycle

In multicellular organisms, not all cells keep their ability to divide. The ones that do follow a process called the cell cycle. The cell cycle starts when a cell has been produced by cell division and ends with the cell dividing to produce two identical cells. The cell cycle (see Figure 1) consists of a period of cell growth and DNA replication, called **interphase**, and a period of cell division, called **mitosis**. Interphase (cell growth) is subdivided into three separate growth stages. These are called G_1, S and G_2.

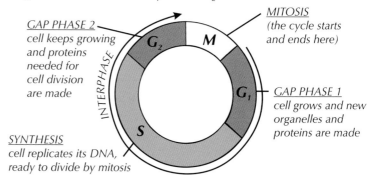

GAP PHASE 2
cell keeps growing and proteins needed for cell division are made

MITOSIS
(the cycle starts and ends here)

GAP PHASE 1
cell grows and new organelles and proteins are made

SYNTHESIS
cell replicates its DNA, ready to divide by mitosis

INTERPHASE

Figure 1: *Stages of the cell cycle.*

Interphase

During interphase the cell carries out normal functions, but also prepares to divide. The cell's DNA is unravelled and replicated, to double its genetic content. The organelles are also replicated so it has spare ones, and its ATP content is increased (ATP provides the energy needed for cell division).

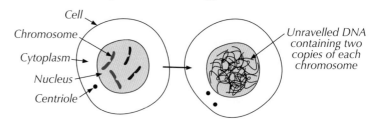

Cell
Chromosome
Cytoplasm
Nucleus
Centriole

Unravelled DNA containing two copies of each chromosome

Mitosis

There are two types of cell division — mitosis and meiosis (see p. 216 for more on meiosis). Mitosis is the form of cell division that occurs during the cell cycle. In mitosis, a parent cell divides to produce two genetically identical daughter cells (they contain an exact copy of the DNA of the parent cell). Mitosis is needed for the growth of multicellular organisms (like us) and for repairing damaged tissues. How else do you think you get from being a baby to being a big, strapping teenager — it's because the cells in our bodies grow and divide.

Mitosis is really one continuous process, but it's described as a series of division stages — prophase, metaphase, anaphase and telophase (see the next page).

The structure of chromosomes in mitosis

Before we go into the detail of mitosis, you need to know more about the structure of chromosomes. As mitosis begins, the chromosomes are made of two strands joined in the middle by a **centromere**. The separate strands are called **chromatids**. Two strands on the same chromosome are called **sister chromatids**. There are two strands because each chromosome has already made an identical copy of itself during interphase. When mitosis is over, the chromatids end up as one-strand chromosomes in the new daughter cells.

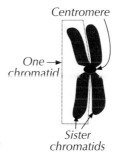

Centromere

One → chromatid

Sister chromatids

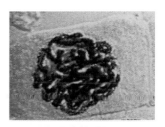

Figure 2: *Interphase in bluebell cells.*

1. Prophase

The chromosomes condense, getting shorter and fatter. Tiny bundles of protein called centrioles start moving to opposite ends of the cell, forming a network of protein fibres across it called the spindle. The nuclear envelope (the membrane around the nucleus) breaks down and chromosomes lie free in the cytoplasm.

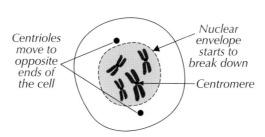

Centrioles move to opposite ends of the cell

Nuclear envelope starts to break down

Centromere

Figure 3: *Prophase in bluebell cells.*

2. Metaphase

The chromosomes (each with two chromatids) line up along the middle of the cell and become attached to the spindle by their centromere.

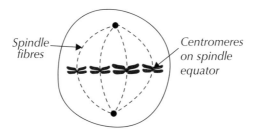

Spindle fibres

Centromeres on spindle equator

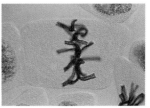

Figure 4: *Metaphase in bluebell cells.*

3. Anaphase

The centromeres divide, separating each pair of sister chromatids. The spindles contract, pulling chromatids to opposite poles (ends) of the spindle, centromere first. This makes the chromatids appear v-shaped.

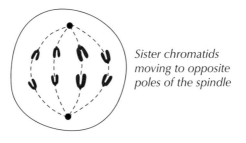

Sister chromatids moving to opposite poles of the spindle

Figure 5: *Anaphase in bluebell cells.*

4. Telophase

The chromatids reach the opposite poles on the spindle. They uncoil and become long and thin again. They're now called chromosomes again. A nuclear envelope forms around each group of chromosomes, so there are now two nuclei. The cytoplasm divides (**cytokinesis**) and there are now two daughter cells that are genetically identical to the original cell and to each other. Mitosis is finished and each daughter cell starts the interphase part of the cell cycle to get ready for the next round of mitosis.

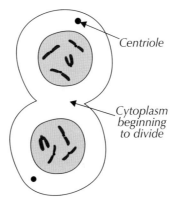

Centriole

Cytoplasm beginning to divide

Figure 6: *Telophase in bluebell cells.*

How long does each stage of mitosis take?

The time taken for each stage of mitosis varies depending on the cell type
and the environmental conditions. You can calculate how long each stage of
mitosis lasts if you're given the right information.

Example — Maths Skills

A scientist observes a section of growing tissue under the microscope.
He counts 100 cells undergoing mitosis. Of those, 10 cells are in
metaphase. One complete cell cycle of the tissue lasts 15 hours.
How long do the cells spend in metaphase? Give your answer in minutes.

- The scientist has observed that 10 out of 100 cells are in metaphase.
  This suggests that the proportion of time the cells spend in metaphase
  must be 10/100th of the cell cycle.

- You're told that the cell cycle in these cells lasts 15 hours.
  That's (15 × 60 =) 900 minutes.

- So the cells spend: $\frac{10}{100} \times 900 = $ **90 minutes in metaphase**.

Practice Questions — Application

Q1 The photo on the right shows
mitosis in onion cells.

Which cell (A-C) is undergoing
the following:

a) metaphase,

b) anaphase?

Give a reason for each of your answers.

Q2 The graph below shows changes in the mass of a cell and its DNA
during the cell cycle.

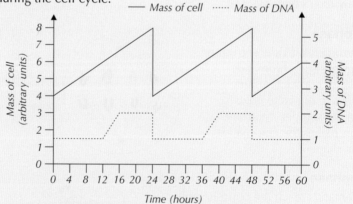

a) During which hours does synthesis take place?
Explain your answer.

b) At which hours does mitosis take place? Explain your answer.

c) i) How many cell divisions are shown on the graph?

   ii) At what time will the next cell division take place?

Q3 A scientist is looking at a tissue sample under a microscope.
She counts 150 cells undergoing mitosis. Of those, 12 cells are in
prophase. One complete cell cycle of the tissue lasts 0.70 days.
How long do the cells spend in prophase? Give your answer in hours.

Cancer

Mitosis and the cell cycle are controlled by genes. Normally, when cells have divided enough times to make enough new cells, they stop. But if there's a mutation in a gene that controls cell division, the cells can grow out of control. The cells keep on dividing to make more and more cells, which form a tumour. Cancer is a tumour that invades surrounding tissue.

Tip: Mutations are changes in the base sequence of an organism's DNA (see page 221).

Cancer treatments

Some treatments for cancer are designed to control the rate of cell division in tumour cells by disrupting the cell cycle. This kills the tumour cells. These treatments don't distinguish tumour cells from normal cells though — they also kill normal body cells that are dividing. However, tumour cells divide much more frequently than normal cells, so the treatments are more likely to kill tumour cells.

Tip: Cancer is basically uncontrolled cell division.

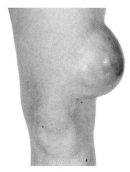

Figure 7: Cancer of the knee — the tumour is sticking out of the leg.

Examples

Some cell cycle targets of cancer treatments include:

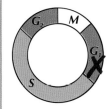

G_1 (cell growth and protein production)

Some chemical drugs (chemotherapy) prevent the synthesis of enzymes needed for DNA replication. If these aren't produced, the cell is unable to enter the synthesis phase (S), disrupting the cell cycle and forcing the cell to kill itself.

S phase (DNA replication)

Radiation and some drugs damage DNA. At several points in the cell cycle, the DNA in the cell is checked for damage. If severe DNA damage is detected, the cell will kill itself — preventing further tumour growth.

Tip: Rapidly dividing cells, like hair cells and cells that line the gut, are often affected by cancer treatments. This can cause side effects like hair loss.

Practice Question — Application

Q1 Methotrexate and vincristine are drugs used to treat cancer. Methotrexate blocks the formation of nucleotides within cells and vincristine prevents the formation of spindle fibres within the nuclei of cells. Which stage of the cell cycle is disrupted by:

    a) methotrexate   b) vincristine?

Tip: Don't let the tricky names of the drugs throw you when answering Q1 here. Just apply your knowledge to the information given in the question.

Practice Questions — Fact Recall

Q1 What is the cell cycle?

Q2 Why is mitosis needed?

Q3 In what stage of the cell cycle does all the DNA unravel?

Q4 Describe what happens during prophase.

Q5 Describe what happens during telophase.

Q6 What is cytokinesis?

Q7 What is cancer?

- Be able to prepare stained squashes of cells from plant root tips, and set up and use an optical microscope, to identify the stages of mitosis in the stained squashes and calculate the mitotic index (Required Practical 2).

- Know how to measure the size of an object viewed with an optical microscope.

- Be able to measure the apparent size of cells in the root tip and calculate their actual size using the formula:

Actual size =

$$\frac{\text{size of image}}{\text{magnification}}$$

Specification Reference 3.2.2

Tip: Make sure you carry out a risk assessment (see p. 3) before you do this experiment, including assessing the specific risks for the particular staining technique you're using.

Tip: If you're using ethano-orcein as a stain, the tips will also need to be fixed in ethanoic acid before step 2.

Tip: Applying too much pressure to the slide or coverslip can break them. Be careful not to shatter the slide when cutting the root tip and be careful not to break the cover slip when squashing the cells.

5. Investigating Mitosis

You need to know how to carry out an experiment to investigate mitosis in cells — that includes preparing a root tip cell squash, using an optical microscope to view the cells and doing a few calculations based on what you see.

Preparing a root tip cell squash

REQUIRED PRACTICAL **2**

You need to know how to prepare and stain a root tip in order to observe the stages of mitosis. Make sure you're wearing safety goggles and a lab coat before you start. You should also wear gloves when using stains.

1. Add some 1 M hydrochloric acid to a boiling tube. There should be just enough acid in the tube to cover the root tip (see step 3) — so the acid should only be a few millimetres deep. Put the tube in a water bath that has been allowed to reach 60 °C.

2. Use a scalpel to cut 1 cm from the tip from a growing root (e.g. of an onion). It needs to be the tip because that's where growth occurs and so that's where mitosis takes place.

3. Carefully transfer the root tip into the boiling tube containing the acid. Incubate it for about 5 minutes.

4. Use tweezers to remove the root tip from the tube and use a pipette to rinse it well with cold water. Leave the tip to dry on a paper towel.

5. Place the root tip on a microscope slide (see Figure 1) and cut 2 mm from the very tip of it. Get rid of the rest.

6. Use a mounted needle to break the tip open and spread the cells out thinly.

7. Add a few drops of stain and leave it for a few minutes. The stain will make the chromosomes easier to see under a microscope. There are loads of different stains, all with crazy names — toluidine blue O, ethano-orcein, Feulgen stain. (If you're using the Feulgen stain, you'll need an extra rinse.)

8. Place a cover slip over the cells and put a piece of folded filter paper on top. Push down firmly to squash the tissue. Squashing will make the tissue thinner and allow light to pass through it. Don't smear the cover slip sideways or you'll damage the chromosomes.

9. Now you can look at all the stages of mitosis under an optical microscope (see next page). You should see something that looks like Figure 2.

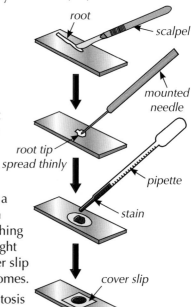

Figure 1: *Preparing a root tip squash slide.*

root
scalpel
mounted needle
root tip spread thinly
pipette
stain
cover slip

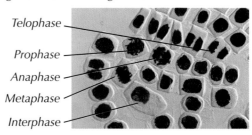

Figure 2: *Optical microscope image of a stained root tip squash, showing cells in different stages of mitosis.*

Telophase
Prophase
Anaphase
Metaphase
Interphase

Using an optical microscope

REQUIRED PRACTICAL **2**

You need to know how to set up and use an optical microscope (see Figure 3) to observe your prepared root tip cells:

- Start by clipping the slide you've prepared onto the stage.
- Select the lowest-powered **objective lens** (i.e. the one that produces the lowest magnification).
- Use the coarse adjustment knob to move the objective lens down to just above the slide.
- Look down the eyepiece (which contains the **ocular lens**) and adjust the focus with the fine adjustment knob, until you get a clear image of what's on the slide.
- If you need to see the slide with greater magnification, swap to a higher-powered objective lens and refocus.

Tip: The objective and ocular lenses magnify the specimen.

Tip: The <u>objective lenses</u> on your school microscope are likely to provide x 4, x 10 and x 40 magnification. The <u>ocular lens</u> probably also provides x 10 magnification. You need to multiply the magnification of the two lenses together to get the overall magnification. E.g. if you're using the x 40 objective lens and the x 10 ocular lens, the overall magnification will be x 10 multiplied by x 40 = x 400.

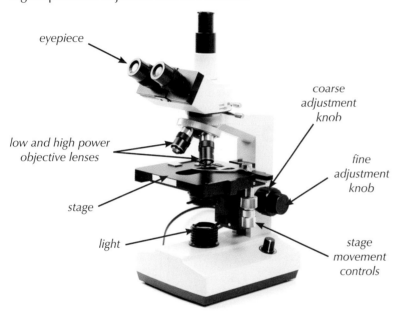

Figure 3: An optical microscope.

Tip: Not all optical microscopes look the same, but they all have similar controls. You should be able to work out what does what on your school microscope from this diagram.

If you're asked to draw cells undergoing mitosis under the microscope, make sure the relative sizes of objects in your drawing are accurate and that you write down the magnification the specimen was viewed under. You'll also need to label your drawing and give it a title.

Calculating the mitotic index

REQUIRED PRACTICAL **2**

The mitotic index is the proportion of cells in a tissue sample that are undergoing mitosis. It lets you work out how quickly the tissue is growing and if there's anything weird going on. You can calculate the mitotic index of your squash cells using this formula:

Tip: Your drawing should be done using a sharp pencil (not pen). Don't colour in or shade your drawing and make sure outlines are drawn neatly, not sketched.

$$\text{mitotic index} = \frac{\text{number of cells with visible chromosomes}}{\text{total number of cells observed}}$$

A plant root tip is constantly growing, so you'd expect a high mitotic index (i.e. lots of cells in mitosis). In other tissue samples, a high mitotic index could mean that tissue repair is taking place or that there is cancerous growth in the tissue.

Example — Maths Skills

If you observed 30 cells, and 4 of them had visible chromosomes:

$$\text{mitotic index} = \frac{4}{30} = \textbf{0.13}$$

The mitotic index can also be presented as a percentage.
All you have to do is multiply the figure by 100:

$$0.13 \times 100 = \textbf{13\%}$$

Calculating the actual size of cells

You need to be able to calculate the size of the cells you're looking at. That's where the eyepiece graticule and stage micrometer come in — they're a bit like rulers.

An **eyepiece graticule** is fitted onto the eyepiece. It's like a transparent ruler with numbers, but no units. The **stage micrometer** is placed on the stage — it is a microscope slide with an accurate scale (it has units) and it's used to work out the value of the divisions on the eyepiece graticule at a particular magnification. This means that when you take the stage micrometer away and replace it with the slide containing your tissue sample, you'll be able to measure the size of the cells.

Example — Maths Skills

- Line up the eyepiece graticule and the stage micrometer (see Figure 4).

- Each division on the stage micrometer is 0.1 mm long.

- At this magnification, 1 division on the stage micrometer is the same as 4.5 divisions on the eyepiece graticule.

- To work out the size of 1 division on the eyepiece graticule, you need to divide 0.1 by 4.5: $0.1 \div 4.5 = 0.022...$ mm.

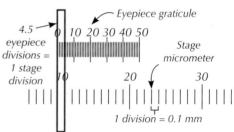

Figure 4: Lining up the eyepiece graticule and stage micrometer.

So if you look at a cell under the microscope at this magnification and it's 4 eyepiece divisions long (see Figure 5), you know it measures: $4 \times 0.022...$
$= 0.088...$
$= \textbf{0.09 mm}$ (1 s.f.)

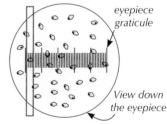

Figure 5: Using the calibrated eyepiece graticule to measure cells.

If you're given an image of cells under the microscope in the exam, you can calculate their actual size using this formula:

$$\text{actual size} = \frac{\text{size of image}}{\text{magnification}}$$

Example — Maths Skills

If the image of a cell measures 5 mm and the magnification is x 100, then the actual size of the cell will be:

$$\text{actual size} = \frac{5}{100} = \textbf{0.05 mm}$$

Practice Questions — Application

Q1 A student prepared a stained squash slide of cells from a hyacinth root tip, in order to investigate mitosis.

   a) Why was it necessary for the student to add a stain?

   b) Name one suitable stain that he could have used.

   c) Describe how the student should have squashed the tissue on the slide to avoid damaging the chromosomes.

   d) Would you expect the mitotic index of these root tip cells to be higher or lower than the mitotic index of cells taken from a mature hyacinth leaf? Explain your answer.

Q2 A microscope is set up with an eyepiece graticule and a stage micrometer. Each division on a stage micrometer is 10 μm long. At × 10 magnification, 1 division of the stage micrometer is equal to 6.5 divisions on the eyepiece graticule.

   a) Calculate the size of 1 division on the eyepiece graticule. Give your answer to the nearest 0.1 μm.

   b) A specimen is viewed under this microscope at × 10 magnification. It is 14 eyepiece divisions long. Use your answer to part a) to calculate the specimen's length. Give your answer to the nearest μm.

Q3 A clinical scientist was analysing a tissue sample from a patient. He observed 750 cells and found that 207 of them had visible chromosomes.

   a) Calculate the mitotic index for this tissue sample. Give your answer as a percentage.

   b) What does an abnormally high mitotic index suggest could be occurring in the tissue sample?

   The scientist also recorded the size of the cells.

   c) When using his optical microscope with a x 200 magnification, one of the cells appeared to be 9.0 mm across. What is the actual size of this cell? Give your answer in millimetres.

Exam Tip
Be prepared for exam questions on the apparatus and techniques you've used in your Required Practicals.

Practice Questions — Fact Recall

Q1 Describe how to focus an optical microscope on a specimen.

Q2 What is an eyepiece graticule?

Q3 What is the purpose of a stage micrometer?

Section Summary

Make sure you know:

- The structure, function and appearance of the following eukaryotic organelles: cell-surface membrane, nucleus (including the chromosomes and nucleolus), mitochondria, chloroplasts (plant and algal cells only), Golgi apparatus, Golgi vesicles, lysosomes, ribosomes, rough and smooth endoplasmic reticulum, cell wall (plant, algal and fungal cells) and cell vacuole (plant cells only).

- How in complex multicellular organisms, eukaryotic cells become specialised for a specific function.

- How to apply your knowledge of organelles to explain why different cells are suited to their function.

- That specialised cells are organised into tissues, tissues into organs and organs into systems.
- That prokaryotic cells are smaller and less complex than eukaryotic cells.
- How the structure of prokaryotic cells is different to eukaryotic cells — no membrane bound organelles in the cytoplasm (e.g. no nucleus), circular DNA and a murein cell wall.
- That some prokaryotic cells also have a capsule, flagella and plasmids.
- How a prokaryotic cell replicates by binary fission — the circular DNA and plasmids are replicated and then the cell divides to produce two daughter cells, each with a single copy of the circular DNA and a variable number of copies of plasmids.
- That viruses are non-living and acellular, so they don't undergo cell division. Instead, they invade host cells and use the host cell 'machinery' to replicate themselves.
- The structure of a typical virus, including the genetic material, capsid and attachment proteins.
- How to calculate magnification using the formula: magnification = size of image ÷ size of real object.
- The difference between magnification (how much bigger the image is than the sample) and resolution (how detailed the image is, based on the microscope's ability to distinguish between two points that are close together).
- The principles and limitations of optical microscopes, transmission electron microscopes (TEMs) and scanning electron microscopes (SEMs).
- How to prepare temporary mount microscope slides for viewing specimens with optical microscopes.
- That it wasn't always easy for early scientists using microscopes to distinguish between artefacts and cell organelles — and how they eventually did this.
- How cell fractionation separates out organelles — homogenisation, filtration and ultracentrifugation.
- That in multicellular organisms, not all cells are able to keep dividing.
- All about the eukaryotic cell cycle, including that DNA replication takes place in interphase and that the division of cells occurs during mitosis.
- That mitosis produces two daughter cells that are genetically identical to each other and to the parent cell.
- How the chromosomes behave during interphase, prophase, metaphase, anaphase and telophase of mitosis and the role of spindle fibres during mitosis.
- That mitosis ends with cytokinesis — division of the cytoplasm.
- How to recognise the stages of the cell cycle, including being able to explain the appearance of cells at each stage of mitosis.
- That when mitosis becomes uncontrolled, tumours and cancers can form.
- That cancer treatments are often aimed at controlling the rate of cell division.
- How to prepare stained squashes of root tip cells, use an optical microscope to observe the stages of mitosis in those cells, and calculate the mitotic index (the proportion of cells undergoing mitosis) of the cells (Required Practical 2).
- How to measure the size of an object viewed with an optical microscope, including how to use an eyepiece graticule and stage micrometer.
- How to use the formula actual size = size of image ÷ magnification, to calculate the actual size of an object viewed through a microscope.

Exam-style Questions

1   A scientist is studying secretory epithelial cells from the stomach under an optical microscope. The microscope has a magnification of × 100 and a resolution of 0.2 μm.

1.1   The ribosomes in the epithelial cells are 25 nm in diameter. Will the scientist be able to see them using the light microscope? Explain your answer.

(1 mark)

1.2   The scientist sees an image of an epithelial cell that is 4 mm in diameter. Calculate the actual diameter of the cell.

(1 mark)

1.3   One of the main functions of secretory epithelial cells in the stomach is to produce and secrete digestive enzymes. Suggest **one** organelle that is likely to be present in large numbers in the epithelial cells to aid this function. Explain your choice.

(2 marks)

1.4   The scientist also separated the organelles by cell fractionation in order to study each one individually. Describe and explain the process of cell fractionation.

(5 marks)

2   Penicillins are a group of antibiotics that are only effective against prokaryotic cells. They work by inhibiting cell wall synthesis, leading to cell lysis (bursting)

2.1   Explain why penicillin antibiotics can clear bacterial infections in humans without harming the infected individual's cells.

(2 marks)

2.2   Antibiotics can be used to target other features of prokaryotic cells. Give an example of a feature that could be targeted and explain why it would be appropriate.

(2 marks)

3   A team of scientists has been investigating the interphase stage of the cell cycle.
The team analysed a sample of dividing cells using a machine called a flow cytometer.

Figure 1 shows the amount of DNA against the number of cells with that amount of DNA.

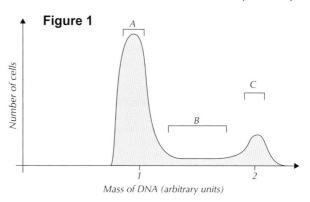

Figure 1

Number of cells

Mass of DNA (arbitrary units)

3.1   Three phases of interphase are shown by the labels **A**, **B** and **C** on the graph. Name each phase and explain your answers.

(3 marks)

3.2   Suggest why there are more cells in phase **A** than in phase **C**.

(1 mark)

4 Proteins control all the different stages of the cell cycle. An experiment was conducted on the effect of protein X on mitosis in one species of yeast cells.

At intervals the activity of the protein was measured and a microscope was used to determine the percentage of dividing yeast cells. The results are shown in **Figure 2**.

Figure 2

Dividing cells
Protein X activity
Activity of protein X
% of cells dividing
100
200
300
400
500
Time (minutes)

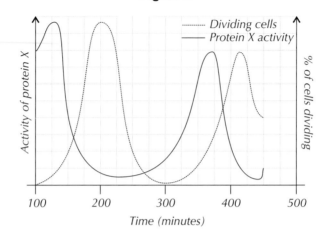

4.1 A scientist uses the data shown in the graph to conclude there is a causal relationship between protein X activity and cell division in all species of yeast. How far does the data support this conclusion?

(3 marks)

4.2 Suggest a control that could have been carried out for this experiment and explain its purpose.

(2 marks)

5 **Figure 3** shows an eye.

Figure 3

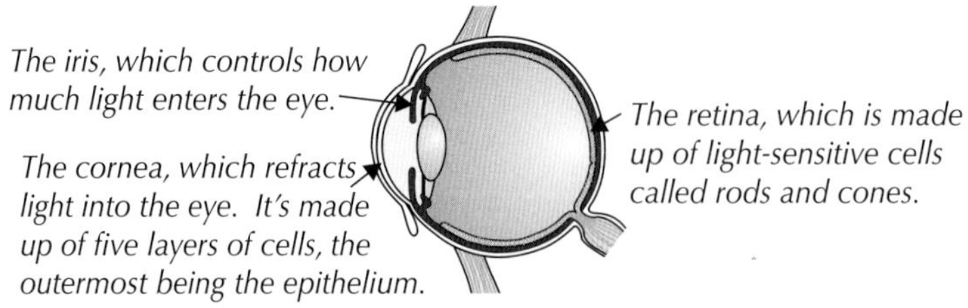

The iris, which controls how much light enters the eye.
The cornea, which refracts light into the eye. It's made up of five layers of cells, the outermost being the epithelium.
The retina, which is made up of light-sensitive cells called rods and cones.

5.1 Is the eye a tissue or an organ?
Use evidence from **Figure 3** to explain your answer.

(2 marks)

5.2 In normal cells there is a protein called Rb that stops the cell from leaving the G_1 phase of the cell cycle unless the cell needs to divide. A mutation in the gene for Rb can cause retinoblastoma — an eye cancer. Explain why.

(3 marks)

1. Cell Membranes — The Basics

Cell membranes are the boundaries of cells, but there's an awful lot more to them than that...

Membrane function

All cells are surrounded by membranes. In eukaryotic cells, many of the organelles are surrounded by membranes too.

Cell-surface membranes

Cell-surface membranes surround cells. They are a barrier between the cell and its environment, controlling which substances enter and leave the cell. They're **partially permeable** — they let some molecules through but not others. Substances can move across the cell-surface membrane by **diffusion**, **osmosis** or **active transport** (see pages 100-110). The cell-surface membrane is sometimes called the plasma membrane.

Membranes within cells

The membranes around organelles divide the cell into different compartments — they act as a barrier between the organelle and the cytoplasm.

┌ Example ───
The substances needed for respiration (like enzymes) are kept together inside a mitochondrion by the membrane surrounding the mitochondrion.
└

They are also partially permeable and control what substances enter and leave the organelle.

┌ Example ───
RNA (see page 51) leaves the nucleus via the nuclear membrane (also called the nuclear envelope). DNA is too large to pass through the partially permeable membrane, so it remains in the nucleus.
└

Membrane structure

The basic structure of all cell membranes is pretty much the same. They're composed of lipids (mainly phospholipids — see page 28), proteins and carbohydrates (attached to proteins or lipids).

In 1972, the **fluid mosaic model** was suggested to describe the arrangement of molecules in the membrane — see Figure 2 (next page). In the model, phospholipid molecules form a continuous, double layer (called a bilayer). This bilayer is 'fluid' because the phospholipids are constantly moving.

Proteins are scattered through the bilayer, like tiles in a mosaic. These include **channel proteins** and **carrier proteins**, which allow large molecules and ions to pass through the membrane. Receptor proteins on the cell-surface membrane allow the cell to detect chemicals released from other cells. The chemicals signal to the cell to respond in some way, e.g. the hormone insulin binds to receptor proteins on liver cells, which tells the cells to absorb glucose.

Learning Objectives:

- Know that the basic structure of all cell membranes, including cell-surface membranes and the membranes around the cell organelles of eukaryotes, is the same.

- Know the arrangement and any movement of phospholipids, proteins, glycoproteins and glycolipids in the fluid mosaic model of membrane structure.

- Understand how the nature of the phospholipid bilayer limits the diffusion of particles across cell membranes.

- Understand that cholesterol may also be present in cell membranes where it restricts the movement of other molecules making up the membrane.

- Know how to investigate the effect of a named variable on the permeability of cell-surface membranes (Required Practical 4).

Specification Reference 3.2.3

Tip: The phospholipid bilayer is about 7 nm thick.

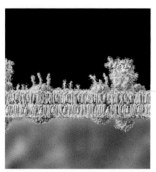

Figure 1: A computer model of the fluid mosaic model.

Some proteins are able to move sideways through the bilayer, while others are fixed in position. Some proteins have a carbohydrate attached — these are called **glycoproteins**. Some lipids also have a carbohydrate attached — these are called **glycolipids**. **Cholesterol** molecules are also present within the bilayer.

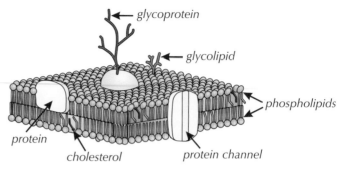

Figure 2: The fluid mosaic model of a cell membrane.

Membrane components

You need to know the roles of these two membrane components:

Phospholipids

Phospholipid molecules form a barrier to dissolved (water-soluble) substances. Phospholipids have a 'head' and a 'tail'. The head is **hydrophilic** — it attracts water. The tail is **hydrophobic** — it repels water.

Tip: A polar molecule has one end with a slightly positive charge and one end with a slightly negative charge — see page 61. These charges are nowhere near as strong as the positive or negative charge on an ion, but they do help polar molecules to dissolve in water. Non-polar substances have no charges.

The molecules automatically arrange themselves into a bilayer — the heads face out towards the water on either side of the membrane (see Figure 3).

The centre of the bilayer is hydrophobic so the membrane doesn't allow water-soluble substances (like ions and polar molecules) to diffuse through it. Small, non-polar substances (e.g. carbon dioxide) and water can diffuse through the membrane (see page 100).

Figure 3: Phospholipid bilayer.

Cholesterol

Tip: Water is actually a polar molecule, but it can diffuse (by osmosis) through the cell membrane because it's so small (see page 104).

Cholesterol gives the membrane stability. It is a type of lipid that's present in all cell membranes (except bacterial cell membranes). Cholesterol fits between the phospholipids (see Figure 4).

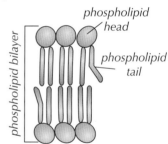

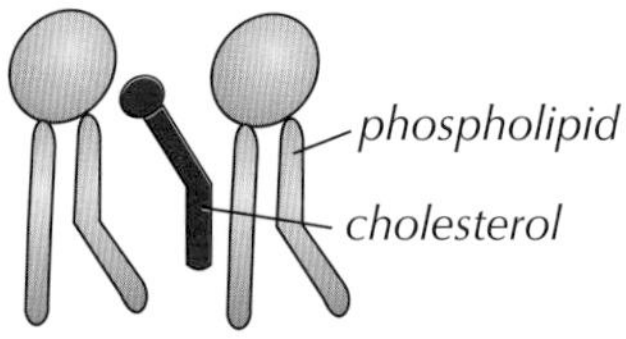

Figure 4: Cholesterol in the membrane.

Cholesterol binds to the hydrophobic tails of the phospholipids, causing them to pack more closely together. This restricts the movement of the phospholipids, making the membrane less fluid and more rigid.

Tip: There's more on phospholipids on pages 28-29.

Cholesterol helps to maintain the shape of animal cells (which don't have cell walls). This is particularly important for cells that aren't supported by other cells, e.g. red blood cells, which float free in the blood.

Cholesterol also has hydrophobic regions, so it's able to create a further barrier to polar substances moving through the membrane.

Temperature and membranes

Cell membranes are affected by temperature — it affects how much the phospholipids in the bilayer can move, which affects membrane structure and permeability.

Temperatures below 0 °C

The phospholipids don't have much energy, so they can't move very much. They're packed closely together and the membrane is rigid. But channel proteins and carrier proteins in the membrane denature (lose structure and function), increasing the permeability of the membrane (see Point 1, Figure 5). Ice crystals may form and pierce the membrane, making it highly permeable when it thaws.

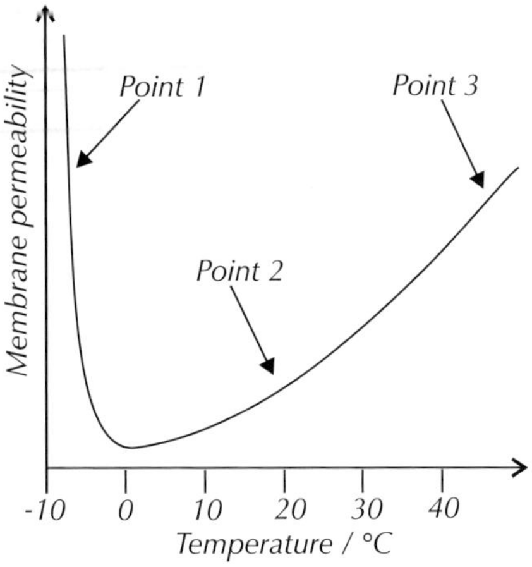

Temperatures between 0 and 45 °C

The phospholipids can move around and aren't packed as tightly together — the membrane is partially permeable (see Point 2, Figure 5). As the temperature increases the phospholipids move more because they have more energy — this increases the permeability of the membrane.

Figure 5: Graph to show the effect of temperature on membrane permeability.

Tip: You may remember from Topic 1A that proteins (e.g. enzymes) denature at high temperatures. Well, very cold temperatures (i.e. those below 0 °C) can cause proteins to denature too.

Temperatures above 45 °C

The phospholipid bilayer starts to melt (break down) and the membrane becomes more permeable. Water inside the cell expands, putting pressure on the membrane. Channel proteins and carrier proteins in the membrane denature so they can't control what enters or leaves the cell — this increases the permeability of the membrane (Point 3, Figure 5).

Tip: Think about what happens when you cook fruit or vegetables — as you apply heat, the food softens and liquid is released. This is partly because the cell membranes start to break down and become more permeable.

Practice Questions — Application

Q1 Suggest a function of each of the following membranes:
   a) the membrane surrounding a chloroplast.
   b) the membrane surrounding a bacterial cell.

Q2 Chloride ions (Cl⁻) need to pass through the cell-surface membrane to get inside the cell. How might they move across the membrane?

Q3 The protein content of a typical cell membrane is around 50%. In energy-releasing organelles, such as mitochondria, the amount rises to around 75%. Suggest a reason for this difference.

Q4 A person removes some raspberries from the freezer that have frozen solid and leaves them on a plate to defrost. When he returns, there's a red puddle on the plate around the fruit. Use your knowledge of cell membranes to explain what has happened.

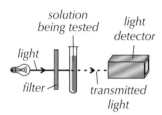

Figure 6: A diagram showing how a colorimeter works.

Figure 7: A cuvette being placed inside a colorimeter.

Investigating cell membrane permeability

You can investigate how different variables (e.g. temperature and solvent concentration) affect cell membrane permeability by doing experiments using beetroot. Beetroot cells contain a coloured pigment that leaks out — the higher the permeability of the membrane, the more pigment leaks out of the cell.

REQUIRED PRACTICAL **4**

Example — Investigating temperature

Here's how you could investigate how temperature affects beetroot membrane permeability:

1. Use a scalpel to carefully cut five equal sized pieces of beetroot. (Make sure you do your cutting on a cutting board.) Rinse the pieces to remove any pigment released during cutting.

2. Add the five pieces to five different test tubes, each containing 5 cm^3 of water. Use a measuring cylinder or pipette to measure the water.

3. Place each test tube in a water bath at a different temperature, e.g. 10 °C, 20 °C, 30 °C, 40 °C, 50 °C, for the same length of time (measured using a stopwatch).

4. Remove the pieces of beetroot from the tubes, leaving just the coloured liquid.

5. Now you need to use a **colorimeter** — a machine that passes light of a specific wavelength through a liquid and measures how much of that light is absorbed. Many colorimeters use filters to make sure the light passing through the liquid is at the desired wavelength.

6. Firstly, switch the colorimeter on and allow five minutes for it to stabilise. Then set up the colorimeter so you're using a blue filter (or a wavelength of about 470 nm).

7. Add distilled water to a cuvette so it is three quarters full (a cuvette is a small container that fits inside a colorimeter — see Figure 7). Put the cuvette into the colorimeter. Two of the cuvette's sides may be ridged or frosted — you need to make sure you put the cuvette into the colorimeter the correct way, so that the light will be passing through the clear sides. Calibrate the machine to zero.

8. Next, use a pipette to transfer a sample of the liquid from the first test tube to a clean cuvette — again it should be about three quarters full.

9. Put the cuvette in the colorimeter and read and record the absorbance of the solution.

10. Repeat steps 8-9 for the liquids in the remaining four test tubes (using a clean pipette and cuvette each time).

11. You're now ready to analyse your results — bear in mind, the higher the absorbance reading, the more pigment released, so the higher the permeability of the membrane.

Depending on the resources you have available, you may be able to connect the colorimeter to a computer and use software to collect the data and draw a graph of the results.

Investigating the effect of solvents

You could do a similar experiment with beetroot to investigate the effect of solvents on the permeability of cell membranes, i.e. by placing the beetroot cubes in different concentrations of a particular solvent (such as alcohol or acetone). Surrounding cells in an increasing concentration of a solvent increases membrane permeability because the solvent dissolves the lipids in the cell membrane, causing it to lose its structure.

Tip: If you're investigating the effect of solvents, remember to keep all other variables the same. Also, make sure you wear eye protection when working with solvents and that there are no naked flames around.

Practice Question — Application

Q1 An experiment was carried out to investigate the effect of increasing methanol concentration on the permeability of beetroot cell membranes. Beetroot cubes were soaked in varying concentrations of methanol for a set amount of time, then a colorimeter was used to read the absorbance of the liquid once the beetroot cubes had been removed. The results of the experiment were used to produce a graph.

a) Give four variables that should be controlled in this experiment.

b) Give two things that should be done with the colorimeter before it is used to measure the absorbance of the liquid samples.

c) Suggest which of the graphs below (A or B) was produced using the results of the experiment. Explain your answer.

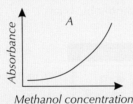

Practice Questions — Fact Recall

Q1 Identify the structures labelled A-E in the diagram below.

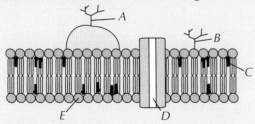

Q2 Why is the phospholipid bilayer described as fluid?

Q3 Describe the movement of proteins within the bilayer.

Q4 What is a glycoprotein?

Q5 Explain the meaning of the terms 'hydrophilic' and 'hydrophobic'.

Q6 Explain why a cell membrane is an effective barrier against water-soluble substances.

Q7 How does the cell-surface membrane control what enters and leaves the cell?

Q8 Describe the role of cholesterol in a cell membrane.

Q9 Briefly describe how you could investigate the effect of temperature on the permeability of cell membranes.

Exam Tip
Not all diagrams of the fluid mosaic model look the same, so don't just memorise the pictures — make sure you learn what all the different components actually are and how they fit together.

- Know that movement across cell membranes can occur by simple diffusion.

- Be able to explain how differences in gradients of concentration affect the rate of movement across cell membranes.

- Know that cells may be adapted for rapid transport across their internal or external membranes by an increase in surface area of their membranes, and be able to explain how this adaptation of specialised cells affects the rate of transport.

- Know that movement across cell membranes can also occur by facilitated diffusion (including the roles of carrier and channel proteins).

- Know that cells may be adapted for rapid transport across their internal or external membranes by an increase in the number of channel proteins and carrier proteins in their membranes, and be able to explain how this adaptation of specialised cells affects the rate of transport.

Specification Reference 3.2.3

Tip: Internal cell membranes are ones surrounding organelles, e.g. the mitochondria.

2. Diffusion

There are many ways substances move in and out of cells across the membrane. First up we have simple and facilitated diffusion...

The process of diffusion

Diffusion is the net movement of particles (molecules or ions) from an area of higher concentration to an area of lower concentration. Molecules will diffuse both ways, but the **net movement** will be to the area of lower concentration. This continues until particles are evenly distributed throughout the liquid or gas. The **concentration gradient** is the path from an area of higher concentration to an area of lower concentration. Particles diffuse down a concentration gradient.

Diffusion is a passive process — no energy is needed for it to happen. Particles can diffuse across cell membranes, as long as they can move freely through the membrane. When molecules diffuse directly through a cell membrane, it's also known as **simple diffusion**.

┌─ Example ───
Oxygen and carbon dioxide can diffuse easily through cell membranes because they're small, so they can pass through spaces between the phospholipids. They're also non-polar, which makes them soluble in lipids, so they can dissolve in the hydrophobic bilayer.

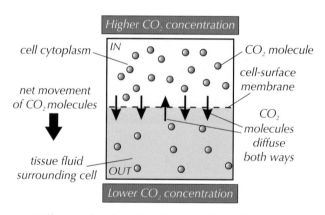

Figure 1: Diffusion of carbon dioxide across the cell-surface membrane.

Factors affecting the rate of diffusion

The rate of diffusion across both external and internal cell membranes can vary. Some specialised cells are adapted for rapid transport across their membranes. The rate of diffusion depends on:

- The concentration gradient — the higher it is, the faster the rate of diffusion. As diffusion takes place, the difference in concentration between the two sides of the membrane decreases until it reaches an equilibrium (i.e. the concentration on both sides is equal). This means that diffusion slows down over time.

- The thickness of the exchange surface — the thinner the exchange surface (i.e. the shorter the distance the particles have to travel), the faster the rate of diffusion.

- The surface area — the larger the surface area (e.g. of the cell-surface membrane), the faster the rate of diffusion.

Facilitated diffusion

Some larger molecules (e.g. amino acids, glucose) would diffuse extremely slowly through the phospholipid bilayer because they're so big. Charged particles, e.g. ions and polar molecules, would also diffuse slowly — that's because they're water soluble, and the centre of the bilayer is hydrophobic (see page 96). So to speed things up, large or charged particles diffuse through **carrier proteins** or **channel proteins** in the cell membrane instead — this is called facilitated diffusion.

Like diffusion, facilitated diffusion moves particles down a concentration gradient, from a higher to a lower concentration. It's also a passive process — it doesn't use energy. There are two types of protein involved — carrier proteins and channel proteins.

Tip: Remember — small, non-polar substances and water can diffuse directly through the membrane.

Exam Tip
Always say <u>down</u> the concentration gradient in the exam, not across or along — or you won't get the marks.

Carrier proteins

Carrier proteins move large molecules across the membrane, down their concentration gradient. Different carrier proteins facilitate the diffusion of different molecules. Here's how they work:

▪ First, a large molecule attaches to a carrier protein in the membrane.
▪ Then, the protein changes shape.
▪ This releases the molecule on the opposite side of the membrane — see Figure 2.

Tip: Carrier proteins and channel proteins are called transport proteins.

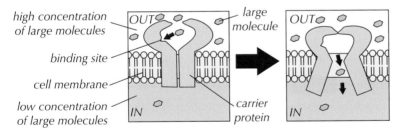

Figure 2: *Movement of a molecule by carrier proteins.*

Channel proteins

Channel proteins form pores in the membrane for charged particles to diffuse through (down their concentration gradient). Different channel proteins facilitate the diffusion of different charged particles.

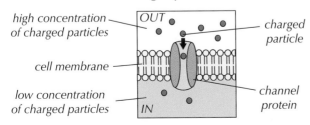

Figure 3: *Movement of a charged particle by channel proteins.*

Figure 4: *Computer model showing a cross section of a channel protein in the phospholipid bilayer.*

Factors affecting the rate of facilitated diffusion

The rate of facilitated diffusion depends on:

- The **concentration gradient** — the higher the concentration gradient, the faster the rate of facilitated diffusion (up to a point, see below). As equilibrium is reached, the rate of facilitated diffusion will level off.

- The number of **channel** or **carrier proteins** — once all the proteins in a membrane are in use, facilitated diffusion can't happen any faster, even if you increase the concentration gradient.

Tip: The green line on this graph shows the rate of uptake if glucose was absorbed by simple diffusion — it's much slower than facilitated diffusion.

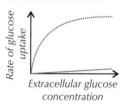

Rate of glucose uptake

Extracellular glucose concentration

Example

Glucose is absorbed from blood plasma into red blood cells via facilitated diffusion, using GLUT 1 carrier proteins. As the red line on the graph shows, the rate of uptake increases as the extracellular glucose concentration increases. The rate of uptake levels off as equilibrium is reached. After this, the rate of facilitated diffusion increases only slightly even at much greater glucose concentrations, as many of the GLUT 1 proteins are already in use.

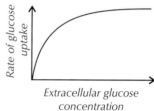

Rate of glucose uptake

Extracellular glucose concentration

So the greater the number of channel or carrier proteins in the cell membrane, the faster the rate of facilitated diffusion.

Example

Aquaporins are special channel proteins that allow the facilitated diffusion of water through cell membranes. Some kidney cells are adapted to have lots of aquaporins. The aquaporins allow the cells to reabsorb a lot of the water that would otherwise be excreted by the body.

Tip: About 180 litres of water need re-absorbing every day.

Calculating the rate of diffusion

In the exams, you might be asked to calculate the rate of diffusion (or any other form of transport across a membrane) from a graph. For a straight line graph, this means finding the **gradient** of the line. For a curved graph, it means drawing a **tangent** and finding the gradient of the tangent.

Tip: There's more on calculating rates from a graph on pages 13-15.

Example — Maths Skills

The graph below shows the concentration of a particle in a cell over time. The concentration is decreasing as the particle diffuses out of the cell. Find the rate of diffusion at 3 seconds.

<u>Step 1</u>: Draw a tangent to the curve at 3 s.

<u>Step 2</u>: Calculate the gradient of the tangent:

$$\text{gradient} = \frac{\text{change in } y}{\text{change in } x}$$

$$= \frac{0.2}{2.8} = 0.07$$

Tip: To find the units, divide the units on the y-axis by the units on the x-axis, just as you find the gradient.

<u>Step 3</u>: Find the units to give the rate of diffusion:

$$\text{rate of diffusion} = \textbf{0.07 Ms}^{-1}$$

Tip: Ms^{-1} means the same as M/s or moles per second.

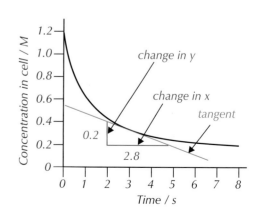

Concentration in cell / M

change in y

change in x

tangent

0.2

2.8

Time / s

Q1 The photograph on the right shows ink
diffusing through a beaker of water.
Explain what is happening
to the ink molecules.

Q2 Carbon dioxide is a waste product
of respiration and must be removed
from cells. How will each of the
following affect the rate of diffusion
of carbon dioxide across a cell-surface
membrane? Explain your answer
in each case.

a) Increasing the thickness of the cell membrane.

b) Increasing the number of folds in the cell membrane.

c) Reducing the concentration of carbon dioxide outside of the cell.

Q3 Simple diffusion and facilitated diffusion both move particles down
their concentration gradient across a cell membrane. Suggest how
you could determine whether a particular particle is being transported
by simple or facilitated diffusion in an experimental setting.
Explain your answer.

Q4 Following oral administration,
a particular drug diffuses
across the cell-surface
membranes of cells in the
digestive tract into the
blood plasma. The graph
on the right shows how
the concentration of the
drug in the blood plasma
changes over time.

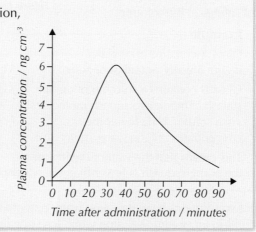

Calculate the rate of
diffusion 10-30 minutes
after taking the drug.

Q1   What is diffusion?

Q2   Is simple diffusion an active or passive process?

Q3   Give three factors that affect the rate of simple diffusion.

Q4   Is facilitated diffusion an active or passive process?

Q5   Briefly describe how a carrier protein transports molecules across a
cell membrane.

Q6   What is a channel protein?

Q7   Describe the role of channel proteins in the transport of particles
across a cell membrane.

Q8   Explain how increasing the number of carrier and channel proteins
in a membrane would affect the rate of facilitated diffusion.

Exam Tip
Make sure you don't get
the roles of carrier and
channel proteins mixed
up in the exam — you
could be throwing away
easy marks.

- Know that transport across the cell membrane can occur by osmosis.
- Be able to describe the process of osmosis in terms of water potential.
- Be able to explain how differences in water potential and a cell membrane's surface area affect the rate of movement across cell membranes.
- Know how to produce a dilution series of a solute and use it to produce a calibration curve with which to identify the water potential of plant tissue (Required Practical 3).

Specification Reference 3.2.3

3. Osmosis

Osmosis is a special case of diffusion for water molecules...

What is osmosis?

Osmosis is the diffusion of water molecules across a partially permeable membrane, from an area of higher water potential (i.e. higher concentration of water molecules) to an area of lower water potential (i.e. lower concentration of water molecules). **Water potential** is the potential (likelihood) of water molecules to diffuse out of or into a solution.

Water molecules are small and can diffuse easily through the cell membrane, but large solute molecules can't.

Pure water has a water potential of zero. Adding solutes to pure water lowers its water potential — so the water potential of any solution is always negative. The more negative the water potential, the stronger the concentration of solutes in the solution.

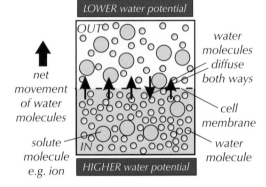

Figure 1: Osmosis across a cell membrane.

Example

Glass A contains pure water — it's got a water potential of zero.

Glass B contains a solution of orange squash. The orange squash molecules are a solute. They lower the concentration of the water molecules.

This means that the water potential of the orange squash is lower than the water potential of pure water.

If two solutions have the same water potential they're said to be **isotonic**. Cells in an isotonic solution won't lose or gain any water — there's no net movement of water molecules because there's no difference in water potential between the cell and the surrounding solution.

If a cell is placed in a solution that has a higher water potential it will swell as water moves into it by osmosis. Solutions with a higher water potential compared with the inside of the cell are called **hypotonic**. If a cell is placed in a solution that has a lower water potential it may shrink as water moves out of it by osmosis. Solutions with a lower water potential than the cell are called **hypertonic**.

Cell in an <u>isotonic</u> solution — no net movement of water.   *Cell in a <u>hypertonic</u> solution — net movement of water <u>out</u> of the cell.*   *Cell in a <u>hypotonic</u> solution — net movement of water <u>into</u> the cell.*

Factors affecting the rate of osmosis

The factors affecting the rate of osmosis are similar to those affecting the rate of diffusion (see page 100).

- The **water potential gradient** — the higher the water potential gradient, the faster the rate of osmosis. As osmosis takes place, the difference in water potential on either side of the membrane decreases, so the rate of osmosis levels off over time.

- The thickness of the exchange surface — the thinner the exchange surface, the faster the rate of osmosis.

- The surface area of the exchange surface — the larger the surface area, the faster the rate of osmosis.

Investigating water potential

REQUIRED PRACTICAL 3

You can do a simple experiment, using potato cylinders, to find out the water potential of plant tissue (see next page). There are three main steps involved:

> **Tip:** Before you start your investigation, make sure you do a risk assessment so you are aware of any potential hazards.

1. Making serial dilutions

Firstly you need to make up several solutions of different, known concentrations to test the cylinders in. You can do this using a **serial dilution** technique. A serial dilution is when you create a set of solutions that decrease in concentration by the same factor each time. It's a useful technique, particularly when you need to create a very weak solution, as it means you don't have to measure out very small volumes of liquid.

┌ **Example — Making serial dilutions** ─────────────

This is how you'd make five serial dilutions of a sucrose solution, starting with an initial sucrose concentration of 2 M and diluting each solution by a factor of 2...

1. Line up five test tubes in a rack.
2. Add 10 cm³ of the initial 2 M sucrose solution to the first test tube and 5 cm³ of distilled water to the other four test tubes (see Figure 2).
3. Then, using a pipette, draw 5 cm³ of the solution from the first test tube, add it to the distilled water in the second test tube and mix the solution thoroughly. You now have 10 cm³ of solution that's half as concentrated as the solution in the first test tube (it's 1 M).
4. Repeat this process three more times to create solutions of 0.5 M, 0.25 M and 0.125 M.

> **Tip:** Making serial dilutions is something you need to know how to do for your Required Practical, so you need to make sure you understand the process. See the next page for more on how to make up a solution of any given concentration.

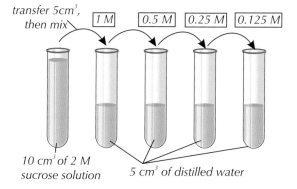

transfer 5cm³, then mix | 1 M | 0.5 M | 0.25 M | 0.125 M

10 cm³ of 2 M sucrose solution   5 cm³ of distilled water

Figure 2: How to make serial dilutions.

> **Tip:** You don't have to dilute solutions by a factor of 2. E.g. to dilute by a factor of 10, take 1 cm³ from your original sample and add it to 9 cm³ of water.

Example — Maths Skills

If you want to make 15 cm³ of 0.4 M sucrose solution...

1. Start with a solution of a known concentration, e.g. 1 M.

2. Find the scale factor by dividing the concentration of this solution by the concentration of the solution you want to make. So in this case the scale factor = 1 M ÷ 0.4 M = **2.5**.

3. This means that the solution you want to make is 2.5 times weaker than the one you have. To make the solution 2.5 times weaker, use 2.5 times less of it, i.e. 15 cm³ ÷ 2.5 = **6 cm³**. Transfer this amount to a clean test tube.

4. Top up the test tube with distilled water to get the volume you want to make. In this case you want to make 15 cm³ of solution, so you need to add: 15 – 6 = **9 cm³** of distilled water.

2. Measuring change in mass

Once you have made up a set of serial dilutions, you can use them to find the water potential of potato cells. First you need to measure how much mass the potato cells gain or lose in each solution...

1. Use a cork borer to cut potatoes into identically sized chips, about 1 cm in diameter. Divide the chips into groups of three and measure the mass of each group using a mass balance.

2. Place one group into each of your sucrose solutions and leave the chips in the solutions for at least 20 minutes (making sure that they all get the same amount of time).

3. Remove the chips and pat dry gently with a paper towel. Weigh each group again and record your results. Calculate the percentage change in mass for each group.

The potato chips will gain water (and therefore mass) in solutions with a higher water potential than the chips, and lose water in solutions with a lower water potential.

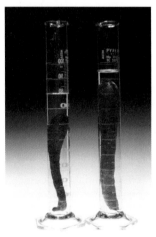

Figure 3: Osmosis in carrot cells. The carrot on the left has been placed in salty water (low water potential) and the carrot on the right has been placed in pure water.

3. Producing a calibration curve

Next, you can use your results to produce a calibration curve by plotting percentage change in mass against the concentration of sucrose solution. You can then use your calibration curve to determine the water potential of the potato cells:

Example — Maths Skills

The point at which your calibration curve crosses the x-axis (where the percentage change in mass is 0) is the point at which the water potential of the sucrose solution is the same as the water potential of the potato cells (see Figure 4). Find the concentration at this point, then look up the water potential for that concentration of sucrose solution in, e.g. a textbook.

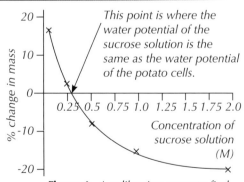

This point is where the water potential of the sucrose solution is the same as the water potential of the potato cells.

Concentration of sucrose solution (M)

Figure 4: A calibration curve to find the water potential of potato cells.

Practice Questions — Application

Q1 Describe the net movement of water molecules in each of the following situations:

   a) Human cheek cells with a water potential of -300 kPa are placed in a salt solution with a water potential of -325 kPa.

   b) Apple slices with a water potential of -750 kPa are placed in a beaker of pure water.

   c) Orange squash with a water potential of -450 kPa is sealed in a length of Visking tubing and suspended in a solution of equal water potential.

Q2 Potato cells with a water potential of -350 kPa are placed in sucrose solutions with varying water potentials. The water potential of each solution is shown in the table below.

Solution	Water potential
1	-250 kPa
2	-500 kPa
3	-1000 kPa

   a) After 15 minutes, the potato cells in solution 1 have increased in volume. Explain why this is the case.

   b) Predict whether the cells in solutions 2 and 3 will increase or decrease in volume. Explain your answers.

Q3 A scientist has a 1.5 M saline solution. For her experiment she needs 30 cm³ of 125 mM solution.

   a) Calculate the volume of the original solution and distilled water that she needs to make the new solution.

   b) From her 30 cm³ of 125 mM solution, she needs to make two more solutions. She will make serial dilutions, diluting by a factor of 5 each time. Describe fully how she would do this.

Tip: Water potential is usually measured in kilopascals (or kPa). It's actually a unit of pressure.

Tip: Visking tubing is a partially permeable membrane — it's used a lot in osmosis and diffusion experiments.

Tip: Remember, a higher water potential is closer to 0 (the water potential of pure water).

Tip: 1 M = 1000 mM.

Practice Questions — Fact Recall

Q1 Define osmosis.

Q2 Define the term 'water potential'.

Q3 Give three factors that affect the rate of osmosis.

Q4 Describe an investigation that you could do to find the water potential of potato cells.

Tip: You should include the use of a calibration curve in your answer to Q4.

Learning Objectives:

- Know that movement across cell membranes can occur by active transport (including the role of carrier proteins and the importance of the hydrolysis of ATP).

- Know that movement across cell membranes can occur by co-transport.

- Understand how co-transporters are involved in the absorption of sodium ions and glucose by cells lining the mammalian ileum.

- Explain how the number of carrier proteins affects the rate of movement across cell membranes.

Specification Reference 3.2.3

4. Active Transport

Another method of transport across a cell membrane, this time using energy...

Active transport — the basics

Active transport uses energy to move molecules and ions across plasma membranes, usually against a concentration gradient. Carrier proteins and co-transporters are involved in active transport.

Carrier proteins

The process is pretty similar to facilitated diffusion — a molecule attaches to the carrier protein, the protein changes shape and this moves the molecule across the membrane, releasing it on the other side (see Figure 1). There are two main differences between active transport and facilitated diffusion though:

- Active transport usually moves solutes from a low to a high concentration — in facilitated diffusion, they always move from a high to a low concentration.

- Active transport requires energy — facilitated diffusion does not.

ATP (a molecule produced by respiration) is a common source of energy in the cell, so it's important for active transport. ATP undergoes a hydrolysis reaction, splitting into ADP and P_i (inorganic phosphate). This releases energy so that the solutes can be transported.

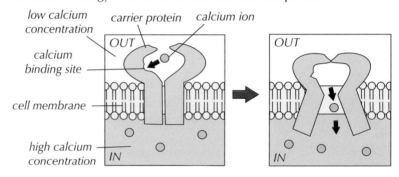

Figure 1: The active transport of calcium ions.

Co-transporters

Co-transporters are a type of **carrier protein**. They bind two molecules at a time. The concentration gradient of one of the molecules is used to move the other molecule against its own concentration gradient.

Figure 2 shows the co-transport of sodium ions and glucose. Sodium ions move across the membrane down their concentration gradient. This moves glucose across the membrane too, against its concentration gradient.

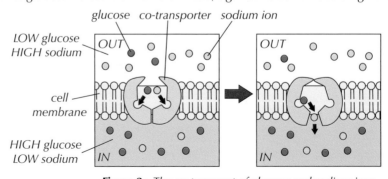

Figure 2: The co-transport of glucose and sodium ions.

Co-transport and the absorption of glucose

Glucose is absorbed into the bloodstream in the small intestine. In the mammalian ileum (the final part of a mammal's small intestine) the concentration of glucose is too low for glucose to diffuse out into the blood. So glucose is absorbed from the lumen (middle) of the ileum by **co-transport**.

Exam Tip
You need to learn this example. Make sure you understand how co-transporters are involved in the process.

Step 1

Sodium ions are actively transported out of the epithelial cells in the ileum, into the blood, by the sodium-potassium pump.

This creates a concentration gradient — there's now a higher concentration of sodium ions in the lumen of the ileum than inside the cell.

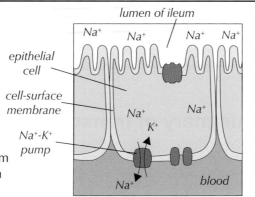

Step 2

This causes sodium ions to diffuse from the lumen of the ileum into the epithelial cell, down their concentration gradient. They do this via the sodium-glucose co-transporter proteins.

The co-transporter carries glucose into the cell with the sodium. As a result the concentration of glucose inside the cell increases.

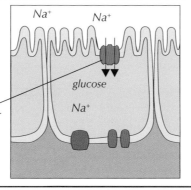

Tip: Remember, co-transporters use the concentration gradient of one molecule (in this case the sodium ions) to move another molecule against its concentration gradient (in this case glucose).

Step 3

Glucose diffuses out of the cell, into the blood, down its concentration gradient through a protein channel, by facilitated diffusion.

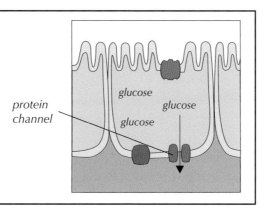

Figure 3: *Coloured TEM image of microvilli (red) on epithelial cells in the small intestine. In the ileum, glucose is absorbed from the lumen (yellow) into the cytoplasm (blue) by co-transport.*

As you can see from this example, the same substance can be transported into or out of a cell in different ways. Sometimes several methods of transport are needed to move a substance from A to B.

Factors affecting the rate of active transport

When active transport moves molecules and ions against their concentration gradient, a decreasing concentration gradient doesn't affect the rate of active transport. The rate of active transport is affected by:

- The speed of individual carrier proteins — the faster they work, the faster the rate of active transport.

- The number of carrier proteins present — the more proteins there are, the faster the rate of active transport.

- The rate of respiration in the cell and the availability of ATP. If respiration is inhibited, active transport can't take place.

Summary of transport mechanisms

In this section, you've covered a lot of different mechanisms that are used to transport substances across cell membranes. Here's a handy table to help you remember the similarities and differences:

Type of transport:	Description
Diffusion (see pages 100-101)	- Net movement of particles from an area of higher concentration to an area of lower concentration. - Passive process — doesn't require energy.
Facilitated diffusion (see pages 101-102)	- Net movement of particles from an area of higher concentration to an area of lower concentration. - Uses carrier proteins and channel proteins to aid the diffusion of large molecules and charged particles through the membrane. - Passive process — doesn't require energy.
Osmosis (see pages 104-105)	- Movement of water molecules across a partially permeable membrane from an area of higher water potential to an area of lower water potential. - Passive process — doesn't require energy.
Active transport (see pages 108-110)	- Movement of molecules, usually from an area of lower concentration to an area of higher concentration. - Uses carrier proteins and co-transporters to transport molecules. - Active process — requires energy.

Figure 4: Summary table of transport mechanisms.

Exam Tip
Make sure you know what types of molecules (e.g. large/small, polar/non-polar/ionic) are moved by the different types of transport.

Exam Tip
Make sure you know that active transport is the only process that uses energy.

Practice Questions — Application

ATP is produced by mitochondria during aerobic respiration. The overall equation for this process can be written as:

glucose + oxygen $\rightarrow$ carbon dioxide + water + ATP

The graph below shows the relationship between the relative rates of oxygen consumption and the active transport of sodium ions across epithelial cells.

Q1 a) Describe the relationship shown by the graph.

   b) Suggest an explanation for this relationship.

   c) Suggest one other factor that may affect the rate of sodium ion active transport.

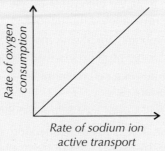

Rate of oxygen consumption

Rate of sodium ion active transport

Exam Tip
Questions asking you to explain graphical relationships are dead common in exams — make sure you're comfortable with doing them.

Q2 The thyroid gland needs iodide ions (I⁻) to make hormones, so there is a higher concentration of I⁻ ions inside the thyroid cells than in the blood plasma. The Na^+/I^- co-transporter is involved in transporting I⁻ ions into the thyroid gland. The concentration of sodium ions is higher in the blood plasma than in the thyroid gland.

   a) Which ion needs to be actively transported by the Na^+/I^- co-transporter? Explain your answer.

   b) Using your knowledge of co-transporters, describe and explain how active transport is carried out by the Na^+/I^- co-transporter.

Practice Questions — Fact Recall

Q1 Describe the chemical reaction that occurs to release energy from ATP.

Q2 Describe how the following are used to transport substances across a cell membrane during active transport:

   a) carrier proteins.

   b) co-transporters.

Q3 Why are sodium ions important in the transport of glucose from the ileum into the blood?

Q4 Will the rate of active transport increase or decrease with an increasing number of carrier proteins?

Section Summary

Make sure you know...

- That the basic structure of cell-surface membranes (those surrounding a cell, also known plasma membranes) and internal cell membranes (e.g. those surrounding many organelles in eukaryotic cells) is the same.

- That the fluid mosaic model describes the structure of a cell membrane — this includes phospholipids arranged in a bilayer with proteins, glycoproteins, glycolipids and sometimes cholesterol scattered throughout.

- That the phospholipids in a cell membrane are always moving, and that some proteins in a membrane move sideways and some proteins are fixed in position.

- How the arrangement of phospholipids in a cell membrane forms a barrier to water-soluble substances.

- That cholesterol in a cell membrane gives the membrane stability.

- How to investigate the effect of a variable, such as temperature or solvent concentration, on cell membrane permeability, e.g. by using cubes of beetroot (Required Practical 4).

- That diffusion is the net movement of particles from an area of higher concentration to an area of lower concentration and is a passive process.

- That the phospholipid bilayer allows small, nonpolar molecules to diffuse directly through a cell membrane — this is called simple diffusion.

- How the rate of simple diffusion of a particle across a cell membrane is affected by the concentration gradient of the particle and the thickness and surface area of the membrane.

- How some specialised cells are adapted for rapid transport across their membranes. For example, cells in the small intestine have microvilli which increase their surface area for rapid diffusion.

- That facilitated diffusion is a passive process that transports large molecules (via carrier proteins) and charged particles (via channel proteins) down a concentration gradient across a cell membrane.

- How the rate of facilitated diffusion of a particle across a cell membrane is affected by the concentration gradient of the particle and the number of channel or carrier proteins in the membrane.

- That some cells are adapted for rapid facilitated diffusion across their membranes by having more transport proteins in their membranes (e.g. some kidney cells have lots of aquaporins).

- That osmosis is the diffusion of water molecules across a partially permeable membrane from an area of higher water potential to an area of lower water potential.

- How the rate of osmosis across a cell membrane is affected by the water potential gradient and the thickness and surface area of the membrane.

- How to investigate the water potential of plant tissue by producing serial dilutions of a given scale factor, placing samples of the plant tissue in the solutions and then producing a calibration curve to find the water potential of the tissue, e.g. producing serial dilutions of sucrose solution and measuring the change in mass of potato cylinders that have been immersed in the solutions (Required Practical 3).

- That active transport usually moves solutes from a low to a high concentration and requires energy (from ATP).

- That ATP releases energy during a hydrolysis reaction, in which it splits into ADP and P_i.

- That active transport, like facilitated diffusion, uses carrier proteins to transport molecules across the membrane.

- That co-transporters bind two molecules at a time, enabling the concentration gradient of one of the molecules to transport the other molecule against its concentration gradient.

- How sodium ions and glucose are absorbed by cells in a mammal's ileum by co-transport.

- That the rate of active transport is affected by the number of carrier proteins in a cell membrane.

Exam-style Questions

1   **Figures 1** and **2** show onion cells under a light microscope. The cytoplasm appears dark grey. One of the figures shows the onion cells after they have been placed in a weak salt solution. The solution has a lower water potential than the onion cells.

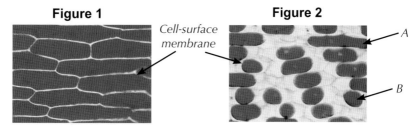

1.1   Which figure shows the cells after they have been placed in the salt solution? Explain your answer.

(2 marks)

1.2   Look at the cells labelled **A** and **B** on **Figure 2**. By comparing the size of their membranes, suggest which of these cells is most likely to experience the fastest transport of water molecules into and out of its cytoplasm. Explain your answer.

(1 mark)

1.3   The cells' surface membranes contain phospholipids. Describe the arrangement of the phospholipids based on the fluid mosaic model of membrane structure.

(2 marks)

1.4   The cell membranes also contain proteins. Some of the proteins have carbohydrates attached. What name is given to these molecules?

(1 mark)

1.5   An onion cell membrane contains less cholesterol than an animal cell membrane. Suggest and explain why this is.

(2 marks)

2   Glucose is a product of digestion. It is also a relatively large polar molecule. Once glucose has been digested, it must be absorbed into the bloodstream from the cells of the ileum. Part of the absorption process happens using active transport.

2.1   Explain what is meant by the term active transport.

(2 marks)

2.2   State the type of molecule that actively transports glucose across the cell-surface membranes of the ileum and briefly describe how it does so.

(2 marks)

2.3   Another stage of the absorption process happens by facilitated diffusion. Suggest why glucose must use facilitated diffusion rather than simple diffusion to cross the cell-surface membranes of the ileum.

(3 marks)

3   A group of students investigated the water potential of potato cells.

They cut cubes of potato of equal size and shape, weighed them and placed a single cube into one of four different concentrations of sucrose solution. One cube was placed in pure water. They re-weighed each of the cubes every hour and after 12 hours the mass of all the cubes remained constant. The overall change in mass for each cube is shown in **Figure 3**.

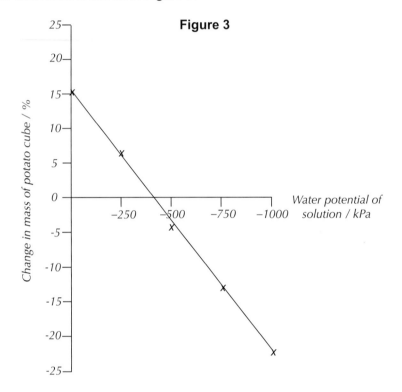

Figure 3

3.1   The students recorded the difference in mass between the cubes at the start and end of the experiment in grams, but plotted the overall change as a percentage. Suggest why the graph was plotted in this way.

(1 mark)

3.2   What was the change in mass for the potato cube placed in pure water?

(1 mark)

3.3   Explain why the cubes in the −500, −750 and −1000 kPa solutions lost mass.

(2 marks)

3.4   Use **Figure 3** to estimate the water potential of the potato cells.

(1 mark)

3.5   Suggest how the students could make their results more precise.

(1 mark)

3.6   If the experiment was repeated with cubes that had a larger surface area would you expect the mass of all the cubes to become constant before 12 hours, at 12 hours or after 12 hours? Explain your answer.

(2 marks)

C: Cells and The Immune System

1. Antigens

Cell-surface membranes contain proteins that act as antigens. These antigens allow the immune system to tell the difference between your own, healthy body cells (known as 'self' cells) and 'foreign' invaders...

What are antigens?

Antigens are molecules (usually proteins) that can generate an **immune response** when detected by the body — see pages 116-119. They are usually found on the surface of cells, including all your body cells. Antigens that aren't normally found in the body are referred to as **foreign antigens** — it's these antigens that the immune system usually responds to. Antigens allow the immune system to identify:

Pathogens

These are organisms that cause disease, e.g. bacteria, viruses and fungi. All pathogens have antigens on their surface — these are identified as foreign by immune system cells, which then respond to destroy the pathogen.

Abnormal body cells

Cancerous or pathogen-infected cells have abnormal antigens on their surface, which trigger an immune response.

Toxins

These are poisons. They're also molecules, not cells. Some toxins are produced by bacteria, e.g. the bacterium *Clostridium botulinum* releases a protein toxin that affects the nervous system, causing the symptoms of botulism. The immune system can respond to toxins, as well as the pathogens that release them.

Cells from other individuals of the same species

When you receive cells from another person, such as in an organ transplant or blood transfusion, those cells will have some antigens that are different to your own (unless the donor is genetically identical to you). The foreign antigens trigger an immune response. This response leads to the rejection of transplanted organs if drugs aren't taken to suppress the recipient's immune system.

For blood transfusions, the most important antigens are the ABO blood group antigens — if the donated blood contains A or B antigens that aren't recognised by the recipient's immune system, they will generate an immune response.

Learning Objectives:
- Recall the definition of an antigen.
- Know that each type of cell has specific molecules (antigens) on its surface that identify it.
- Understand that these molecules include proteins and enable the immune system to identify pathogens, cells from other organisms of the same species, abnormal body cells and toxins.

Specification Reference 3.2.4

Tip: The toxin itself is an antigen — it doesn't have antigens on its surface.

Tip: The ABO blood groups are A, B, AB and O. Type A blood has A antigens on its red blood cells, type B blood has B antigens and type AB blood has both A and B antigens. Type O blood doesn't have any A or B antigens. So if a person has type B blood, for example, their immune system won't recognise type A antigens on blood cells from other people.

Practice Questions — Fact Recall

Q1 What are antigens?

Q2 Why do some antigens generate an immune response?

Learning Objectives:

- Recall the process of phagocytosis of pathogens and the subsequent destruction of ingested pathogens by lysozymes.

- Know the response of T lymphocytes to a foreign antigen (the cellular response).

- Understand the role of antigen-presenting cells in the cellular response.

- Understand the role of helper T-cells in stimulating cytotoxic T-cells, B cells and phagocytes.

- Know the response of B lymphocytes to a foreign antigen (the humoral response), including clonal selection and the release of monoclonal antibodies.

- Recall the definition of an antibody and know its general structure.

- Understand how an antigen-antibody complex is formed, leading to the destruction of the antigen by agglutination and phagocytosis of bacterial cells.

- Understand the roles of plasma cells and of memory cells in producing primary and secondary immune responses.

Specification Reference 3.2.4

2. The Immune Response

There's an army of cells in the body that helps to protect us from disease — together, they're called the immune system.

The main stages of the immune response

1. Phagocytosis

A **phagocyte** (e.g. a macrophage) is a type of white blood cell that carries out phagocytosis (engulfment of pathogens). They're found in the blood and in tissues and are the first cells to respond to an immune system trigger inside the body. Here's how they work:

- A phagocyte recognises the foreign antigens (see previous page) on a pathogen.

- The cytoplasm of the phagocyte moves round the pathogen, engulfing it.

- The pathogen is now contained in a **phagocytic vacuole** (a bubble) in the cytoplasm of the phagocyte.

- A **lysosome** (an organelle that contains enzymes called **lysozymes**) fuses with the phagocytic vacuole. The lysozymes break down the pathogen.

- The phagocyte then presents the pathogen's antigens — it sticks the antigens on its surface to activate other immune system cells. The phagocyte is acting as an antigen-presenting cell.

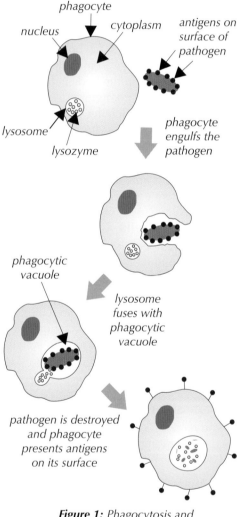

Figure 1: Phagocytosis and antigen presentation.

2. T-Cells

A **T-cell** (also called a T-lymphocyte) is another type of white blood cell. It has receptor proteins on its surface that bind to complementary antigens presented to it by phagocytes. This activates the T-cell.

Different types of T-cells respond in different ways. For example, **helper T-cells** (T_H cells) release chemical signals that activate and stimulate phagocytes and **cytotoxic T-cells** (T_C cells), which kill abnormal and foreign cells. T_H cells also activate **B-cells**, which secrete antibodies (see next page).

3. B-Cells

B-cells (also called B-lymphocytes) are also a type of white blood cell. They're covered with antibodies — proteins that bind to antigens to form an **antigen-antibody complex**. Each B-cell has a different shaped antibody on its membrane, so different ones bind to different shaped antigens (see Figure 2).

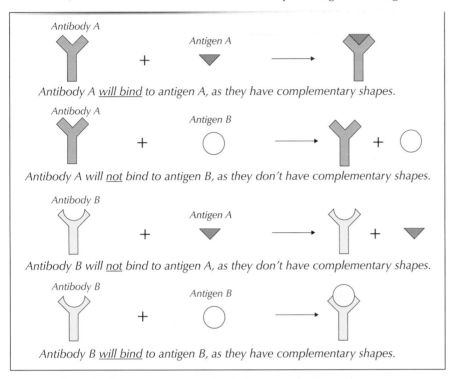

Antibody A *will bind* to antigen A, as they have complementary shapes.

Antibody A will *not* bind to antigen B, as they don't have complementary shapes.

Antibody B will *not* bind to antigen A, as they don't have complementary shapes.

Antibody B *will bind* to antigen B, as they have complementary shapes.

Figure 2: *Complementary binding between antibodies and antigens.*

When the antibody on the surface of a B-cell meets a complementary shaped antigen, it binds to it. This, together with substances released from helper T-cells, activates the B-cell. This process is called **clonal selection**. The activated B-cell divides into **plasma cells**.

4. Antibody production

Plasma cells are identical to the B-cell (they're clones). They secrete loads of antibodies specific to the antigen. These are called **monoclonal antibodies**. They bind to the antigens on the surface of the pathogen to form lots of **antigen-antibody complexes** (see Figure 5 on the next page).

An antibody has two binding sites, so can bind to two pathogens at the same time. This means that pathogens become clumped together — this is called **agglutination**. Phagocytes then bind to the antibodies and phagocytose many pathogens at once. This process leads to the destruction of pathogens carrying this antigen in the body.

You need to learn the general structure of an antibody for your exam — this is also shown in Figure 5. Antibodies are proteins — they're made up of chains of amino acids. The specificity of an antibody depends on its **variable regions**, which form the antigen binding sites. Each antibody has a variable region with a unique tertiary structure (due to different amino acid sequences) that's complementary to one specific antigen. All antibodies have the same **constant regions**.

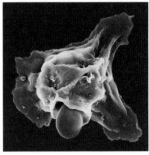

Figure 3: *An electron micrograph of a phagocyte (blue) engulfing a pathogen (red).*

Figure 4: A molecular model of an antibody.

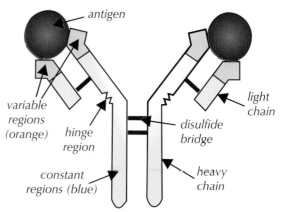

Figure 5: Antigen-antibody complex and antibody structure.

Cellular and humoral responses

Just to add to your fun, the immune response is split into two — the cellular response and the humoral response.

- Cellular — The T-cells and other immune system cells that they interact with, e.g. phagocytes, form the cellular response.
- Humoral — B-cells, clonal selection and the production of monoclonal antibodies form the humoral response.

Both types of response are needed to remove a pathogen from the body and the responses interact with each other, e.g. T-cells help to activate B-cells, and antibodies coat pathogens making it easier for phagocytes to engulf them.

Primary and secondary immune responses

The primary response

When an antigen enters the body for the first time it activates the immune system. This is called the primary response. The primary response is slow because there aren't many B-cells that can make the antibody needed to bind to it. Eventually the body will produce enough of the right antibody to overcome the infection. Meanwhile the infected person will show symptoms of the disease.

After being exposed to an antigen, both T- and B-cells produce **memory cells**. These memory cells remain in the body for a long time. Memory T-cells remember the specific antigen and will recognise it a second time round. Memory B-cells record the specific antibodies needed to bind the antigen. The person is now immune — their immune system has the ability to respond quickly to a second infection.

The secondary response

If the same pathogen enters the body again, the immune system will produce a quicker, stronger immune response — the secondary response. Clonal selection happens faster. Memory B-cells are activated and divide into plasma cells that produce the right antibody to the antigen. Memory T-cells are activated and divide into the correct type of T-cells to kill the cell carrying the antigen. The secondary response often gets rid of the pathogen before you begin to show any symptoms (see Figure 6 on the next page).

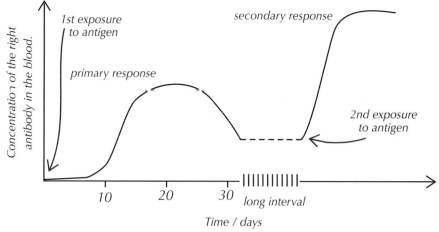

Figure 6: A graph of antibody concentration against time since antigen exposure.

Tip: The secondary response is always faster than the primary response. This is shown by a steeper line in graphs of blood antibody concentration against time.

Practice Questions — Application

Q1 The graph below shows the immune responses of two mice exposed to a pathogen. Both mice were exposed on day 0 of the experiment.

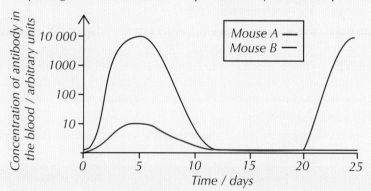

a) How much antibody did each mouse have in its blood on day 5?

b) Which mouse was already immune to the pathogen? Explain your answer.

c) i) On which day was Mouse A exposed to the pathogen again?

ii) Describe what happened to Mouse A's immune system after it was exposed again.

Q2 Rheumatic fever is a disease where the immune system attacks cells in the heart. It's often triggered by an infection with the bacterium *Streptococcus pyogenes*. Antigens on the surface of *S. pyogenes* have a very similar shape to antigens on the surface of heart cells. Suggest why *S. pyogenes* infection can lead to rheumatic fever.

Practice Questions — Fact Recall

Q1 What is the function of helper T-cells?

Q2 What is the function of plasma cells?

Q3 What is the difference between the cellular immune response and the humoral immune response?

Q4 Give three differences (other than speed) between a primary and a secondary immune response.

- Know the differences between active and passive immunity.
- Understand the use of vaccines to provide protection for individuals and populations against disease.
- Understand the concept of herd immunity.
- Be able to discuss ethical issues associated with the use of vaccines.

Specification Reference 3.2.4

3. Immunity and Vaccines

After you've been infected once by a pathogen you'll be immune to it, but being infected in the first place can be pretty unpleasant. Vaccination can make you immune without the being ill part.

Active and passive immunity

Immunity can be active or passive:

Active immunity

This is the type of immunity you get when your immune system makes its own antibodies after being stimulated by an antigen. There are two different types of active immunity:

1. **Natural** — this is when you become immune after catching a disease.
2. **Artificial** — this is when you become immune after you've been given a vaccination containing a harmless dose of antigen (see below).

Passive immunity

This is the type of immunity you get from being given antibodies made by a different organism — your immune system doesn't produce any antibodies of its own. Again, there are two types:

1. **Natural** — this is when a baby becomes immune due to the antibodies it receives from its mother, through the placenta and in breast milk.
2. **Artificial** — this is when you become immune after being injected with antibodies from someone else. E.g. If you contract tetanus you can be injected with antibodies against the tetanus toxin, collected from blood donations.

In the exam you might be asked about the differences between these types of immunity:

Active Immunity	Passive Immunity
Requires exposure to antigen	Doesn't require exposure to antigen
It takes a while for protection to develop	Protection is immediate
Memory cells are produced	Memory cells aren't produced
Protection is long-term because the antibody is produced (after activation of memory cells) in response to complementary antigen being present in the body	Protection is short-term because the antibodies given are broken down

Vaccination

While your B-cells are busy dividing to build up their numbers to deal with a pathogen (i.e. the primary response — see page 118), you suffer from the disease. Vaccination can help avoid this.

Vaccines contain antigens that cause your body to produce memory cells against a particular pathogen, without the pathogen causing disease. This means you become immune without getting any symptoms.
Vaccines protect individuals that have them and, because they reduce the occurrence of the disease, those not vaccinated are also less likely to catch the disease (because there are fewer people to catch it from). This is called **herd immunity** — see Figure 1 on the next page.

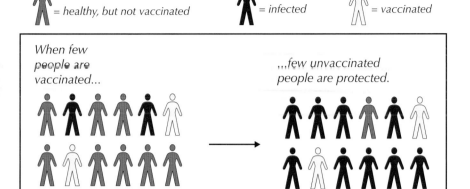

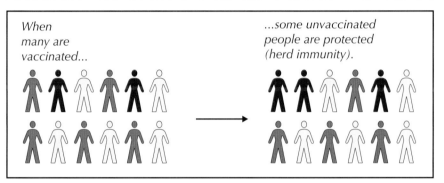

Figure 1: Herd immunity

Tip: Vaccinations are sometimes called immunisations.

Vaccines always contain antigens — these may be free or attached to a dead or attenuated (weakened) pathogen. Vaccines may be injected or taken orally. The disadvantages of taking a vaccine orally are that it could be broken down by enzymes in the gut or the molecules of the vaccine may be too large to be absorbed into the blood. Sometimes booster vaccines are given later on (e.g. after several years) to make sure that more memory cells are produced.

Tip: Attenuated viruses have usually been genetically or chemically modified so that they can't produce toxins or attach to and infect host cells.

Ethical issues surrounding the use of vaccines

All vaccines are tested on animals before being tested on humans — some people disagree with animal testing. Also, animal based substances may be used to produce a vaccine, which some people disagree with.

Testing vaccines on humans can be risky, e.g. volunteers may put themselves at unnecessary risk of contracting the disease because they think they're fully protected (e.g. they might have unprotected sex because they have had a new HIV vaccine and think they're protected — and the vaccine might not work).

Some people don't want to take the vaccine due to the risk of side effects, but they are still protected because of herd immunity — other people think this is unfair.

If there was an epidemic of a new disease (e.g. a new influenza virus) there would be a rush to receive a vaccine and difficult decisions would have to be made about who would be the first to receive it.

Practice Questions — Application

Whooping cough is an infection of the respiratory system. The graph below shows the number of cases of whooping cough in Scotland between 1960 and 1999, and the vaccine uptake from the 1970s to 1999.

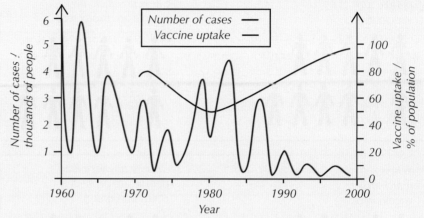

Q1 What percentage of the population were vaccinated in 1990?

Q2 How many cases of whooping cough were there in 1965?

Q3 The whooping cough vaccine was introduced in Scotland in the 1950s. Describe and explain the overall trend in the number of cases of whooping cough between 1960 and 1975.

Q4 In the 1970s some people were concerned that the vaccine caused neurological problems, such as seizures.

    a) What happened to the uptake of the vaccine in the 1970s?

    b) Explain how this change affected the number of cases between the mid 1970s and the mid-1980s.

Practice Questions — Fact Recall

Q1 Define the terms active and passive immunity.

Q2 How do vaccines give people immunity?

Q3 What is herd immunity?

Q4 Describe two issues surrounding the use of vaccinations.

4. Antigenic Variation

Just to complicate things, pathogens can change their antigens to trick the immune system.

What is antigenic variation?

Antigens on the surface of pathogens activate the primary response. When you're infected a second time with the same pathogen (which has the same antigens on its surface) they activate the secondary response and you don't get ill.

However, some sneaky pathogens can change their surface antigens. This is called **antigenic variation**. (Different antigens are formed due to changes in the genes of a pathogen.) This means that when you're infected for a second time, the memory cells produced from the first infection will not recognise the different antigens. So the immune system has to start from scratch and carry out a primary response against these new antigens. This primary response takes time to get rid of the infection, which is why you get ill again.

Antigenic variation also makes it difficult to develop vaccines against some pathogens for the same reason. Examples of pathogens that show antigenic variation include HIV and the influenza virus. Here's how antigenic variation affects the production of vaccines to help prevent people catching influenza:

> ### ⌐ Example
>
> The influenza (flu) vaccine changes every year. That's because the antigens on the surface of the influenza virus change regularly, forming new strains of the virus.
>
> Memory cells produced from vaccination with one strain of the flu will not recognise other strains with different antigens. The strains are immunologically distinct. Every year there are different strains of the influenza virus circulating in the population, so a different vaccine has to be made.
>
> New vaccines are developed and one is chosen every year that is the most effective against the recently circulating influenza viruses. Governments and health authorities then implement a programme of vaccination using the most suitable vaccine.

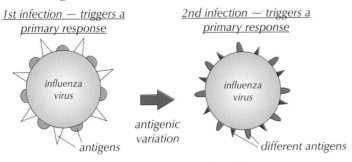

1st infection — triggers a primary response

2nd infection — triggers a primary response

antigenic variation

antigens

different antigens

influenza virus

influenza virus

Figure 2: *Antigenic variation in the influenza virus.*

Learning Objective:

- Understand the effect of antigen variability on disease and disease prevention.

Specification Reference 3.2.4

Tip: Pathogens of the same type that show antigenic variation are often referred to as <u>strains</u>.

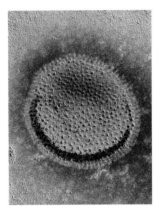

Figure 1: *A TEM of an influenza virus.*

Practice Questions — Fact Recall

Q1 What is antigenic variation?

Q2 Explain why you can become ill with flu even if you've been infected by the influenza virus before.

Learning Objectives:

- Understand the use of monoclonal antibodies in targeting medication to specific cell types by attaching a therapeutic drug to an antibody, and in medical diagnosis.
- Understand the use of antibodies in the ELISA test.
- Be able to discuss ethical issues associated with the use of monoclonal antibodies.

Specification Reference 3.2.4

5. Antibodies in Medicine

Scientists can make antibodies in the lab and use them for all sorts of stuff...

The use of monoclonal antibodies

Monoclonal antibodies are antibodies produced from a single group of genetically identical B-cells (plasma cells). This means that they're all identical in structure.

As you know, antibodies are very specific because their binding sites have a unique tertiary structure (see p. 32) that only an antigen with a complementary shape can fit into. You can make monoclonal antibodies that bind to anything you want, e.g. a cell antigen or other substance, and they will only bind to (target) this molecule. This can be useful for both treating illnesses and in medical diagnosis.

Tip: The unique tertiary structure of the antibody binding sites is due to the unique order of the amino acids in the protein (its primary structure — see p. 32).

> ### Example — Anti-cancer drugs targeted to cancer cells
>
> Different cells in the body have different surface antigens. Cancer cells have antigens called tumour markers that are not found on normal body cells. Monoclonal antibodies can be made that will bind to the tumour markers. You can also attach anti-cancer drugs to the antibodies. When the antibodies come into contact with the cancer cells they will bind to the tumour markers. This means the drug will only accumulate in the body where there are cancer cells. So, the side effects of an antibody-based drug are lower than other drugs because they accumulate near specific cells.
>
>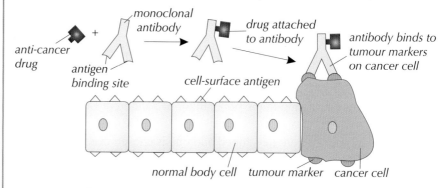
>
> **Figure 1:** *Targeting anti-cancer drugs to cancerous cells.*

Tip: Anti-cancer drugs are basically toxic chemicals that kill cells — they cause side effects because they also kill cells that aren't cancerous. Targeting the drugs using antibodies helps reduce this problem.

> ### Example — Pregnancy tests
>
> Pregnancy tests detect the hormone human chorionic gonadotropin (hCG) that's found in the urine of pregnant women:
>
> - The application area contains antibodies that are complementary to the hCG protein, bound to a coloured bead (blue).
> - When urine is applied to the application area any hCG will bind to the antibody on the beads, forming an antigen-antibody complex.
> - The urine moves up the stick to the test strip, carrying any beads with it.
> - The test strip contains antibodies to hCG that are stuck in place (immobilised).
> - If there is hCG present the test strip turns blue because the immobilised antibody binds to any hCG — concentrating the hCG-antibody complex with the blue beads attached. If no hCG is present, the beads will pass through the test area without binding to anything, and so it won't go blue.

Tip: The steps in this Example are illustrated in Figure 2 on the next page.

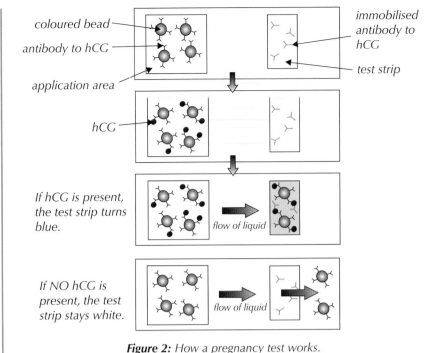

coloured bead

antibody to hCG

application area

immobilised antibody to hCG

test strip

hCG

If hCG is present, the test strip turns blue.

flow of liquid

If NO hCG is present, the test strip stays white.

flow of liquid

Figure 2: How a pregnancy test works.

Figure 3: A lab technician testing a urine sample for hCG.

You can use similar test strips in other areas of medical diagnosis, e.g. malaria can be diagnosed using a test strip that detects malaria antigens in the blood.

ELISA test

The enzyme-linked immunosorbent assay (ELISA) allows you to see if a patient has any antibodies to a certain antigen or any antigen to a certain antibody. It can be used in medical diagnosis to test for pathogenic infections (e.g. for HIV infection), for allergies (e.g. to nuts or lactose) and for just about anything you can make an antibody for.

In an ELISA test, an antibody is used which has an enzyme attached to it. This enzyme can react with a substrate to produce a coloured product. This causes the solution in the reaction vessel to change colour.

If there's a colour change, it demonstrates that the antigen or antibody of interest is present in the sample being tested (e.g. blood plasma). In some types of ELISA, the quantity of this antigen/antibody can be worked out from the intensity of the colour change.

There are several different types of ELISA — the simplest is the direct ELISA.

Direct ELISA

A direct ELISA uses a single antibody that is complementary to the antigen you're testing for.

Antigens from a patient sample are bound to the inside of a well in a well plate (a plastic tray with loads of little circular pits in it). A detection antibody (with an attached enzyme) that is complementary to the antigen of interest is added. If the antigen of interest is present in the patient sample, it will be immobilised on the inside surface of the well and the detection antibody will bind to it — see Figure 4 on the next page. The well is then washed out to remove any unbound antibody and a substrate solution is added. If the detection antibody is present, the enzyme reacts with the substrate to give a colour change. This is a positive result for presence of the antigen.

Tip: An allergy is an inappropriate reaction of the immune system to an antigen that shouldn't normally trigger a response, e.g. a protein in food.

Tip: The intensity of the colour change can be measured by reading the absorbance of the solution (how much light it absorbs). This absorbance value can then be compared to the absorbance of a known concentration of antibody or antigen to work out the concentration in the sample.

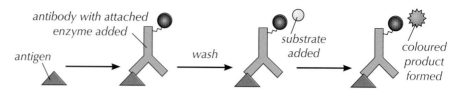

Figure 4: A direct ELISA test.

Indirect ELISA

Indirect ELISA is different because it uses two different antibodies. This method is outlined in the example below:

Example

An indirect ELISA test can be used to see if a patient possesses antibodies to HIV (Human Immunodeficiency Virus):

1. HIV antigen is bound to the bottom of a well in a well plate.

2. A sample of the patient's blood plasma, which might contain several different antibodies, is added to the well. If there are any HIV-specific antibodies in the plasma (i.e. antibodies against HIV) these will bind to the HIV antigen stuck to the bottom of the well. The well is then washed out to remove any unbound antibodies.

3. A secondary antibody, that has a specific enzyme attached to it, is added to the well. This secondary antibody can bind to the HIV-specific antibody (which is also called the primary antibody). The well is washed out again to remove any unbound secondary antibody. If there's no primary antibody in the sample, all of the secondary antibody will be washed away because there will be nothing for it to bind to.

4. A solution is added to the well. This solution contains a substrate, which is able to react with the enzyme attached to the secondary antibody and produce a coloured product. If the solution changes colour, it indicates that the patient has HIV-specific antibodies in their blood and is infected with HIV.

1. HIV antigen bound to the bottom of a well

HIV antigen

well in a well plate

2. Plasma sample added

antibodies not specific to HIV antigen

antibody specific to HIV antigen

wash out

3. Secondary antibody added

secondary antibody with attached enzyme

wash out

4. Substrate added

colour change = HIV is present (positive result)

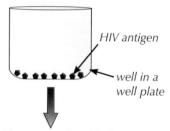

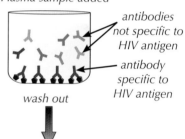

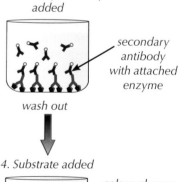

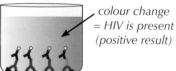

Figure 6: Stages in an ELISA test for HIV. A positive result is shown.

Tip: The colour change you see varies depending on the enzyme and substrate that are used.

Tip: A person is only likely to have antibodies to HIV if they're infected with HIV. An exception to this is babies born to mothers with HIV — see page 132.

Tip: The washing steps are important to make sure unbound antibodies aren't left in the well which could affect the results. E.g. unbound secondary antibodies could cause the test to appear positive when there are no HIV antibodies present.

Tip: If the ELISA result was negative, there would be no colour change because there would be no HIV-specific antibodies for the secondary antibodies to bind to.

Figure 5: ELISA test results for HIV. The coloured wells show a positive result.

Ethical issues surrounding the use of monoclonal antibodies

Ethical issues surrounding monoclonal antibody therapy often involve animal rights issues. Animals are used to produce the cells from which the monoclonal antibodies are produced. Some people disagree with the use of animals in this way.

Practice Questions — Application

Q1 Donated blood is tested to see which type it is. There are four main blood types — A (containing antigen A), B (containing antigen B), AB (containing antigens A and B) and type O (containing neither). The blood type test can be done using monoclonal antibodies produced against these antigens. The table below shows the results for four people.

Person	Result with anti-antigen A	Result with anti-antigen B
1	Positive — binding occurs	Negative — no binding
2	Positive — binding occurs	Positive — binding occurs
3	Negative — no binding	Negative — no binding
4	Negative — no binding	Positive — binding occurs

Tip: Antibody names can get a bit confusing — usually, whatever comes after 'anti-' will be what the antibody will bind to.

a) What blood type is:

   i) Person 1?   ii) Person 3?

b) People with blood type B carry anti-antigen A antibodies in their blood. If these antibodies meet antigen A the blood clots, which can kill the patient. Could they accept blood from:

   i) Person 2?   ii) Person 4?

Q2 A scientist is using an indirect ELISA to test a patient for an allergy to gluten. First she coats a well plate with gluten protein. She then adds the patient serum sample to three of the wells. She then washes the well plate and adds a secondary antibody that has an attached enzyme. The scientist washes the well plate again, then adds a substrate solution.

Tip: Serum is the liquid remaining when all the blood cells and clotting agents have been removed from a blood sample. Proteins such as antibodies remain in the serum.

a) Why is the well plate washed out after the secondary antibody is added?

b) The substrate will change colour if it reacts with the enzyme bound to the secondary antibody. What would you expect the scientist to observe if the patient is allergic to the gluten protein? Explain your answer.

c) Suggest why the scientist adds the patient serum sample to more than one well.

d) Two control wells are used in this test. In one well, antibodies specific to the gluten protein are used instead of patient serum. In the other well, a salt solution is used instead of patient serum. Suggest what each of these controls are designed to show. State what you would expect the result of the test to be in each case.

Tip: A control is an experiment designed to either check that only the independent variable is affecting the dependent variable, or to check that a positive result is possible (see p. 2 for more on controls).

Learning Objective:

- Be able to evaluate methodology, evidence and data relating to the use of vaccines and monoclonal antibodies.

Specification Reference 3.2.4

6. Interpreting Data About Vaccines and Antibodies

When a study presents evidence for a new theory (e.g. a vaccine has a dangerous side effect) it's important that other scientists come up with more evidence to validate (confirm) the theory. Other scientists may repeat the study and try to reproduce the results, or conduct other studies to try to prove the same theory.

Tip: Sample size is really important in scientific studies — the bigger the better. See page 3 for more on sample size.

Tip: Bias is when someone intentionally, or unintentionally, favours a particular result.

Example 1: The MMR Vaccine

In 1998, a study was published about the safety of the measles, mumps and rubella (MMR) vaccine. The study was based on 12 children with autism (a life-long developmental disability) and concluded that there may be a link between the MMR vaccine and autism.

Not everyone was convinced by this study because it had a very small sample size of 12 children, which increased the likelihood of the results being due to chance. The study may have been biased because one of the scientists was helping to gain evidence for a lawsuit against the MMR vaccine manufacturer. Also, studies carried out by different scientists found no link between autism and the MMR vaccine.

There have been further scientific studies to sort out the conflicting evidence. In 2005, a Japanese study was published about the incidence of autism in Yokohama (an area of Japan). They looked at the medical records of 30 000 children born between 1988 and 1996 and counted the number of children that developed autism before the age of seven. The MMR jab was first introduced in Japan in 1989 and was stopped in 1993. During this time the MMR vaccine was administered to children at 12 months old. Figure 1 shows the results of the study.

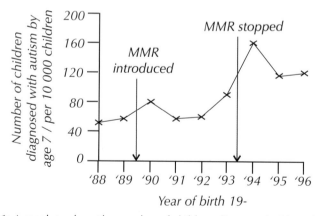

Figure 1: A graph to show the number of children diagnosed with autism by age 7.

In the exam you could be asked to evaluate evidence like this.

You might be asked to describe the data...

The graph shows that the number of children diagnosed with autism continued to rise after the MMR vaccine was stopped. For example, from all the children born in 1992, who did receive the MMR jab, about 60 out of 10 000 were diagnosed with autism before the age of seven. However, from all the children born in 1994, who did not receive the MMR jab, about 160 out of 10 000 of them were diagnosed with autism before the age of seven.

...or draw conclusions

There is no link between the MMR vaccine and autism.

...or evaluate the methodology

You can be much more confident in this study, compared to the 1998 study, because the sample size was so large — 30 000 children were studied. A larger sample size means that the results are less likely to be due to chance.

Tip: See pages 15-16 for more about drawing conclusions from data and page 17 for more on evaluating methods.

Example 2: Herceptin® — Monoclonal antibodies

About 20% of women with breast cancer have tumours that produce more than the usual amount of a receptor called HER2. Herceptin® is a drug used to treat this type of breast cancer — it contains monoclonal antibodies that bind to the HER2 receptor on a tumour cell and prevent the cells from growing and dividing.

In 2005, a study tested Herceptin® on women who had already undergone chemotherapy for HER2-type breast cancer. 1694 women took the drug for a year after chemotherapy and another 1694 women who were not given the drug were observed for the same time (the control group). The results are shown in Figure 2.

Describe the data: Almost twice as many women in the control group developed breast cancer again or died compared to the group taking Herceptin®.

Draw conclusions: A one-year treatment with Herceptin®, after chemotherapy, increases the disease-free survival rate for women with HER2-type breast cancer.

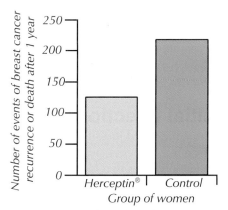

Figure 2: A graph to show the recurrence of breast cancer with and without Herceptin® treatment.

Practice Questions — Application

A vaccination programme was conducted in China in 2009 to protect against influenza type A. A study analysed the side effects of 86.9 million vaccines given between September 2009 and March 2010. Figure 3 shows the results of the study.

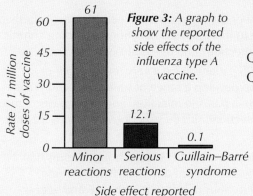

Figure 3: A graph to show the reported side effects of the influenza type A vaccine.

Q1 If 12 million people had the vaccine, how many minor reactions would you expect to see?

Q2 Describe the data.

Q3 The background rate of Guillain-Barré syndrome is 1 per 100 000 people. Does this study support the idea that influenza A vaccination increases the risk of this disease? Explain your answer.

Tip: A background rate is the incidence of something in the general population.

Learning Objectives:

- Understand how the human immunodeficiency virus (HIV) causes the symptoms of AIDS.
- Recall the structure of HIV.
- Recall the stages of HIV replication in helper T-cells.
- Understand why antibiotics are ineffective against viruses.

Specification Reference 3.2.4

7. HIV and Viruses

Viruses aren't living things — they can only reproduce inside the cells of another organism. The organism that they infect is called the host.

HIV and AIDS

HIV (**human immunodeficiency virus**) is a virus that affects the human immune system. It eventually leads to **acquired immune deficiency syndrome** (AIDS). AIDS is a condition where the immune system deteriorates and eventually fails. This makes someone with AIDS more vulnerable to other infections, like pneumonia.

HIV host cells

HIV infects and eventually kills **helper T-cells**, which act as the **host cells** (see page 76) for the virus. Helper T-cells send chemical signals that activate phagocytes, cytotoxic T-cells and B-cells (see pages 116-117) so they're hugely important cells in the immune response.

Without enough helper T-cells, the immune system is unable to mount an effective response to infections because other immune system cells don't behave how they should. People infected with HIV develop AIDS when the helper T-cell numbers in their body reach a critically low level.

Initial infection

During the initial infection period, HIV replicates rapidly and the infected person may experience severe flu-like symptoms. After this period, HIV replication drops to a lower level. This is the **latency period**. During the latency period (which can last for years) the infected person won't experience any symptoms.

The symptoms of AIDS

People with HIV are classed as having AIDS when symptoms of their failing immune system start to appear or their helper T-cell count drops below a certain level. The length of time between infection with HIV and the development of AIDS varies between individuals but without treatment it's usually around 10 years. People with AIDS generally develop diseases that wouldn't cause serious problems in people with a healthy immune system.

- The initial symptoms of AIDS include minor infections of mucous membranes (e.g. the inside of the nose, ears and genitals), and recurring respiratory infections.

- As AIDS progresses the number of immune system cells decreases further. Patients become susceptible to more serious infections including chronic diarrhoea, severe bacterial infections and tuberculosis.

- During the late stages of AIDS patients have a very low number of immune system cells and can develop a range of serious infections such as toxoplasmosis of the brain (a parasite infection) and candidiasis of the respiratory system (fungal infection). It's these serious infections that kill AIDS patients, not HIV itself.

The length of time that people survive with AIDS varies a lot. Factors that affect progression of HIV to AIDS and survival time with AIDS include existing infections, the strain of HIV they're infected with, age and access to healthcare.

Tip: The initial (acute) stage of a HIV infection can cause flu-like symptoms as the immune system mounts a response to the virus. This immune response is not able to destroy all of the virus though, so a small amount remains in the cells and continues to replicate.

Tip: As HIV replicates and the amount of virus increases, the helper T-cell count drops, which leads to AIDS.

Tip: Antiviral drugs (see page 132) can delay the time between HIV and AIDS.

Tip: The infections become more and more serious as there are fewer and fewer immune system cells to fight them.

HIV structure

You might get asked about the structure of HIV in your exam.
The basic structure of HIV is shown in Figure 1.

The virus particle has a spherical structure. It's made up of a core containing the genetic material (RNA) and some proteins (including the enzyme **reverse transcriptase**, which is needed for virus replication). It has an outer coating of protein called a capsid and an extra outer layer called an envelope, which is made of membrane stolen from the cell membrane of a previous host cell. Sticking out from the envelope are loads of copies of an attachment protein that help HIV attach to the host helper T-cell.

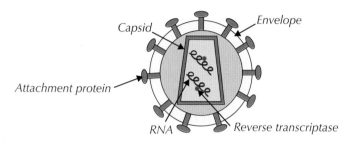

Tip: HIV attachment proteins are foreign antigens that can be recognised by the immune system. During replication, the virus can change parts of the structure of its attachment proteins — this is antigenic variation (see p. 123), and it helps HIV evade destruction by the immune system.

Figure 1: The structure of HIV.

Tip: The attachment proteins are also called envelope proteins.

HIV replication

HIV (and all other viruses) can only reproduce inside the cells of the organism it has infected. HIV replicates inside the helper T-cells of the host. It doesn't have the equipment (such as enzymes and ribosomes) to replicate on its own, so it uses those of the host cell. The following text and Figure 3 show how HIV replicates:

1. The attachment protein attaches to a receptor molecule on the cell membrane of the host helper T-cell.

2. The capsid is released into the cell, where it uncoats and releases the genetic material (RNA) into the cell's cytoplasm.

3. Inside the cell, reverse transcriptase is used to make a complementary strand of DNA from the viral RNA template.

4. From this, double-stranded DNA is made and inserted into the human DNA.

5. Host cell enzymes are used to make viral proteins from the viral DNA found within the human DNA.

6. The viral proteins are assembled into new viruses, which bud from the cell and go on to infect other cells.

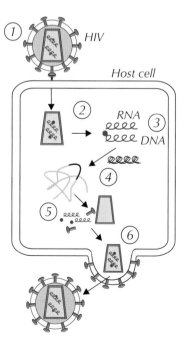

Figure 2: An electron micrograph of a cell (blue sphere) infected by HIV (yellow dots).

Tip: See pages 51-54 for loads more on DNA and RNA and how the two are inter-linked.

Tip: When HIV particles emerge from a cell, the cell ruptures and dies.

Figure 3: Replication of HIV using a host cell.

Antibiotics and viruses

Tip: Antibiotics don't kill viruses, which is why you don't get prescribed antibiotics for a cold. Colds are caused by rhinoviruses.

Antibiotics kill bacteria by interfering with their metabolic reactions. They target the bacterial enzymes and ribosomes used in these reactions. Bacterial enzymes and ribosomes are different from human enzymes and ribosomes. Antibiotics are designed to only target the bacterial ones so they don't damage human cells. Makes sense.

Viruses don't have their own enzymes and ribosomes — they use the ones in the host's cells. So because human viruses use human enzymes and ribosomes to replicate, antibiotics can't inhibit them because they don't target human processes. Most **antiviral drugs** are designed to target the few virus-specific enzymes (enzymes that only the virus uses) that exist.

Tip: HIV is a type of virus called a retrovirus. So HIV antiviral therapy is also known as antiretroviral therapy.

— Example

HIV uses reverse transcriptase to replicate (see previous page). Human cells don't use this enzyme, so drugs can be designed to inhibit it without affecting the host cell. These drugs are called reverse-transcriptase inhibitors.

Controlling HIV infection

There's currently no cure or vaccine for HIV but antiviral drugs can be used to slow down the progression of HIV infection and AIDS in an infected person.

Tip: HIV testing, based on HIV antibody detection, before a baby is 18 months old can be inaccurate. This is because the baby of an HIV-positive mother may have some HIV antibodies in their blood (passed over from their mother in the womb) regardless of whether or not they're infected.

The best way to control HIV infection in a population is by reducing its spread. HIV can be spread via unprotected sexual intercourse, through infected bodily fluids (e.g. blood from sharing contaminated needles) and from a HIV-positive mother to her fetus. Not all babies from HIV-positive mothers are born infected with HIV and taking antiviral drugs during pregnancy can reduce the chance of the baby being HIV-positive.

Practice Questions — Application

Q1 Figure 4 shows the estimated number of deaths from AIDS, number of people diagnosed with AIDS and number of people living with HIV infection aged ≥ 13 years in the United States between the years 1981 and 2008.

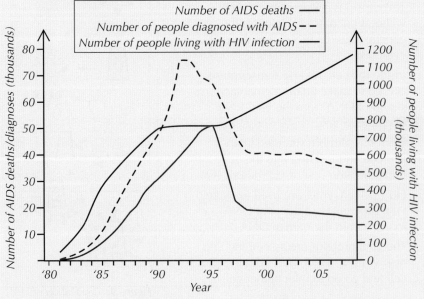

Figure 4: HIV and AIDS statistics from the US between 1981 and 2008

Highly active antiretroviral therapy (HAART) is a combination of several antiretroviral drugs that reduce the amount of HIV in the body.

a) Use information from Figure 4 to suggest the year that HAART was first introduced. Give two reasons for your answer.

b) Calculate the percentage decrease in the number of AIDS deaths between 1995 and 1998.

Tip: See page 7 for info on how to calculate percentage decreases.

c) Suggest and explain the effect HAART has on the progression of HIV to AIDS.

Q2 Initial infection with HIV stimulates an immune response, producing antibodies specific to HIV. However, the immune system does not completely destroy the virus.

a) Suggest why the immune response is not sufficient to destroy the virus.

b) HIV can vary the structure of its attachment proteins. Suggest how this helps the virus evade the immune response when replicating.

Practice Questions — Fact Recall

Q1 What does HIV stand for?

Q2 What disease does HIV cause?

Q3 Look at the diagram of a HIV particle below:

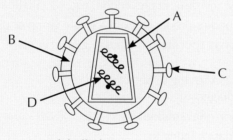

Name the structures labelled A-D.

Q4 Describe how HIV replicates.

Q5 Why can't antibiotics be used against viruses?

Section Summary

Make sure you know...

- That antigens are molecules (usually proteins) that can generate an immune response.
- That each type of cell has specific antigens on its surface that are used to identify it.
- That the immune system uses antigens to identify foreign cells (e.g. pathogens and cells from another individual), abnormal cells (e.g. cancer cells) and toxins.
- The four main stages of the immune response — phagocytosis, T-cell activation, B-cell activation, and plasma cell and antibody production.
- How phagocytes engulf pathogens, destroy them (using lysozymes) and present their antigens to T-cells.

- That T-cells are activated by foreign antigens presented by phagocytes.
- The helper T-cell response to a foreign antigen — activation of phagocytes, cytotoxic (killer) T-cells and B-cells (clonal selection).
- The B-cell response to a foreign antigen — including division into identical plasma cells and the production and release of monoclonal antibodies specific to the antigen.
- That an antibody is a protein that binds antigens to form an antigen-antibody complex.
- That the formation of antigen-antibody complexes leads to the agglutination and phagocytosis of pathogens.
- The structure of antibodies   including the variable regions (with a unique tertiary structure for antigen binding) and constant regions.
- What the cellular immune response (T-cells) and the humoral immune response (B-cells) are.
- That the primary immune response involves the production of memory cells in response to an antigen.
- That if the same antigen enters the body again, these memory cells will be activated and some will divide to produce plasma cells that produce the right type of antibody to this antigen — and that this is the secondary immune response.
- The differences between active immunity (when your immune system makes its own antibodies) and passive immunity (when you receive antibodies from a different organism).
- How vaccines make people immune to disease by stimulating memory cell production.
- How vaccines protect populations by herd immunity.
- The ethical issues surrounding vaccine use.
- That antigenic variation is when pathogens change their surface antigens.
- The effect antigenic variation has on immunity and disease prevention, e.g. vaccination programmes.
- That monoclonal antibodies are identical antibodies produced from a single group of plasma cells.
- How antibodies can be used in medicine to target specific cell types (e.g. cancer cells) and in medical diagnosis.
- How enzyme-linked antibodies are used in ELISA testing to detect antibodies or antigens of interest for medical diagnosis.
- The ethical issues surrounding the use of monoclonal antibodies.
- How to evaluate methodology, evidence and data relating to the use of vaccines and monoclonal antibodies.
- That human immunodeficiency virus (HIV) causes the symptoms of AIDS by reducing the number of helper T-cells in the body.
- The structure of the HIV and how it replicates in helper T-cells.
- That antibiotics are ineffective against viruses because viruses use host enzymes and ribosomes (so can't be targeted by antibiotics).

Exam-style Questions

1 Tetanus is a disease caused by the bacterium *Clostridium tetani*. Symptoms of the disease include extreme muscle spasms caused by the release of a toxin by the bacterium. **Figure 1** shows the global incidence of tetanus along with the percentage vaccine coverage.

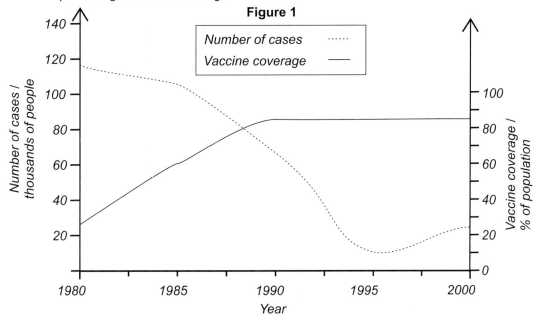

Figure 1

1.1 Calculate the average rate at which the number of tetanus cases decreased between 1985 and 1990. Give your answer in cases / thousands of people year^{-1}.

(2 marks)

1.2 In 2011 a newspaper used this data to conclude that, 'Cases of tetanus in the UK are on the increase'. Does the evidence support this conclusion? Explain your answer.

(2 marks)

1.3 Suggest a possible reason for the increase in cases from 1995 to 2000.

(1 mark)

1.4 If someone has been potentially exposed to *Clostridium tetani* then they are given a post-exposure injection of antibodies against the toxin.

Explain how this prevents them suffering from the disease, but does not prevent them from contracting the disease in the future.

(2 marks)

2 Phagocytosis is the first stage of the immune response.

2.1 Describe the process of phagocytosis.

(4 marks)

2.2 Outline the main stages of the immune response after phagocytosis.

(5 marks)

3   The illegal drug amphetamine can be tested for using monoclonal antibodies. Antibodies that bind to amphetamine are created in the laboratory and used to test urine samples.

3.1   State what monoclonal antibodies are and explain why they are specific to one substance.

(3 marks)

3.2   Describe the structure of an antibody.

(4 marks)

3.3   **Figure 2** shows the structures of amphetamine and the prescription drug bupropion.

Taking bupropion can cause a positive result on an amphetamine drug test. Suggest why this happens.

(2 marks)

3.4   Describe **one** ethical issue surrounding the use of monoclonal antibodies.

(1 mark)

Figure 2

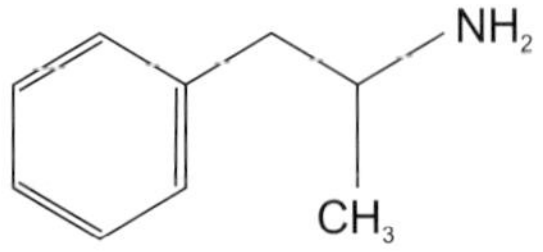

Amphetamine

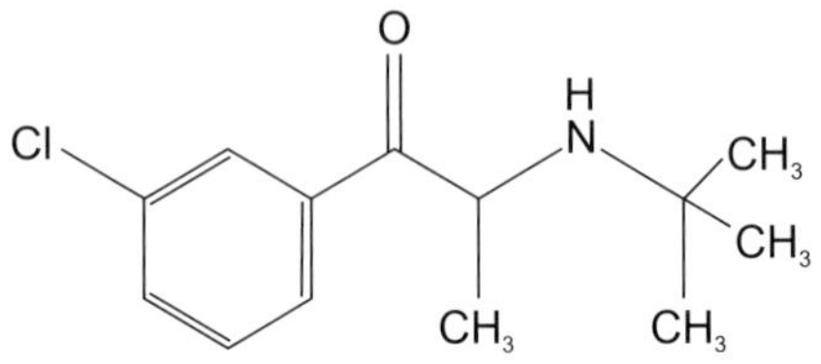

Bupropion

4   Read the following passage:

In 1918 there was a worldwide outbreak of influenza called 'Spanish flu'. It killed approximately 50-100 million people. The virus responsible was the H1N1 strain of influenza — it had type 1 haemagglutinin and type 1 neuraminidase antigens on its surface. Spanish flu circulated the globe for over a year. Survivors of the Spanish flu did not contract the disease when exposed for a second time.   5

The outbreak of Spanish flu killed an unusually high number of young, healthy adults. Some scientists think that in these cases, the patients' helper T-cells produced an excess of chemical signalling molecules. The effect this had on the patients' immune systems may have eventually contributed to their deaths.

In 1957 there was another outbreak of influenza called 'Asian flu'.   10
This outbreak was caused by the H2N2 strain of influenza.

Use the information above and your own scientific knowledge to answer these questions:

4.1   Explain why survivors of the Spanish flu did not contract it when exposed for a second time (lines 4-5).

(3 marks)

4.2   What effect would an excess of chemical signalling molecules have had on the Spanish flu patients' immune systems (lines 7-9)? Explain your answer.

(2 marks)

4.3   Suggest why children and the elderly may not have been affected by Spanish flu in the same way as young adults.

(2 marks)

4.4   Survivors of the Spanish flu may have been able to contract Asian flu (line 10). Explain why.

(3 marks)

Topic 3 | A: Exchange and Transport Systems

1. Size and Surface Area

Learning Objectives:
- Understand the relationship between the size of an organism or structure and its surface area to volume ratio.
- Know how adaptations, such as changes to body shape and the development of systems in larger organisms, facilitate exchange as the surface area to volume ratio reduces.
- Understand the relationship between surface area to volume ratio and metabolic rate.

Specification Reference 3.3.1

Every organism has substances it needs to take in and others it needs to get rid of in order to survive. An organism's size and surface area affect how quickly this is done.

Exchange of substances with the environment

Every organism, whatever its size, needs to exchange things with its environment. Cells need to take in oxygen (for aerobic respiration) and nutrients. They also need to excrete waste products like carbon dioxide and urea. Most organisms need to stay at roughly the same temperature, so heat needs to be exchanged too.

Surface area : volume ratio

An organism's surface area : volume ratio affects how quickly substances are exchanged. But before going into the effects of surface area : volume ratios, you need to understand a bit more about them. Smaller organisms have higher surface area : volume ratios than larger organisms, as shown in the example below.

> **Example** — **Maths Skills**
>
> A mouse has a bigger surface area relative to its volume than a hippo. This can be hard to imagine, but you can prove it mathematically.
>
> Imagine these animals as cubes...
>
> The mouse could be represented by a cube measuring 1 cm × 1 cm × 1 cm.
>
> 1 cm   1 cm
> 1 cm
> *"cube mouse"*
>
> Its volume is: $1 \times 1 \times 1 = 1$ cm³
>
> Its surface area is: $6 \times 1 \times 1 = 6$ cm²
>
> So the mouse has a surface area : volume ratio of **6 : 1**.
>
> Compare this to a cube hippo measuring 2 cm × 4 cm × 4 cm.
>
> Its volume is: $2 \times 4 \times 4 = 32$ cm³
>
> Its surface area is:
>
> $2 \times 4 \times 4 = 32$ cm²
> (top and bottom surfaces of cube)
>
> $+ (4 \times 2 \times 4) = 32$ cm²
> (four sides of the cube)
>
> 4 cm   4 cm   2 cm
> *"cube hippo"*
>
> Total surface area = 64 cm²
>
> So the hippo has a surface area : volume ratio of 64 : 32 or **2 : 1**.
>
> The cube mouse's surface area is six times its volume, but the cube hippo's surface area is only twice its volume. Smaller animals have a bigger surface area compared to their volume.

Tip: A ratio shows how big one value is <u>in relation</u> to another.

Figure 1: *A hippo (top) has a small surface area:volume ratio. A mouse (bottom) has a large surface area:volume ratio.*

Calculating volume and surface area

You might be asked to calculate volume or surface area in the exam. For example, you could be asked to calculate the volume or surface area of a cell.

─ **Example** ── **Maths Skills** ─────────

Bacillus are rod-shaped bacteria — as shown in Figure 2.

To calculate the volume of this cell, you need to split the bacterium into parts: the cylindrical centre and the hemispheres on either end.

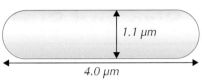

Figure 2: A Bacillus *cell.*

1. Start by calculating the volume of the cylinder. The formula you need is **πr²h** or **π x radius² x height**. First find the radius, then the height:

   radius (r) = 1.1 ÷ 2   height (h) = 4.0 − 0.55 − 0.55
   = **0.55 μm**   = **2.9 μm**

   Then use them to calculate the volume of the cylinder:
   Volume of a cylinder = πr²h
   = π x 0.55² x 2.9 = **2.755...**

2. Now find the volume of the two hemispheres.
   The formula for the volume of a sphere is $\frac{4}{3}\pi r^3$.

   A sphere is made of two hemispheres,
   so the total volume of the two hemispheres = $\frac{4}{3}\pi$ x 0.55³
   = **0.696...**

3. Finally, add the volume of the cylinder and the two hemispheres together to find the total volume of the cell:

   Total volume = 2.755... + 0.696...
   = **3.5 μm³** (2 s.f.)

Practice Question — Application

Q1 Below are three 3D shapes of different sizes (not drawn to scale).

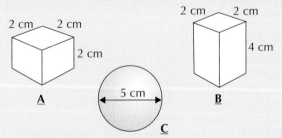

a) For each 3D shape work out its:
   i) surface area.
   ii) volume.
   iii) surface area: volume ratio.
b) Which 3D shape has the greatest surface area: volume ratio?

Exchange organs and mass transport systems

An organism needs to supply every one of its cells with substances like glucose and oxygen (for respiration). It also needs to remove waste products from every cell to avoid damaging itself. Different sized organisms do this in different ways:

Single-celled organisms

In single-celled organisms, these substances can **diffuse** directly into (or out of) the cell across the cell-surface membrane. The diffusion rate is quick because of the small distances the substances have to travel (see p. 100).

Multicellular organisms

In multicellular organisms, diffusion across the outer membrane is too slow, for two reasons:

1. Some cells are deep within the body — there's a big distance between them and the outside environment.

2. Larger animals have a low surface area to volume ratio — it's difficult to exchange enough substances to supply a large volume of animal through a relatively small outer surface.

So rather than using straightforward diffusion to absorb and excrete substances, multicellular organisms need specialised **exchange organs** (like lungs — see page 146).

They also need an efficient system to carry substances to and from their individual cells — this is **mass transport**. In mammals, 'mass transport' normally refers to the circulatory system, which uses blood to carry glucose and oxygen around the body. It also carries hormones, antibodies and waste like CO_2. Mass transport in plants involves the transport of water and solutes in the xylem and phloem.

Figure 3: *A bacterium — an example of a single-celled organism.*

Tip: Remember, diffusion is the net movement of particles from an area of higher concentration to an area of lower concentration — see page 100.

Tip: There's more about the circulatory system on page 173. There's more about xylem and phloem on pages 189 and 193.

Heat exchange

As well as creating waste products that need to be transported away, the metabolic activity inside cells creates heat. Staying at the right temperature is difficult, and it's pretty heavily influenced by your size and shape...

Body size

The rate of heat loss from an organism depends on its surface area. As you saw on page 137, if an organism has a large volume, e.g. a hippo, its surface area is relatively small. This makes it harder for it to lose heat from its body. If an organism is small, e.g. a mouse, its relative surface area is large, so heat is lost more easily. This means smaller organisms need a relatively high metabolic rate, in order to generate enough heat to stay warm.

Body shape

Animals (of any size) with a compact shape have a small surface area relative to their volume — minimising heat loss from their surface. Animals with a less compact shape (those that are a bit gangly or have sticky outy bits) have a larger surface area relative to their volume — this increases heat loss from their surface.

Adaptations for heat exchange

Whether an animal is compact or not depends on the temperature of its environment — the animal's body shape is **adapted** to suit its environment.

Examples

Arctic fox

Body temperature — 37 °C
Average outside
temperature — 0 °C

The Arctic fox has small ears and a round head to reduce its surface area : volume ratio and heat loss.

African bat-eared fox

Body temperature — 37 °C
Average outside
temperature — 25 °C

The African bat-eared fox has large ears and a more pointed nose to increase its surface area : volume ratio and heat loss.

European fox

Body temperature — 37 °C
Average outside
temperature — 12 °C

The European fox is intermediate between the two, matching the temperature of its environment.

Behavioural and physiological adaptations to aid exchange

Not all organisms have a body size or shape to suit their climate — some have other adaptations to aid exchange instead...

- Animals with a high surface area : volume ratio tend to lose more water as it evaporates from their surface. This is a problem particularly for animals living in hot regions where water evaporates quickly. Some small desert mammals have kidney structure adaptations so that they produce less urine to compensate.

- To support their high metabolic rates, small mammals living in cold regions need to eat large amounts of high energy foods such as seeds and nuts.

- Smaller mammals may have thick layers of fur or hibernate when the weather gets really cold.

- Larger organisms living in hot regions, such as elephants and hippos, find it hard to keep cool as their heat loss is relatively slow. Elephants have developed large flat ears which increase their surface area, allowing them to lose more heat. Hippos spend much of the day in the water — a behavioural adaptation to help them lose heat.

Figure 4: *A squirrel eats high energy foods to fuel its high metabolic rate.*

Figure 5: *An elephant's large, flat ears help it keep cool.*

Exam Tip
Make sure you write about surface area : volume ratio in the exam and not just surface area.

Practice Questions — Application

Q1 An Emperor penguin is much larger than an Adélie penguin.

a) Which penguin would you expect to have the larger surface area : volume ratio?

b) Which penguin would you expect to find in the coldest regions? Explain your answer.

An Adélie penguin has a compact shape with short wings and legs. A Rockhopper penguin is less compact with longer wings and legs.

c) Assuming the two penguins are roughly the same size, explain which one you would expect to live in the colder regions.

Q2 In snowy, winter months small animals such as mice and voles live in underground tunnels. Suggest why they have developed this behaviour.

Q3 In winter some birds 'fluff' their feathers to trap more warm air close to their body. Would you expect this physiological adaptation to be more common among small or large birds? Explain your answer.

Q4 Some large desert animals, such as coyotes, sleep during the day and are only active at night. Suggest why they have this behaviour.

Practice Questions — Fact Recall

Q1 a) Name two substances an animal needs to take in from its environment.

   b) Name two substances an animal needs to release into its environment.

Q2 Do most large animals have a higher or lower surface area : volume ratio than small animals?

Q3 Give two reasons why diffusion is too slow in multicellular organisms for them to absorb and excrete substances this way.

Q4 What is meant by a 'mass transport' system?

Q5 Will the rate of heat loss at a given temperature be greater for an animal with a high or low surface area : volume ratio?

Q6 Explain how an animal's shape can help to control its temperature.

Q7 Other than body size or shape, give two adaptations a small animal may have to survive in a cold environment.

Q8 Other than body size or shape, give two adaptations a large animal might have to survive in a hot environment.

Learning Objectives:

- Know the adaptations of gas exchange surfaces, shown by gas exchange:
  - across the body surface of a single-celled organism,
  - across the gills of fish (gill lamellae and filaments including the counter-current principle),
  - by the leaves of dicotyledonous plants (mesophyll and stomata),
  - in the tracheal system of an insect (tracheae, tracheoles and spiracles).
- Understand the structural and functional compromises between the opposing needs for efficient gas exchange and the limitation of water loss shown by terrestrial insects and xerophytic plants.
  Specification Reference 3.3.2

Tip: There's more on factors that increase the rate of diffusion on page 100.

Tip: The gills are located inside a fish's head underneath gill slits or a bony flap called the operculum.

Figure 1: *The gills inside a mackerel.*

2. Gas Exchange

Organisms are constantly exchanging gases with their environment. In large organisms that's not always easy — so many plants and animals have adaptations to aid gas exchange.

Gas exchange surfaces

Gas exchange occurs over a **gas exchange surface** — a boundary between the outside environment and the internal environment of an organism. Organisms need oxygen and carbon dioxide to diffuse across gas exchange surfaces as quickly as possible. Most gas exchange surfaces have two things in common that increase the rate of diffusion:

1. They have a large surface area.
2. They're thin (often just one layer of epithelial cells) — this provides a short diffusion pathway across the gas exchange surface.

The organism also maintains a steep concentration gradient of gases across the exchange surface, which increases the rate of diffusion.

Gas exchange in single-celled organisms

Single-celled organisms absorb and release gases by diffusion through their cell-surface membranes. They have a relatively large surface area, a thin surface and a short diffusion pathway (oxygen can take part in biochemical reactions as soon as it diffuses into the cell) — so there's no need for a specialised gas exchange system.

Gas exchange in fish

There's a lower concentration of oxygen in water than in air. So fish have special adaptations to get enough of it. In a fish, the gas exchange surface is the gills.

Structure of gills

Water, containing oxygen, enters the fish through its mouth and passes out through the gills. Each gill is made of lots of thin plates called **gill filaments**, which give a large surface area for exchange of gases (and so increase the rate of diffusion). The gill filaments are covered in lots of tiny structures called **lamellae**, which increase the surface area even more — see Figure 2. The lamellae have lots of blood capillaries and a thin surface layer of cells to speed up diffusion, between the water and the blood.

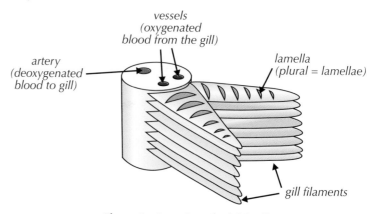

Figure 2: *A section of a fish's gill.*

The counter-current system

In the gills of a fish, blood flows through the lamellae in one direction and water flows over them in the opposite direction — see Figure 3. This is called a counter-current system. The counter-current system means that the water with a relatively high oxygen concentration always flows next to blood with a lower concentration of oxygen. This in turn means that a steep concentration gradient is maintained between the water and the blood — so as much oxygen as possible diffuses from the water into the blood.

Exam Tip
In the exam it's not enough to write that the counter-current system creates a steep concentration gradient — you need to say that the concentration gradient is <u>maintained</u> over the <u>whole length</u> of the gill to get the marks.

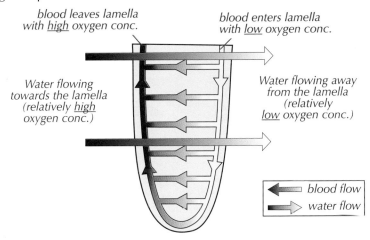

blood leaves lamella with <u>high</u> oxygen conc.

blood enters lamella with <u>low</u> oxygen conc.

Water flowing towards the lamella (relatively <u>high</u> oxygen conc.)

Water flowing away from the lamella (relatively <u>low</u> oxygen conc.)

| ← | blood flow |
| → | water flow |

Figure 3: *The counter-current system across a lamella.*

Tip: The normal circulation of the fish replaces the oxygenated blood that leaves the gill with more deoxygenated blood. The normal ventilation of the fish ensures that more water with a relatively high oxygen concentration is taken in. Both of these help to maintain the steep concentration gradient.

Gas exchange in dicotyledonous plants

Plants need CO_2 for photosynthesis, which produces O_2 as a waste gas. They need O_2 for respiration, which produces CO_2 as a waste gas. The main gas exchange surface is the surface of the **mesophyll cells** in the leaf. They're well adapted for their function — they have a large surface area.

The mesophyll cells are inside the leaf. Gases move in and out through special pores in the epidermis (mostly the lower epidermis) called **stomata** (singular = stoma). The stomata can open to allow exchange of gases, and close if the plant is losing too much water. **Guard cells** control the opening and closing of stomata.

Tip: You don't need to worry too much about what dicotyledonous means — it's a category of plant that includes most green and non-woody plants, bushes and trees.

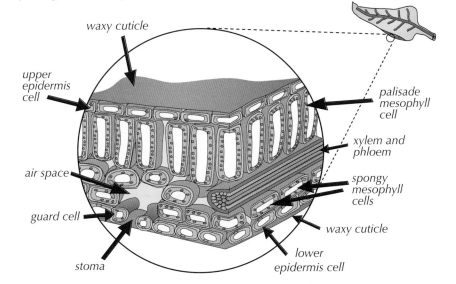

waxy cuticle

upper epidermis cell

palisade mesophyll cell

xylem and phloem

air space

spongy mesophyll cells

guard cell

waxy cuticle

stoma

lower epidermis cell

Figure 4: *Structure of a dicotyledonous plant leaf.*

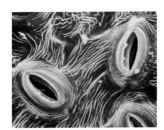

Figure 5: *Open stomata on the epidermis of a leaf.*

Gas exchange in insects

Tip: Terrestrial insects are just insects that live on land.

Terrestrial insects have microscopic air-filled pipes called **tracheae** which they use for gas exchange. Air moves into the tracheae through pores on the surface called **spiracles**. Oxygen travels down the concentration gradient towards the cells. The tracheae branch off into smaller **tracheoles** which have thin, permeable walls and go to individual cells. This means that oxygen diffuses directly into the respiring cells — the insect's circulatory system doesn't transport O_2. Carbon dioxide from the cells moves down its own concentration gradient towards the spiracles to be released into the atmosphere. Insects use rhythmic abdominal movements to move air in and out of the spiracles.

Figure 6: A spiracle on the surface of a garden tiger moth caterpillar.

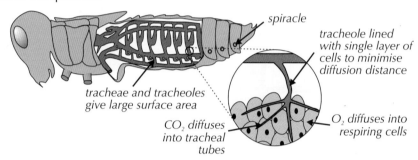

spiracle

tracheole lined with single layer of cells to minimise diffusion distance

tracheae and tracheoles give large surface area

CO_2 diffuses into tracheal tubes

O_2 diffuses into respiring cells

Figure 7: Gas exchange across the tracheal system of an insect.

Control of water loss

Exchanging gases tends to make you lose water — there's a sort of trade-off between the two. Luckily for plants and insects though, they've evolved adaptations to minimise water loss without reducing gas exchange too much.

Tip: Being <u>turgid</u> means the guard cells become swollen/plump. Being <u>flaccid</u> means they become limp.

If insects are losing too much water, they close their spiracles using muscles. They also have a waterproof, waxy cuticle all over their body and tiny hairs around their spiracles, both of which reduce evaporation.

Plants' stomata are usually kept open during the day to allow gaseous exchange. Water enters the guard cells, making them turgid, which opens the stomatal pore. If the plant starts to get dehydrated, the guard cells lose water and become flaccid, which closes the pore.

Tip: Marram grass and cacti are good examples of xerophytic plants.

Some plants are specially adapted for life in warm, dry or windy habitats, where water loss is a problem. These plants are called **xerophytes**. Examples of xerophytic adaptations include:

- Stomata sunk in pits to trap water vapour, reducing the concentration gradient of water between the leaf and the air. This reduces evaporation of water from the leaf.

Figure 8: Marram grass.

- A layer of 'hairs' on the epidermis to trap water vapour round the stomata.

- Curled leaves with the stomata inside, protecting them from wind (windy conditions increase the rate of diffusion and evaporation).

Tip: See page 190 for more on water loss in plants.

- A reduced number of stomata, so there are fewer places for water to escape.

- Thicker waxy, waterproof cuticles on leaves and stems to reduce evaporation.

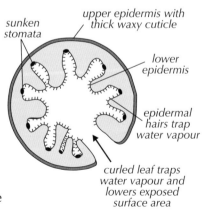

upper epidermis with thick waxy cuticle

sunken stomata

lower epidermis

epidermal hairs trap water vapour

curled leaf traps water vapour and lowers exposed surface area

Figure 9: Adaptations of a xerophytic plant.

Q1 The photographs below show sections of leaves from two different plants.

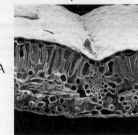

A

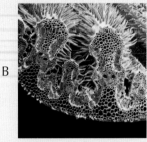

B

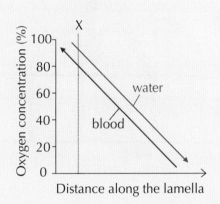

Tip: To help you answer Q1, think of all the adaptations that a xerophytic plant has and then see which photo you can spot them on.

Which leaf belongs to a xerophyte? Explain your answer.

Q2 In polluted water the dissolved oxygen concentration is lower than it is in clean water. Explain how this would affect gas exchange across the gills of a fish.

Q3 The graph on the right shows how the relative oxygen concentrations of blood and water change with distance along a lamella.

a) What happens to the oxygen concentration of blood as it moves along the lamella?

b) What happens to the oxygen concentration of water as it moves along the lamella?

c) What is the oxygen concentration of the blood at distance X on the graph?

d) Use evidence from the graph to explain why the oxygen concentration of the blood increases straight after point X.

Q1 Give two things that all gas exchange surfaces have in common.

Q2 Explain why single-celled organisms don't need a gas exchange system.

Q3 Describe the structure of fish gills.

Q4 Describe how the 'counter-current' system in fish aids gas exchange.

Q5 What is the main gas exchange surface for a dicotyledonous plant?

Q6 Where do gases move in and out of a leaf?

Q7 How does air get into an insect's tracheae?

Q8 Describe how carbon dioxide moves out of an insect's cells into the atmosphere.

Q9 What is a xerophyte?

Q10 Give three adaptations that xerophytic plants have to reduce water loss.

- Know the gross structure of the human gas exchange system including the alveoli, bronchioles, bronchi, trachea and lungs.

- Understand ventilation and the exchange of gases in the lungs.

- Know the mechanism of breathing, including the role of the diaphragm and the antagonistic interaction between external and internal intercostal muscles in bringing about pressure changes in the thoracic cavity.

- Know the essential features of the alveolar epithelium as a surface over which gas exchange takes place.

Specification Reference 3.3.2

3. Gas Exchange in Humans

The role of your gas exchange system is to supply your blood with oxygen, and remove carbon dioxide from your body.

Gas exchange

Humans need to get oxygen into the blood (for respiration) and they need to get rid of carbon dioxide (made by respiring cells). This is where breathing (or ventilation as it's sometimes called) and the gas exchange system come in.

Structure of the gas exchange system

The structure of the human gas exchange system is shown in Figure 1.

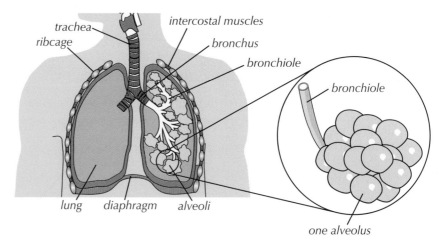

Figure 1: A diagram of the human gas exchange system with the alveoli enlarged.

As you breathe in, air enters the trachea (windpipe). The trachea splits into two bronchi — one bronchus leading to each lung. Each bronchus then branches off into smaller tubes called bronchioles. The bronchioles end in small 'air sacs' called alveoli. This is where gases are exchanged (see next page). The ribcage, intercostal muscles and diaphragm all work together to move air in and out.

Intercostal muscles

The intercostal muscles are found between the ribs. There are actually three layers of intercostal muscles, two of which you need to know about for your exams: the internal and external intercostal muscles. Unsurprisingly, the internal intercostal muscles are on the inside of the external intercostal muscles. There's more about how these two sets of muscles interact to help you breathe on the next page.

Ventilation

Ventilation consists of inspiration (breathing in) and expiration (breathing out). It's controlled by the movements of the diaphragm, internal and external intercostal muscles and ribcage. The processes of inspiration and expiration are described in detail on the next page.

Figure 2: A coloured chest X-ray showing the airways in the lungs (pink).

Inspiration

During inspiration the external intercostal and diaphragm muscles contract. This causes the ribcage to move upwards and outwards and the diaphragm to flatten, increasing the volume of the thoracic cavity (the space where the lungs are). As the volume of the thoracic cavity increases, the lung pressure decreases to below atmospheric pressure. Air will always flow from an area of higher pressure to an area of lower pressure (i.e. down a pressure gradient) so air flows down the trachea and into the lungs. Inspiration is an active process — it requires energy.

Tip: Only the <u>external</u> intercostal muscles contract during inspiration — the internal intercostal muscles remain relaxed throughout.

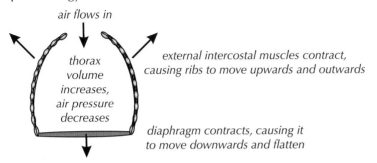

air flows in

thorax volume increases, air pressure decreases

external intercostal muscles contract, causing ribs to move upwards and outwards

diaphragm contracts, causing it to move downwards and flatten

Figure 3: *Diagram showing what happens during inspiration.*

Tip: Remember, when the diaphragm contracts, it's flat. When it relaxes, it bulges upwards. Think of it like trying to hold your stomach in — you contract your muscles to flatten your stomach and relax to release it.

Expiration

During expiration the external intercostal and diaphragm muscles relax. The ribcage moves downwards and inwards, and the diaphragm curves upwards again (so it becomes dome-shaped). The volume of the thoracic cavity decreases, causing the air pressure to increase to above atmospheric pressure. Air is forced down the pressure gradient and out of the lungs.

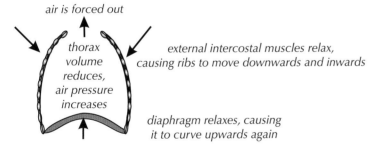

air is forced out

thorax volume reduces, air pressure increases

external intercostal muscles relax, causing ribs to move downwards and inwards

diaphragm relaxes, causing it to curve upwards again

Figure 4: *Diagram showing what happens during expiration.*

Tip: It's the movement of the ribcage and diaphragm and the change in lung pressure that causes air to flow in and out — not the other way round.

Normal expiration is a passive process — it doesn't require energy. Expiration can be forced though, e.g. if you want to blow out the candles on your birthday cake. During forced expiration, the external intercostal muscles relax and internal intercostal muscles contract, pulling the ribcage further down and in. During this time, the movement of the two sets of intercostal muscles is said to be antagonistic (opposing).

Alveoli and gas exchange

Lungs contain millions of microscopic air sacs where gas exchange occurs — called alveoli. The alveoli are surrounded by a network of capillaries — see Figure 5.

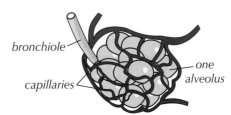

bronchiole

capillaries

one alveolus

Figure 5: *Alveoli covered in a network of capillaries.*

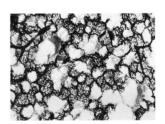

Figure 6: *A light micrograph of capillaries surrounding alveoli.*

Tip: Epithelial tissue is pretty common in the body. It's usually found on exchange surfaces.

Alveoli structure

The wall of each alveolus is made from a single layer of thin, flat cells called alveolar epithelium. The walls of the capillaries are made from capillary endothelium — see Figure 7.

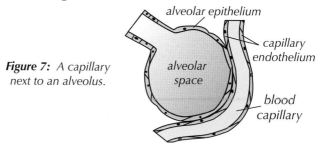

Figure 7: A capillary next to an alveolus.

The walls of the alveoli contain a protein called elastin. Elastin is elastic — it helps the alveoli to return (recoil) to their normal shape after inhaling and exhaling air.

Movement of oxygen and carbon dioxide through the gas exchange system

Air (containing oxygen) moves down the trachea, bronchi and bronchioles into the alveoli. This movement happens down a pressure gradient. Oxygen then moves into the blood where it can be transported round the body — this movement happens down a diffusion gradient.

Carbon dioxide moves down its own diffusion and pressure gradients, but in the opposite direction to oxygen, so that it can be breathed out.

Gas exchange in the alveoli

Tip: Haemoglobin is found in red blood cells. There's more about it on page 168.

Oxygen (O_2) diffuses out of the alveoli, across the alveolar epithelium and the capillary endothelium, and into a compound called haemoglobin in the blood. Carbon dioxide (CO_2) diffuses into the alveoli from the blood — see Figure 8.

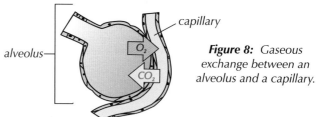

Figure 8: Gaseous exchange between an alveolus and a capillary.

Tip: Don't forget, gases pass through two layers of cells (the alveolar epithelium and the capillary endothelium).

Summary

Figure 9 summarises how oxygen moves through the gas exchange system from when it is first inhaled to reaching the blood. Carbon dioxide moves in the opposite direction.

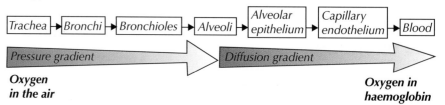

Figure 9: Flow diagram showing how oxygen moves through the gas exchange system.

Factors affecting the rate of diffusion

Alveoli have features that speed up the rate of diffusion so gases can be exchanged quickly:

- A thin exchange surface — the alveolar epithelium is only one cell thick. This means there's a short diffusion pathway (which speeds up diffusion).

- A large surface area — there are millions of alveoli. This means there's a large surface area for gas exchange.

There's also a steep concentration gradient of oxygen and carbon dioxide between the alveoli and the capillaries, which increases the rate of diffusion. This is constantly maintained by the flow of blood and ventilation (Figure 10).

Tip: These features are the same as the features of gas exchange surfaces in other organisms — see pages 142-144.

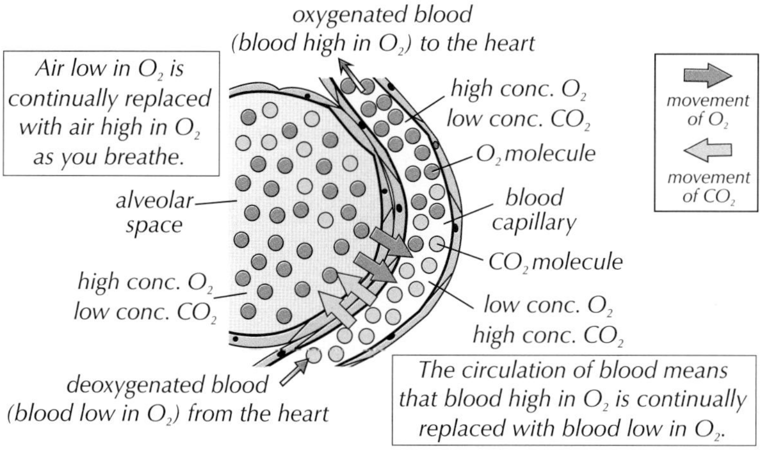

oxygenated blood (blood high in O_2) to the heart

Air low in O_2 is continually replaced with air high in O_2 as you breathe.

alveolar space

high conc. O_2
low conc. CO_2

deoxygenated blood (blood low in O_2) from the heart

high conc. O_2
low conc. CO_2

O_2 molecule

blood capillary

CO_2 molecule

low conc. O_2
high conc. CO_2

movement of O_2

movement of CO_2

The circulation of blood means that blood high in O_2 is continually replaced with blood low in O_2.

Figure 10: *Diagram showing how blood flow and ventilation maintain high concentration gradients of O_2 and CO_2.*

Practice Questions — Application

Q1 The diagram below shows a capillary next to an alveolus. Blood flows from X to Y.

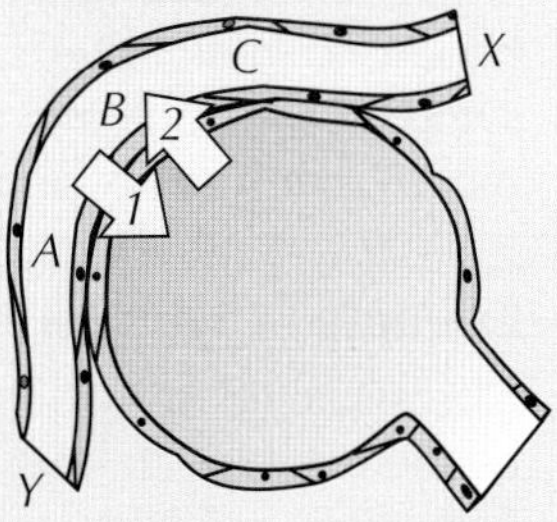

a) Which arrow, 1 or 2, indicates the movement of carbon dioxide?

b) At which letter, A, B or C, would you find the highest concentration of oxygen?

c) Blood takes 2 s to flow from X to Y. The distance between X and Y is 0.82 mm. Calculate the speed of blood flow from X to Y, giving your answer in mm s^{-1}.

Q2 A mountain climber is climbing at altitude, where there's less oxygen. Suggest how this will affect gas exchange in the alveoli.

Exam Tip
You need to be able to use maths in the exam — whatever the topic.

Practice Questions — Fact Recall

Q1 Describe what happens to make the volume of the thorax increase during inspiration.

Q2 What happens to make air leave the lungs during forced expiration?

Q3 Describe how oxygen gets from the lungs into the blood.

Q4 Describe the features of alveoli and explain how they affect the rate of diffusion.

-

Tip: dm^3 stands for decimetres cubed. $1\ dm^3$ is the same as 1 litre or $1000\ cm^3$.

Exam Tip
Don't be thrown if you get an exam question that uses an unfamiliar measure of lung function. The question will tell you what it means, then it's just a case of applying what you already know.

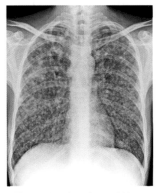

Figure 1: *A coloured X-ray of a patient with pulmonary tuberculosis. The tubercles are shown in pink.*

4. The Effects of Lung Disease

Unfortunately, there can be problems with ventilation and gas exchange. You need to be able to interpret information about this.

Lung function

Lung diseases affect both **ventilation** (breathing) and **gas exchange** in the lungs — in other words, how well the lungs function. Here are some terms you might come across in the exams. They're all measures of lung function:

- **Tidal volume** is the volume of air in each breath — it's usually between $0.4\ dm^3$ and $0.5\ dm^3$ for adults.

- **Ventilation rate** is the number of breaths per minute. For a healthy person at rest it's about 15 breaths.

- **Forced expiratory volume$_1$ (FEV$_1$)** is the maximum volume of air that can be breathed out in 1 second.

- **Forced vital capacity (FVC)** is the maximum volume of air it is possible to breathe forcefully out of the lungs after a really deep breath in.

Lung diseases

Lung diseases affect lung function in different ways.

Example — Tuberculosis

Pulmonary tuberculosis (TB) is a lung disease caused by bacteria. When someone becomes infected with tuberculosis bacteria, immune system cells build a wall around the bacteria in the lungs. This forms small, hard lumps known as tubercles (see Figure 1). Infected tissue within the tubercles dies and the gaseous exchange surface is damaged, so tidal volume is decreased. TB also causes fibrosis (see below), which further reduces the tidal volume.

A reduced tidal volume means less air can be inhaled with each breath. In order to take in enough oxygen, patients have to breathe faster, i.e. ventilation rate is increased. Common symptoms include a persistent cough, coughing up blood and mucus, chest pains, shortness of breath and fatigue.

Example — Fibrosis

Fibrosis is the formation of scar tissue in the lungs (see Figure 2). This can be the result of an infection or exposure to substances like asbestos or dust. Scar tissue is thicker and less elastic than normal lung tissue. This means that the lungs are less able to expand and so can't hold as much air as normal — tidal volume is reduced, and so is FVC (i.e. a smaller volume of air can be forcefully breathed out). There's a reduction in the rate of gaseous exchange — diffusion is slower across a thicker scarred membrane.

Fibrosis sufferers have a faster ventilation rate than normal — to get enough air into their lungs to oxygenate their blood. Symptoms of fibrosis include shortness of breath, a dry cough, chest pain, fatigue and weakness.

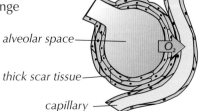

alveolar space

thick scar tissue

capillary

Figure 2: *An alveolus with thick scar tissue, which slows the diffusion of O_2 into the capillary.*

Example — Asthma

Asthma is a respiratory condition where the airways become inflamed and irritated. The causes vary from case to case but it's usually because of an allergic reaction to substances such as pollen and dust.

During an asthma attack, the smooth muscle lining the bronchioles contracts and a large amount of mucus is produced (see Figure 3). This causes constriction of the airways, making it difficult for the sufferer to breathe properly. Air flow in and out of the lungs is severely reduced, so less oxygen enters the alveoli and moves into the blood. Reduced air flow means that FEV_1 is severely reduced (i.e. less air can be breathed out in 1 second).

Symptoms include wheezing, a tight chest and shortness of breath. During an attack the symptoms come on very suddenly. They can be relieved by drugs (often in inhalers) which cause the muscle in the bronchioles to relax, opening up the airways.

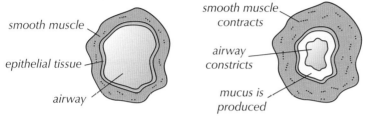

Figure 3: A cross section through a healthy bronchiole (left) and a bronchiole of someone suffering from an asthma attack (right).

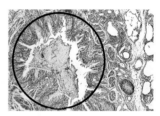

Figure 4: A lung section showing a constricted bronchiole (circled).

Example — Emphysema

Emphysema is a lung disease caused by smoking or long-term exposure to air pollution — foreign particles in the smoke (or air) become trapped in the alveoli. This causes inflammation, which attracts phagocytes to the area. The phagocytes produce an enzyme that breaks down elastin (a protein found in the walls of the alveoli).

Elastin is elastic — it helps the alveoli to return to their normal shape after inhaling and exhaling air. Loss of elastin means the alveoli can't recoil to expel air as well (it remains trapped in the alveoli). It also leads to destruction of the alveoli walls, which reduces the surface area of the alveoli (see Figure 5), so the rate of gaseous exchange decreases.

Symptoms of emphysema include shortness of breath and wheezing. People with emphysema have an increased ventilation rate as they try to increase the amount of air (containing oxygen) reaching their lungs.

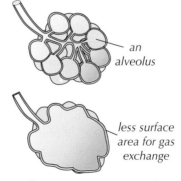

Figure 5: Cross-section of healthy alveoli (top) and damaged alveoli (bottom).

The effect of lung diseases on gas exchange

TB, fibrosis, asthma and emphysema all reduce the rate of gas exchange in the alveoli. Less oxygen is able to diffuse into the bloodstream, the body cells receive less oxygen and the rate of aerobic respiration is reduced. This means less energy is released and sufferers often feel tired and weak.

Interpreting graphs

In the exams, you could be asked to interpret information about lung diseases — and that information includes graphs. Here are two examples of the sort of thing you might get.

Tip: You can also get restrictive lung diseases — these diseases make it difficult to fully breathe in, e.g. fibrosis (in which scar tissue restricts the volume of the lungs).

Exam Tip
You could also be asked to calculate the percentage increase or decrease. Remember that a percentage decrease is always written as a positive number — see page 7.

Tip: If the graph included a line for someone with a restrictive disease, like fibrosis, FVC would be severely reduced because it's hard to get air into the lungs. FEV_1 is likely to be relatively high compared to FVC because someone with a restrictive disease is able to breathe out fairly normally.

Example 1 — Maths Skills

Figure 6 shows a typical forced expiratory volume$_1$ (FEV_1 — the maximum volume of air that can be breathed out in 1 s) and a typical forced vital capacity (FVC — the maximum volume of air it's possible to forcefully breathe out of the lungs) for someone with normal lung function (Line A) and someone with an obstructive lung disease (line B). Obstructive lung diseases are diseases that make it difficult to breathe out, e.g. asthma and emphysema.

You might be asked to do calculations from the data...

For example, you might be asked to calculate the percentage change in FEV_1 for line B compared to line A.

Reading the values off the graph, FEV_1 for line A = 4 dm^3 and FEV_1 for line B = 1 dm^3.

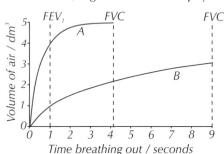

Figure 6: Graph to show typical lung functions.

$$\text{percentage change} = \frac{\text{final value} - \text{original value}}{\text{original value}} \times 100 = \frac{1-4}{4} \times 100 = -75\%$$

... and to explain it

FEV_1 and FVC are much lower than normal for someone with an obstructive lung disease because obstructive diseases make it difficult to breathe out. For example, after an asthma attack, the bronchioles are constricted and full of mucus — this narrows the airways, reducing air flow out of the lungs and leading to a large drop in FEV_1. Because it's harder to breathe out, it may also take longer for someone with an obstructive disease to forcibly breathe out all the air in their lungs (i.e. reach their FVC).

Example 2 — Spirometer data

Doctors can carry out tests to investigate lung function and diagnose lung diseases. A machine called a spirometer is used to measure the volume of air breathed in and out. You can figure out tidal volume, ventilation rate and other measures of breathing from the graph produced from a spirometer (see Figure 8).

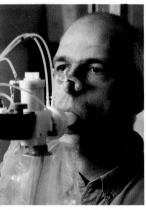

Figure 7: Testing a patient's respiratory function using a spirometer.

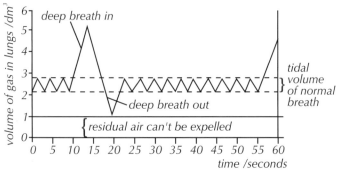

Figure 8: An example of a graph produced by a spirometer.

Practice Questions — Application

Q1 Which one of the spirometer traces below is from a patient with TB, A or B? Give a reason for your answer.

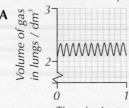

A

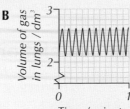

B

> **Exam Tip**
> Don't panic if a question asks you about a disease you've never heard of — just apply your knowledge of what you've learnt about how lungs normally work and you'll be able to work out the answer.

Q2 The pictures on the right show light micrographs of healthy lung tissue (top) and diseased lung tissue from a patient with emphysema (bottom). The alveoli appear white.

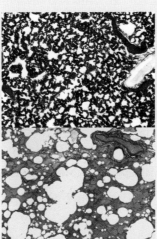

a) Describe the main difference between the healthy lung tissue and the diseased lung tissue.

b) Use your answer to part a) to explain why people with emphysema have a lower level of oxygen in the blood than normal.

Q3 The graph below shows the median area of a bronchial cross-section in healthy volunteers and in people with asthma. The areas were measured both before and after a drug called salbutamol was inhaled.

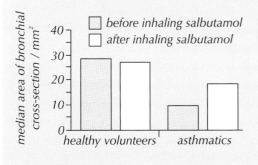

a) Describe the data.

b) Calculate the percentage change in the median bronchial area of asthmatics, after inhaling salbutamol.

c) What do you think salbutamol is used for? Explain your answer.

Practice Questions — Fact Recall

Q1 What is forced vital capacity (FVC)?

Q2 A person with fibrosis scar tissue has a reduced tidal volume. Explain why.

Q3 Explain why the rate of gaseous exchange in someone with fibrosis is slower than in a healthy person.

Q4 What happens to FEV_1 during an asthma attack?

5. Interpreting Lung Disease Data

It's common for exam questions to include a graph or two, so you could well get asked to interpret some data on the risk factors for lung diseases.

- Be able to interpret data relating to the effects of pollution and smoking on the incidence of lung disease.
- Be able to analyse and interpret data associated with specific risk factors and the incidence of lung disease.
- Be able to evaluate the way in which experimental data led to statutory restrictions on the sources of risk factors.
- Be able to recognise correlations and causal relationships.
  Specification Reference 3.3.2

Cause and correlation

All diseases have factors that will increase a person's chance of getting that disease. These are called **risk factors**. For example, it's widely known that if you smoke you're more likely to get lung cancer (smoking is a risk factor for lung cancer). This is an example of a correlation — a link between two things (see page 15). However, a correlation doesn't always mean that one thing causes the other. Smokers have an increased risk of getting cancer but that doesn't necessarily mean smoking causes the disease — there are lots of other factors to take into consideration.

Interpreting data

You need to be able to describe and analyse data given to you in your exams. Here's an example of the sort of thing you might get:

Tip: 'Incidence' just means the number of new cases of a disease.

┌─ **Example 1 — Smoking and lung cancer** ────────────

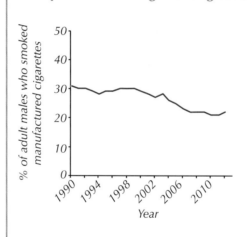

Figure 1: A graph showing the percentage of males aged 16 and over who smoked manufactured cigarettes in Great Britain.

Tip: A risk factor is just something that <u>increases</u> the chance of getting a disease. Having a risk factor doesn't mean you'll definitely get the disease though, it just makes it more likely.

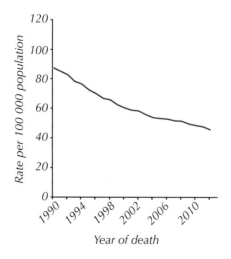

Figure 2: A graph showing age-standardised mortality rates for male lung cancer in the United Kingdom.

You might be asked to describe the data...

Figure 1 shows that the number of adult males in Great Britain who smoke decreased between 1990 and 2012. Figure 2 shows that the male lung cancer mortality (death) rate decreased between 1990 and 2012 in the United Kingdom.

... or draw conclusions

You need to be careful what you say here. There's a correlation (link) between the number of males who smoked and the mortality rate for male lung cancer. But you can't say that one caused the other. There could be other reasons for the trend, e.g. deaths due to lung cancer may have decreased because less asbestos was being used in homes (not because fewer people were smoking).

Other points to consider:

Figure 2 shows mortality (death) rates. The rate of cases of lung cancer may have been increasing but medical advances may mean more people were surviving (so only mortality was decreasing, not the number of people developing the disease).

Exam Tip
It's always a good idea to pick out some numbers from a graph when describing data.

Tip: Mortality rate is the number of deaths in a population in a set period of time (e.g. a year).

Example 2 — Air pollution and asthma

Figure 3 shows the number of new cases of asthma per 100 000 of the population diagnosed in the UK from 1996 to 2000. Figure 4 shows the emissions (in millions of tonnes) of sulfur dioxide (an air pollutant) from 1996 to 2000 in the UK.

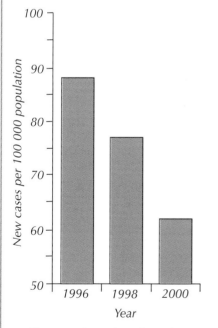

Figure 3: A graph to show the rates of new cases of asthma between 1996 and 2000 in the UK.

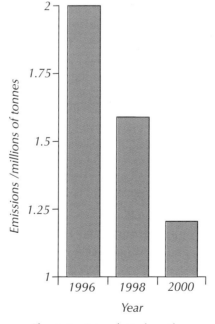

Figure 4: A graph to show the emission of sulfur dioxide between 1996 and 2000 in the UK.

Figure 5: Power stations release sulfur dioxide and other pollutants into the atmosphere.

You might be asked to describe the data...

Figure 3 shows that the number of new cases of asthma in the UK fell between 1996 and 2000, from 87 to 62 per 100 000 people.

Figure 4 shows that the emissions of sulfur dioxide in the UK fell between 1996 and 2000, from 2 to 1.2 million tonnes.

Tip: Figure 4 shows sulfur dioxide emissions in millions of tonnes. So there were 2 million tonnes of emissions in 1996 — not 2 tonnes.

... or draw conclusions

Be careful what you say when drawing conclusions. Here there's a link between the number of new cases of asthma and emissions of sulfur dioxide in the UK — the rate of new cases of asthma has fallen as sulfur dioxide emissions have fallen. You can't say that one causes the other though because there could be other reasons for the trend, e.g. the number of new cases of asthma could be falling due to the decrease in the number of people smoking. You can't say the reduction in asthma cases is linked to a reduction in air pollution (in general) either as only sulfur dioxide levels were studied.

Other points to consider:

Figure 3 shows new cases of asthma. The rate of new cases may be decreasing but existing cases may be becoming more severe. The emissions were for the whole of the UK but air pollution varies from area to area, e.g. cities tend to be more polluted. The asthma data doesn't take into account any other factors that may increase the risk of developing asthma, e.g. allergies, smoking, etc.

Responses to experimental data

You might also need to evaluate the way in which scientific data has led to government restrictions on the sources of risk factors.

Examples — Restrictions on tobacco and smoking

Advertising of tobacco products

Medical studies in the 1950s and 1960s documented the link between smoking and various forms of cancer, particularly lung cancer. The evidence prompted the first voluntary agreement between the UK government and tobacco companies in 1971, which stated that tobacco products and adverts should carry a health warning label.

However, despite further evidence for smoking-related health risks, it was not until 2003 that bans on advertising of tobacco-based products began to replace the voluntary agreements. As of October 2008, picture health warnings were made compulsory on all UK boxes of cigarettes after studies suggested they were more effective than written warnings alone.

Passive smoking

During the 1980s and 1990s a number of reports were published linking lung-cancer (and other diseases) in non-smokers to smoke that they had been passively exposed to. In 1997, the government initiated a voluntary agreement for workplaces, pubs and restaurants to increase provision of smoke-free areas for non-smokers. However, this had a limited impact.

During the early 2000s, evidence for the effects of passive smoking continued to grow and public support for smoke-free areas increased. In 2002, the British Medical Association called for a ban on smoking in public places. Finally, in 2007, workplaces and public areas such as pubs and restaurants were made smoke-free by law. Increasing concern about the impact of passive smoking on children has recently led to a ban on smoking in cars carrying under-18s, which will come into force in October 2015.

Figure 6: *Cigarette packet showing a written health warning.*

Clean Air Programme for Europe

In response to studies connecting air pollution to various diseases and as part of the Clean Air Programme for Europe, the EU adopted the National Emission Ceilings Directive in 2001. This set upper limits on the total emissions of four major pollutants in the atmosphere, to be achieved by 2010. The four pollutants covered were sulfur dioxides, nitrogen oxides, non-methane volatile organic compounds and ammonia. However, twelve member states failed to meet their emissions targets for at least one pollutant in 2010.

Following a review of progress in 2011 and further scientific evidence, e.g. on the effects of particulate matter on lung function, the directive has been revised. New limits are being agreed on for 2020 with tougher enforcement. Particulate matter has now been included in the emissions targets, along with methane.

Clean Power for Transport

The EU also introduced the Clean Power for Transport package to promote cleaner fuels for vehicles and all new cars are required to comply with Euro Standards on emissions, which are tested during the car's annual MOT. The UK government also taxes car owners according to their car's emissions with discounts available for cars that have less-polluting fuels.

Tip: The fact that statutory restrictions on sources of air pollution have only been introduced relatively recently is partly because it is difficult to establish air pollution as a cause of lung diseases. This is because there are a number of different pollutants in the atmosphere and it is difficult to monitor people's exposure to them.

Practice Questions — Application

The graph below shows the per capita consumption of tobacco and the death rates for COPD (chronic obstructive pulmonary disease, which includes emphysema) from 1945 to 1998 in Australia.

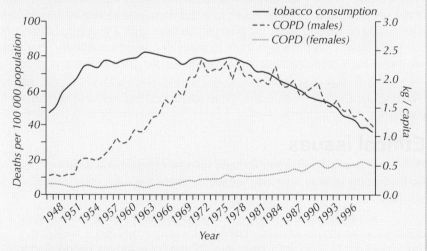

Tip: Per capita basically just means per person.

Q1 Describe in detail the trend in male COPD.

Q2 A scientist concludes from this data that COPD in women is not caused by smoking. Discuss this claim.

Q3 Suggest how the Australian government might make use of data like this.

6. Dissecting Gas Exchange Systems

Here's your chance to see what gas exchange systems really look like inside...

Carrying out dissections

As part of your AS or A-level in Biology, you're expected to carry out at least one dissection. It could be a dissection of a gaseous exchange system or a mass transport system (or an organ within one of those systems) in either an animal or a plant. You could also be asked about dissections in your exams.

There are examples of mass transport system dissections on pages 178 and 191-192. The next two pages cover some gaseous exchange system dissections that you could do as well or instead. Whatever the dissection, you're expected to know how to carry it out safely and ethically. You might also need to record your observations using labelled diagrams.

Dissection tools

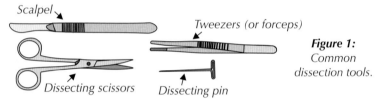

Figure 1: Common dissection tools.

Scalpel

Tweezers (or forceps)

Dissecting scissors

Dissecting pin

Figure 1 shows some of the tools that you might need to use for your dissections. Scalpels have a very sharp detachable blade and can be used for making very fine cuts. Dissecting scissors are also used for precise cutting. They are safer to use than scalpels (because the blades are less likely to snap under pressure) and it can be easier to avoid damaging the tissue underneath when using scissors. Dissecting pins can be used with a wax-filled dissection tray (see Figure 2) to pin a specimen in place during the dissection. Tweezers are useful for holding and manipulating the smaller parts of the specimen.

Figure 2: A wax-filled dissection tray.

Your dissecting tools (e.g. scalpels, dissecting scissors) should all be clean, sharp and free from rust — blunt tools don't cut well and can be dangerous.

Ethical issues

Dissecting animals (including fish and insects) can give you a better understanding of their anatomy. However, there are some ethical issues involved.

Some people argue that it is morally wrong to kill animals just for dissections, as it is unnecessary killing. However many dissections that are carried out in schools involve animals that have already been killed for their meat, e.g. the sheep's lung dissection on the next page. (Some people disagree with killing animals altogether though.)

There are concerns that the animals used for dissections are not always raised in a humane way — they may be subject to overcrowding, extremes of temperature or lack of food — and they may not be killed humanely either. If animals (e.g. insects) are raised in school for dissection, it's important to make sure they are looked after properly and killed humanely to minimise any suffering or distress.

Examples of dissections

REQUIRED PRACTICAL **5**

Example 1 — Dissection of a mammalian lung

1. Lung dissection is messy, so make sure you're wearing a lab coat.
2. Lay the lungs your teacher has given you on a cutting board. They'll probably be sheep or pig lungs from a butcher's shop. You should be able to see the trachea and two bronchi going into the lungs.
3. To see the lungs inflate, pop them in a clear plastic bag, attach a piece of rubber tubing to the trachea and pump air into the lungs using a foot or bicycle pump. The lungs will deflate by themselves because of the elastin in the walls of the alveoli (see p. 148). Never blow down the tube to inflate the lungs — you could end up sucking up stale air from inside the lungs into your mouth. Putting the lungs in a plastic bag stops bacteria inside the lungs from being released into the room.
4. Once you've seen the lungs inflate, you can examine the different tissue types in the lungs.
5. The trachea is supported by C-shaped rings of cartilage. A cross-section of the trachea is shown in Figure 3.

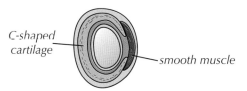

C-shaped cartilage

smooth muscle

Figure 3: *Horizontal cross section through the trachea, showing a C-shaped ring of cartilage.*

6. Cartilage is tough, so if you want to open up the trachea, it's best to cut it lengthways, down the gap in the C-shaped rings (see Figure 4). Use dissecting scissors or a scalpel to make the cut. If using a scalpel, cut downwards (not towards you) and don't apply too much pressure to the blade.

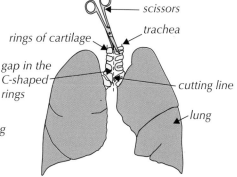

scissors

trachea

rings of cartilage

gap in the C-shaped rings

cutting line

lung

Figure 4: *Diagram showing where to cut in order to open up the trachea.*

7. Continue cutting down one of the bronchi. You should be able to see the bronchioles branching off.
8. Cut off a piece of the lung. The tissue will feel spongy because of the air trapped in all the alveoli.
9. Lungs from a butcher are safe for humans to handle, but they could still contain bacteria that cause food poisoning. Make sure you wash your hands after the dissection and disinfect work surfaces.

Tip: Make sure that you've done a full risk assessment and identified any safety issues before you start any of these dissections. The risks involved in each one will be slightly different.

Tip: You can learn more about the lungs on pages 146-149.

Tip: The lungs you get from a butcher's will contain cuts from the abattoir, which will allow air to escape when you try to inflate them. If the cuts are making inflation tricky, you could try inflating just one of the lobes (parts) of the lung, which hasn't been cut.

Tip: If you do cut the cartilage be careful — you need to wear goggles to protect your eyes.

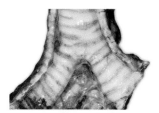

Figure 5: *Rings of cartilage in the trachea and bronchi.*

Example 2 — Dissection of a bony fish

1. Make sure you're wearing an apron or lab coat.
2. Place your chosen fish (something like a perch or salmon works well) in a dissection tray or on a cutting board.

operculum

Figure 6: Perch head showing operculum.

Tip: You can find more information about the gas exchange systems of fish on pages 142-143 and insects on page 144.

Tip: Some live insects, e.g. grasshoppers, can cause allergic reactions in some people. They need to be handled very carefully. A full risk assessment should be carried out before using them.

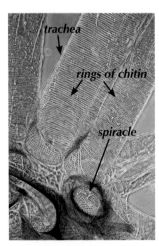

trachea

rings of chitin

spiracle

Figure 9: Optical microscope image of a silkworm's shed skin showing the spiracles, chitin rings and silver/grey tracheae.

3. Gills are located on either side of the fish's head. They're protected on each side by a bony flap called an operculum and supported by gill arches — see Figure 7.

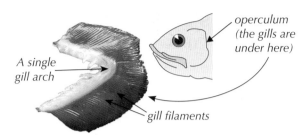

operculum (the gills are under here)

A single gill arch

gill filaments

Figure 7: Photo of a fish gill and diagram to show its location beneath operculum.

4. To remove the gills, push back the operculum and use scissors to carefully remove the gills. Cut each gill arch through the bone at the top and bottom.

5. If you look closely, you should be able to see the gill filaments. With the gills above, it's not possible to see the lamellae without a microscope.

— Example 3 — Dissection of a large insect —

Big insects like grasshoppers or cockroaches are usually best for dissecting because they're easier to handle. For dissection, you'll need to use an insect that's been humanely killed fairly recently.

1. First fix the insect to a dissection tray. You can put dissecting pins through its legs to hold it in place.

2. To examine the tracheae, you'll need to carefully cut and remove a piece of exoskeleton (the insect's hard outer shell) from along the length of the insect's abdomen — see Figure 8.

3. Use a syringe to fill the abdomen with saline solution. You should be able to see a network of very thin, silvery-grey tubes — these are the tracheae. They look silver because they're filled with air.

4. You can examine the tracheae under an optical microscope using a temporary mount slide (see p. 81). Again, the tracheae will appear silver or grey. You should also be able to see rings of chitin in the walls of the tracheae — these are there for support (like the rings of cartilage in a human trachea).

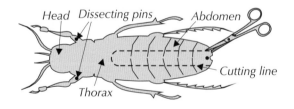

Head   Dissecting pins   Abdomen

Cutting line

Thorax

Figure 8: How to remove a piece of exoskeleton from an insect abdomen.

Practice Question — Application

Q1 A student was dissecting a pair of pig lungs. Her teacher told her to inflate the lungs with a bicycle pump.

   a) Explain why she shouldn't inflate the lungs by blowing into them.

   b) Give one other safety precaution the student should take while inflating the lungs.

   c) Once the lungs are inflated, the student stops pumping air into them. Describe and explain what the student would expect to see next.

d) The student wants to open up the trachea.
Describe where she should make the cut in order to do this.

Practice Questions — Fact Recall

Q1 How can you make sure that your dissecting tools are safe to use?

Q2 Give two ethical issues that might be raised regarding dissections.

Section Summary

Make sure you know:

- That smaller organisms have a bigger surface area : volume ratio than larger organisms.
- How to calculate the volume and surface area of common 3D shapes.
- That multicellular organisms have adaptations such as specialised exchange organs and mass transport systems to help in the exchange of substances.
- That smaller organisms have a relatively high metabolic rate because their relatively large surface area : volume ratio causes them to lose heat quickly.
- How an animal's body size and shape influence heat exchange.
- That animals have behavioural and physiological adaptations that aid heat exchange.
- How gas exchange surfaces are specialised to increase the rate of diffusion — they're thin and have a large surface area.
- How single-celled organisms are adapted for gas exchange.
- How the structure of fish gills (including gill filaments and lamellae) and the counter-current system maximise gas exchange.
- That gas exchange in dicotyledonous plants takes place in the leaves, and how they are adapted for efficient gas exchange (mesophyll with a large surface area and stomata).
- How the structure of the gas exchange system in insects (including tracheae and spiracles) maximises gas exchange.
- How insects and xerophytic plants are adapted to control water loss.
- The structure of the gas exchange system in humans, including the lungs, trachea, bronchi, bronchioles and alveoli.
- The mechanism of breathing, including the role of the diaphragm and intercostal muscles in changing the pressure in the thoracic cavity.
- How the internal and external intercostal muscles act antagonistically during forced expiration.
- How oxygen and carbon dioxide are exchanged via diffusion gradients in the alveoli.
- How the alveoli are adapted for efficient gas exchange — they provide a thin exchange surface and a large surface area.
- How to interpret information relating to the effects of lung disease on gas exchange or ventilation.
- How to interpret data relating to the effects of pollution and smoking on lung disease and explain what the data shows.
- How to evaluate the way in which experimental data has led to statutory restrictions for smoking and air pollution.
- How to safely and ethically dissect an organism's gas exchange system or an organ within that system — for example, sheep lungs, a bony fish's gills or insect tracheae.

Exam-style Questions

1   The gills are the gas exchange organ in fish.
        Figure 1 shows a cross section through a dogfish gill.

Figure 1

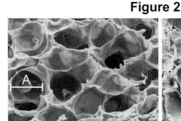

1.1   Name the structures labelled **A** in **Figure 1** and explain how they increase the
        efficiency of gas exchange across the gills.

(3 marks)

1.2   Give **one** other adaptation of the gills for efficient gas exchange.

(1 mark)

1.3   Insects have a tracheal system for exchanging gases with the environment.
        Describe how oxygen gets into an insect's respiring cells.

(2 marks)

1.4   Terrestrial insects lose water as a result of gas exchange.
        Explain **two** features insects have to reduce unwanted water loss.

(2 marks)

Figure 2

2   **Figure 2** shows a scanning
        electron micrograph
        of alveoli in a healthy
        human lung (left) and the
        effects of emphysema on
        the alveoli (right). The
        magnification is x 60.

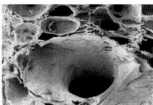

2.1   Calculate the actual width of the labelled alveolus, A.
        Give your answer in μm.

(2 marks)

2.2   Describe **one** difference between the healthy alveoli and the diseased alveoli,
        and explain what effect this would have on gaseous exchange in the alveoli.

(3 marks)

2.3   Oxygen tents contain a higher percentage of oxygen than normal air.
        Suggest how being in an oxygen tent might benefit a patient with emphysema.

(2 marks)

3 Expiratory flow rate is a measure of the volume of air exhaled per second.
In a peak expiratory flow test the person inhales as fully as possible and then
forcefully exhales all air from the lungs as fast as possible.

A doctor measured the expiratory flow rate of two people. The results are shown in
Figure 3. Line **A** is from a healthy person. Line **B** is from a person shortly after they
had an asthma attack. During an asthma attack the bronchioles become inflamed.

Figure 3

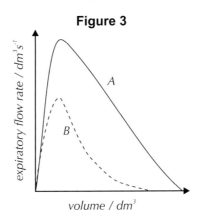

3.1 Describe and explain **one** difference between lines **A** and **B** in **Figure 3**.

(1 mark)

3.2 Some studies have suggested that exercise improves peak expiratory
flow rate in healthy adults. Suggest why this might be the case.

(2 marks)

4 Describe the processes of inspiration and expiration.

(6 marks)

5 **Figure 4** shows a spherical bacterium
with a radius of 0.7 μm.

Figure 4

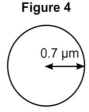

0.7 μm

5.1 Calculate the surface area to volume ratio of this bacterium.

(2 marks)

5.2 Explain why this bacterium doesn't have a specialised gas exchange system.

(3 marks)

1. Digestion and Absorption

Food molecules need to broken down by enzymes into smaller molecules. These molecules can then be absorbed into the bloodstream.

Digestion basics

The large biological molecules (e.g. starch, proteins) in food are too big to cross cell membranes. This means they can't be absorbed from the gut into the blood. During digestion, these large molecules are broken down into smaller molecules (e.g. glucose, amino acids), which can move across cell membranes. This means they can be easily absorbed from the gut into the blood, to be transported around the body for use by the body cells.

You might remember from Topic 1A, that most large biological molecules are polymers, which can be broken down into smaller molecules (monomers) using **hydrolysis reactions**. Hydrolysis reactions break bonds by adding water. During hydrolysis, carbohydrates are broken down into disaccharides and then monosaccharides. Fats are broken down into fatty acids and monoglycerides. Proteins are broken down into amino acids.

Digestive enzymes

Digestive enzymes are used to break down biological molecules in food. A variety of different digestive enzymes are produced by specialised cells in the digestive systems of mammals. These enzymes are then released to mix with food. Since enzymes only work with specific substrates (see page 37), different enzymes are needed to catalyse the breakdown of different food molecules.

The digestion of carbohydrates

Amylase

Amylase is a digestive enzyme that catalyses the breakdown of starch. Starch is a mixture of two polysaccharides, each made from long chains of alpha-glucose molecules (see page 25). Amylase works by catalysing hydrolysis reactions that break the glycosidic bonds in starch to produce maltose (a disaccharide) — see Figure 1. Amylase is produced by the salivary glands, which release amylase into the mouth, and also by the pancreas, which releases amylase into the small intestine — see Figure 3 (next page).

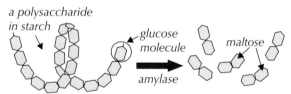

Figure 1: *Amylase catalyses the breakdown of starch into maltose molecules.*

Membrane-bound disaccharidases

Membrane-bound disaccharidases are enzymes that are attached to the cell membranes of epithelial cells lining the ileum (the final part of the small intestine). They help to break down disaccharides into monosaccharides. Again, this involves the hydrolysis of glycosidic bonds.

Learning Objectives:

- Know that during digestion, large biological molecules are hydrolysed to smaller molecules that can be absorbed across cell membranes.
- Understand the digestion in mammals of:
  - carbohydrates by amylases and membrane bound disaccharidases.
  - lipids by lipase, including the action of bile salts.
  - proteins by endopeptidases, exopeptidases and membrane-bound dipeptidases.
- Know the mechanisms for the absorption of the products of digestion by cells lining the ileum, including:
  - co-transport mechanisms for the absorption of monosaccharides.
  - the role of micelles in the absorption of lipids.
  - co-transport mechanisms for the absorption of amino acids.

  Specification Reference 3.3.3

Tip: There's more on polysaccharides, disaccharides and monosaccharides on pages 21-25.

Sucrase is a membrane-bound disaccharidase. It catalyses the breakdown of sucrose into the monosaccharides glucose and fructose.

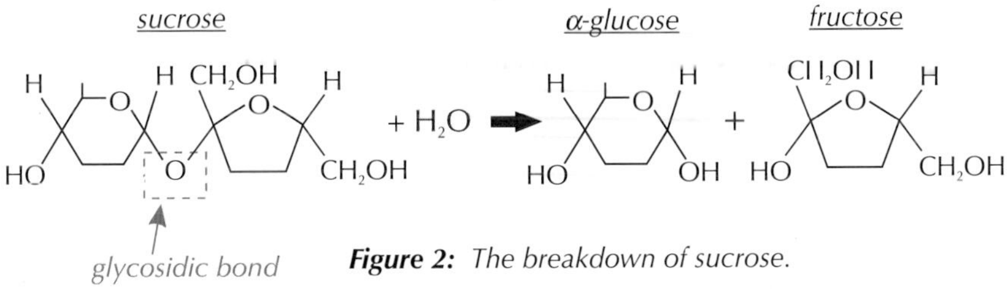

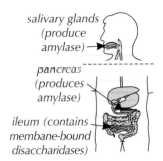

Figure 3: The location of carbohydrate digestive processes in the body.

salivary glands (produce amylase)

pancreas (produces amylase)

ileum (contains membane-bound disaccharidases)

sucrose   _α-glucose_   _fructose_

$+ H_2O \Rightarrow$

glycosidic bond   **Figure 2:** The breakdown of sucrose.

The disaccharides maltose and lactose are broken down in a similar way to sucrose in the example above, i.e. via hydrolysis of the glycosidic bonds. Here's a table showing the enzymes and products involved for all three sugars:

Disaccharide	Disaccharidase	Monosaccharides
sucrose	sucrase	glucose + fructose
maltose	maltase	glucose + glucose
lactose	lactase	glucose + galactose

The monosaccharides can be transported across the epithelial cell membranes in the ileum via specific transporter proteins (see page 167).

Tip: The names of most digestive enzymes end with '<u>ase</u>'. And you can usually figure out what the enzyme breaks down by looking at what comes before that, e.g. <u>malt</u>ase breaks down <u>malt</u>ose, <u>lip</u>ase breaks down <u>lip</u>ids.

The digestion of lipids

Lipase enzymes catalyse the breakdown of lipids into monoglycerides and fatty acids. This involves the hydrolysis of the ester bonds in lipids (see Figure 4). Lipases are mainly made in the pancreas — they're then secreted into the small intestine where they act.

Tip: A monoglyceride is a glycerol molecule with one fatty acid attached.

ester bond

hydrolysis

triglyceride   monoglyceride   fatty acids

Tip: See pages 27-29 for more information on lipids.

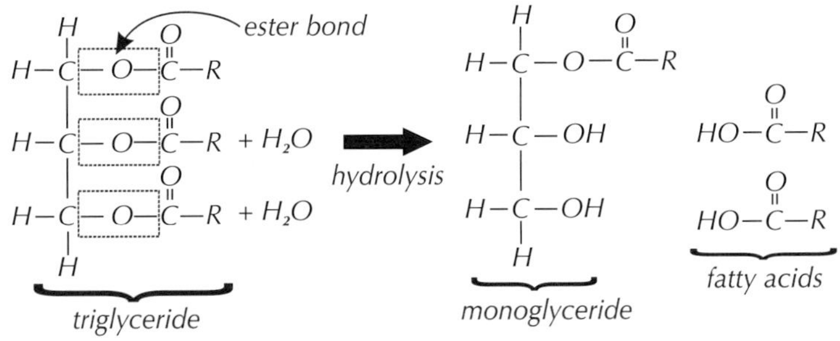

Figure 4: The hydrolysis of ester bonds in a triglyceride.

Bile salts are produced by the liver and **emulsify** lipids — this means they cause the lipids to form small droplets. Although bile salts are not enzymes they are really important in the process of lipid digestion. Several small lipid droplets have a bigger surface area than a single large droplet (for the same volume of lipid). So the formation of small droplets greatly increases the surface area of lipid that's available for lipases to work on.

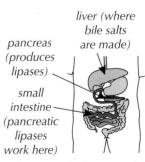

Figure 6: The location of lipid digestive processes in the body.

liver (where bile salts are made)

pancreas (produces lipases)

small intestine (pancreatic lipases work here)

big lipid droplet   +   bile salts   emulsification   smaller lipid droplets — larger surface area

Figure 5: The emulsification of lipids by bile salts.

Once the lipid has been broken down by lipase, the monoglycerides and fatty acids stick with the bile salts to form tiny structures called micelles (see Figure 7). Micelles help the products of lipid digestion to be absorbed (see next page).

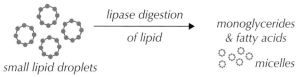

small lipid droplets

lipase digestion of lipid

monoglycerides & fatty acids

micelles

Figure 7: *The action of lipase and the formation of micelles.*

The digestion of proteins

Proteins are broken down by a combination of different peptidases. These are enzymes that catalyse the conversion of proteins into amino acids by hydrolysing the peptide bonds between amino acids. You need to know about endopeptidases and exopeptidases (including dipeptidases).

Tip: Peptidases are also called proteases.

Endopeptidases

Endopeptidases act to hydrolyse peptide bonds within a protein (see Figure 8).

Tip: Remember: endopeptidases break bonds insi**de** the protein.

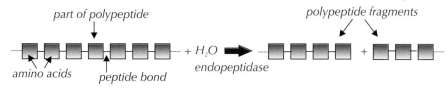

part of polypeptide

polypeptide fragments

$+ H_2O$

endopeptidase

amino acids

peptide bond

Figure 8: *The action of endopeptidases.*

Examples

- Trypsin and chymotrypsin are both endopeptidases. They're synthesised in the pancreas and secreted into the small intestine.

- Pepsin is another endopeptidase. It's released into the stomach by cells in the stomach lining. Pepsin only works in acidic conditions — these are provided by hydrochloric acid in the stomach.

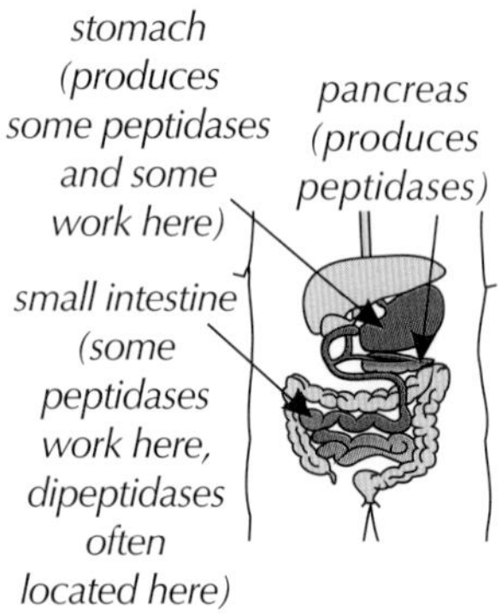

Exopeptidases

Exopeptidases act to hydrolyse peptide bonds at the ends of protein molecules. They remove single amino acids from proteins (see Figure 10).

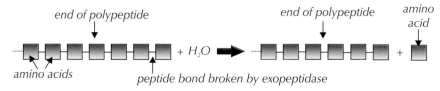

end of polypeptide

end of polypeptide

amino acid

$+ H_2O$

amino acids

peptide bond broken by exopeptidase

Figure 10: *The action of exopeptidases.*

Dipeptidases are exopeptidases that work specifically on dipeptides. They act to separate the two amino acids that make up a dipeptide by hydrolysing the peptide bond between them (see Figure 11). Dipeptidases are often located in the cell-surface membrane of epithelial cells in the small intestine.

Tip: Dipeptidases located on cell-surface membranes are called 'membrane-bound' dipeptidases.

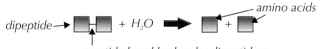

dipeptide $+ H_2O$ *amino acids*

peptide bond broken by dipeptidase

Figure 11: *The action of a dipeptidase.*

stomach (produces some peptidases and some work here)

pancreas (produces peptidases)

small intestine (some peptidases work here, dipeptidases often located here)

Figure 9: *The location of protein digestive processes in the body.*

Absorption of the products of digestion

The products of digestion are absorbed across the ileum epithelium into the bloodstream.

Monosaccharides

Glucose is absorbed by active transport with sodium ions via a **co-transporter protein** (see page 109). Galactose is absorbed in the same way using the same co-transporter protein. Fructose is absorbed via facilitated diffusion (see page 101) through a different transporter protein.

Monoglycerides and fatty acids

Micelles (see previous page) help to move monoglycerides and fatty acids towards the epithelium. Because micelles constantly break up and reform they can 'release' monoglycerides and fatty acids, allowing them to be absorbed — whole micelles are not taken up across the epithelium. Monoglycerides and fatty acids are lipid-soluble, so can diffuse directly across the epithelial cell membrane.

Amino acids

Amino acids are absorbed in a similar way to glucose and galactose. Sodium ions are actively transported out of the epithelial cells into the ileum itself. They then diffuse back into the cells through sodium-dependent transporter proteins in the epithelial cell membranes, carrying the amino acids with them.

Figure 12: *Light micrograph of a transverse section through the ileum. The dense network of capillaries (blue/black) helps the products of digestion be absorbed.*

Practice Questions — Application

A model gut is set up using Visking tubing as shown in the diagram on the right. Sucrose solution and sucrase are placed inside the Visking tubing and incubated at 37 °C. Sucrose is a disaccharide formed from glucose and fructose. The contents inside and outside the Visking tubing are monitored over time.

Visking tubing

sucrose and sucrase

water

Tip: Visking tubing is partially permeable — it allows small molecules like water to pass through but not larger molecules like proteins.

Q1 Sucrase is a membrane-bound disaccharidase. Where in the body would you find sucrase?

Q2 After 30 minutes, the solution outside the Visking tubing was tested. Name three different molecules that would be present.

Q3 Explain the role of sucrase in the body.

Practice Questions — Fact Recall

Q1 What is a hydrolysis reaction?

Q2 What type of enzymes are needed to break down lipids?

Q3 Describe how micelles are formed in digestion.

Q4 Describe the action of exopeptidases.

Q5 Explain how monoglycerides and fatty acids are absorbed across the ileum epithelium.

Q6 How are sodium ions involved in the transport of amino acids?

- Know that the haemoglobins are a group of chemically similar molecules found in many different organisms.

- Know that haemoglobin is a protein with a quaternary structure.

- Understand the role of haemoglobin and red blood cells in the transport of oxygen.

- Understand the loading, transport and unloading of oxygen in relation to the oxyhaemoglobin dissociation curve.

- Understand the cooperative nature of oxygen binding — the change in shape of haemoglobin caused by the binding of the first oxygens makes the binding of further oxygens easier.

- Understand the effects of carbon dioxide concentration on the dissociation of oxyhaemoglobin (the Bohr effect).

- Know that many animals are adapted to their environment by possessing different types of haemoglobin with different oxygen transport properties.

Specification Reference 3.3.4.1

Tip: A protein with a quaternary structure just means it's made up of more than one polypeptide chain — see page 32 for more.

2. Haemoglobin

Many different organisms have haemoglobin in their blood to transport oxygen. But the type of haemoglobin each organism has varies depending on where they live and their way of life...

The role of haemoglobin

Many organisms have to transport substances over large distances to get them to and from their exchange surfaces (see page 139). Mass transport systems, such as the circulatory system in animals, ensure the efficient movement of substances throughout the organism.

Haemoglobin is an important part of the circulatory system. Human haemoglobin is found in red blood cells — its role is to carry oxygen around the body. There are many chemically similar types of haemoglobin found in many different organisms, all of which carry out the same function. As well as being found in all vertebrates, haemoglobin is found in earthworms, starfish, some insects, some plants and even in some bacteria.

Haemoglobin and oxyhaemoglobin

Haemoglobin (Hb) is a large protein with a quaternary structure — it's made up of four polypeptide chains. Each chain has a haem group which contains an iron ion and gives haemoglobin its red colour (see Figure 1). Each molecule of human haemoglobin can carry four oxygen molecules.

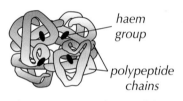

haem group

polypeptide chains

Figure 1: *Human haemoglobin.*

In the lungs, oxygen joins to haemoglobin in red blood cells to form **oxyhaemoglobin**. This is a reversible reaction — near the body cells, oxygen leaves oxyhaemoglobin and it turns back to haemoglobin (see Figure 2). When an oxygen molecule joins to haemoglobin it's referred to as **association** or **loading**, and when oxygen leaves oxyhaemoglobin it's referred to as **dissociation** or **unloading**.

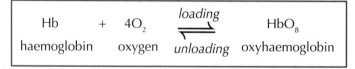

$$Hb \quad + \quad 4O_2 \quad \underset{\textit{unloading}}{\overset{\textit{loading}}{\rightleftharpoons}} \quad HbO_8$$

haemoglobin   oxygen   oxyhaemoglobin

Figure 2: *The formation and dissociation of oxyhaemoglobin.*

Affinity for oxygen and pO_2

Affinity for oxygen means the tendency a molecule has to bind with oxygen. Haemoglobin's affinity for oxygen varies depending on the conditions it's in — one of the conditions that affects it is the **partial pressure of oxygen (pO_2)**.

pO_2 is a measure of oxygen concentration. The greater the concentration of dissolved oxygen in cells, the higher the partial pressure. As pO_2 increases, haemoglobin's affinity for oxygen also increases:

- Oxygen loads onto haemoglobin to form oxyhaemoglobin where there's a high pO_2.

- Oxyhaemoglobin unloads its oxygen where there's a lower pO_2.

Oxygen enters blood capillaries at the alveoli in the lungs. Alveoli have a high pO_2 so oxygen loads onto haemoglobin to form oxyhaemoglobin. When cells respire, they use up oxygen — this lowers the pO_2. Red blood cells deliver oxyhaemoglobin to respiring tissues, where it unloads its oxygen. The haemoglobin then returns to the lungs to pick up more oxygen. Figure 3 summarises this process.

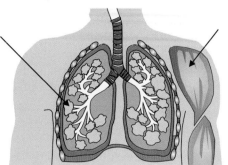

Alveoli in lungs
• HIGH oxygen concentration
• HIGH pO_2
• HIGH affinity
• Oxygen LOADS

Respiring tissue
• LOW oxygen concentration
• LOW pO_2
• LOW affinity
• Oxygen UNLOADS

Figure 3: _Oxygen loading and unloading in the body._

Exam Tip
Always be specific in your exam answers. For example, don't just say that human haemoglobin has a high affinity for oxygen — it only has a high affinity for oxygen _in the lungs_.

Dissociation curves

An oxygen dissociation curve shows how saturated the haemoglobin is with oxygen at any given partial pressure. The affinity of haemoglobin for oxygen affects how saturated the haemoglobin is:

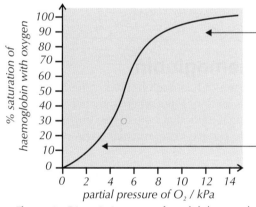

Figure 4: _Dissociation curve for adult haemoglobin._

Where pO_2 is high (e.g. in the lungs), haemoglobin has a high affinity for oxygen, so it has a high saturation of oxygen.

Where pO_2 is low (e.g. in respiring tissues), haemoglobin has a low affinity for oxygen, so it has a low saturation of oxygen.

Tip: These curves are sometimes called oxyhaemoglobin dissociation curves.

Tip: 100% saturation means every haemoglobin molecule is carrying the maximum of 4 molecules of oxygen.

Tip: 0% saturation means none of the haemoglobin molecules are carrying any oxygen.

Weirdly, the saturation of haemoglobin can also affect the affinity — this is why the graph is 'S-shaped' and not a straight line.

When haemoglobin combines with the first O_2 molecule, its shape alters in a way that makes it easier for other O_2 molecules to join too. But as the haemoglobin starts to become saturated, it gets harder for more oxygen molecules to join. As a result, the curve has a steep bit in the middle where it's really easy for oxygen molecules to join, and shallow bits at each end where it's harder — see Figure 5. When the curve is steep, a small change in pO_2 causes a big change in the amount of oxygen carried by the haemoglobin.

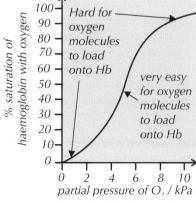

Hard for oxygen molecules to load onto Hb

very easy for oxygen molecules to load onto Hb

Figure 5: _The S-shaped dissociation curve for haemoglobin._

Tip: kPa (kilopascal) is a unit used to measure pressure.

Carbon dioxide concentration

The **partial pressure of carbon dioxide (pCO_2)** is a measure of the concentration of CO_2 in a cell. To complicate matters, pCO_2 also affects oxygen unloading. Haemoglobin gives up its oxygen more readily at a higher pCO_2. It's a cunning way of getting more O_2 to cells during activity.

When cells respire they produce carbon dioxide, which raises the pCO_2. This increases the rate of oxygen unloading (i.e. the rate at which oxyhaemoglobin dissociates to form haemoglobin and oxygen) — so the dissociation curve 'shifts' right (but it stays the same shape). The saturation of blood with oxygen is lower for a given pO_2, meaning that more oxygen is being released — see Figure 6. This is called the **Bohr effect**.

Tip: The word equation for respiration is: glucose + oxygen → carbon dioxide + water + energy.

Tip: When dissociation curves are being compared, the further left the curve is, the higher the haemoglobin's affinity for oxygen is.

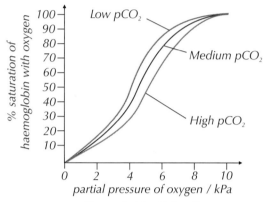

Figure 6: The Bohr effect.

Different types of haemoglobin

Different organisms have different types of haemoglobin with different oxygen transporting capacities — it depends on things like where they live, how active they are and their size. Having a particular type of haemoglobin is an adaptation that helps the organism to survive in a particular environment.

Low oxygen environments

Organisms that live in environments with a low concentration of oxygen have haemoglobin with a higher affinity for oxygen than human haemoglobin. This is because there isn't much oxygen available, so the haemoglobin has to be very good at loading any available oxygen. The dissociation curve of their haemoglobin is to the left of ours.

Tip: Environments with a low oxygen concentration include underground, at high altitudes or close to the seabed.

Tip: The curve shifts to the **l**eft for organisms that live in **l**ow oxygen environments. The curve shifts to the **r**ight for organisms that have a high **r**espiration rate.

> **Example**
>
> A lugworm lives in burrows beneath sand where there's a low oxygen concentration. Its haemoglobin has to be able to pick up as much oxygen as possible — it has a high affinity for oxygen.

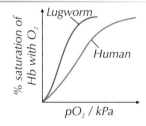

High activity levels

Organisms that are very active and have a high oxygen demand have haemoglobin with a lower affinity for oxygen than human haemoglobin. This is because they need their haemoglobin to easily unload oxygen, so that it's available for them to use. The dissociation curve of their haemoglobin is to the right of the human one.

Example

A hawk has a high respiratory rate (because it is very active) and lives where there's plenty of oxygen. Its haemoglobin has to be able to unload oxygen quickly in order to meet the high oxygen demand — it has a low affinity for oxygen.

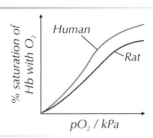

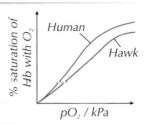

Figure 7: *Hawks have a high oxygen demand.*

Size

Small mammals tend to have a higher surface area to volume ratio than larger mammals. This means they lose heat quickly, so they have a high metabolic rate to help them keep warm — which means they have a high oxygen demand. Mammals that are smaller than humans have haemoglobin with a lower affinity for oxygen than human haemoglobin, because they need their haemoglobin to easily unload oxygen to meet their high oxygen demand. The dissociation curve of their haemoglobin is to the right of the human one.

Tip: See page 137 for more on surface area to volume ratios.

Example

A rat has a higher surface area to volume ratio than a human. Its haemoglobin needs to unload oxygen easily to meet the greater oxygen demand — it has a lower affinity for oxygen.

Tip: Metabolic rate is the rate at which energy is used. A higher metabolic rate leads to a higher respiration rate. This in turn leads to a higher oxygen demand.

Reading values from a dissociation curve

In the exam, you might need to interpret a dissociation curve to answer a question. It's really important you can read data points off a graph correctly.

Example — **Maths Skills**

The graph on the right shows the oxygen dissociation curves for two animals. At a pO_2 of 6 kPa, what is the difference between the percentage saturation of haemoglobin with oxygen for the two animals?

1. Find 6 kPa on the x-axis.

2. Use a ruler to draw a line up to the curve for animal A. Make sure the line is parallel to the y-axis.

3. Then draw a line across to the y-axis. Make sure this line is parallel to the x-axis.

4. Read off the value at this point on the axis — 84%.

5. Repeat for the curve for animal B — 60%.

6. Find the difference between them: 84 − 60 = **24%**

Exam Tip
Graphs crop up a lot in Biology exams. If you're shown one then asked to do a calculation or interpret the data, be aware that you'll probably need to find specific data points from the graph.

Exam Tip
You need to read graphs as accurately as you can — check the scales and the units on the axes very carefully to avoid throwing away marks.

Tip: To help you answer Q1 a), think of the difference in respiration rates between the two activities.

Exam Tip
In the exam you could be asked to interpret dissociation curves from animals you've never even heard of — don't let that throw you. Examiners want to make sure you really know your stuff by applying your knowledge to new situations.

Practice Questions — Application

Q1 The graph to the right shows two oxygen dissociation curves for the same man. One curve was produced based on blood tests when he was watching television and the other was produced based on blood tests immediately after a bike ride.

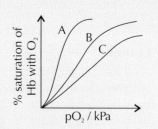

a) Which curve was produced after the bike ride? Explain your answer.

b) What name is given to the effect shown on the graph?

Q2 The table below gives descriptions of three similarly sized animals. The graph shows each animal's dissociation curve. Match each animal to its dissociation curve and give reasons for your choices.

Animal	Description
Badger	Lives in an underground sett
Bush dog	Lives above ground, fairly active
Brown-throated sloth	Lives above ground, very inactive

Practice Questions — Fact Recall

Q1 What is the role of haemoglobin?

Q2 Where is haemoglobin found in humans?

Q3 How many polypeptide chains does a haemoglobin molecule have?

Q4 Describe what is meant by haemoglobin 'loading' and 'unloading' oxygen.

Q5 What is formed when oxygen is loaded onto haemoglobin?

Q6 What is shown on an oxygen dissociation curve?

Q7 Why does the binding of a single oxygen molecule increase haemoglobin's affinity for oxygen?

Q8 Where in the body would you find cells with a high pO_2? Explain your answer.

3. The Circulatory System

The mammalian circulatory system is a mass transport system — it carries raw materials, as well as waste products, around the body of the mammal.

Function of the circulatory system

Multicellular organisms, like mammals, have a low surface area to volume ratio (see p. 139), so they need a specialised mass transport system to carry raw materials from specialised exchange organs to their body cells — this is the circulatory system.

Structure of the circulatory system

The circulatory system is made up of the heart and blood vessels. The heart pumps blood through blood vessels (**arteries**, **arterioles**, **veins** and **capillaries**) to reach different parts of the body. You need to know the names of the blood vessels entering and leaving the heart, lungs and kidneys. These are shown in Figures 1 and 2.

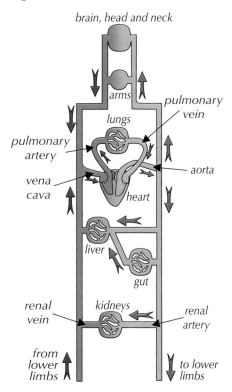

Figure 1: The circulatory system.

Vessel	Carries blood from...	Carries blood to...
Pulmonary artery	heart	lungs
Pulmonary vein	lungs	heart
Aorta	heart	body
Vena cava	body	heart
Renal artery	body	kidneys
Renal vein	kidneys	vena cava

Figure 2: Some of the blood vessels in a mammalian circulatory system.

Blood transports respiratory gases, products of digestion, metabolic wastes and hormones round the body. There are two circuits. One circuit takes blood from the heart to the lungs, then back to the heart. The other loop takes blood around the rest of the body, so the blood has to go through the heart twice to complete one full circuit of the body. The heart has its own blood supply — the left and right **coronary arteries** — see Figure 3.

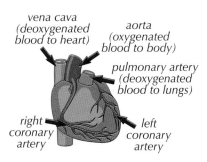

Figure 3: Blood vessels of the heart.

Learning Objectives:

- Know the general pattern of blood circulation in a mammal.
- Know the names of the coronary arteries and the blood vessels entering and leaving the heart, lungs and kidneys.
- Know the structure of arteries, arterioles and veins in relation to their function.
- Know the structure of capillaries and the importance of capillary beds as exchange surfaces.
- Understand how tissue fluid is formed and how it is returned to the circulatory system.

Specification Reference 3.3.4.1

Tip: Blood always flows from a higher pressure to a lower pressure in the circulatory system. The vena cava is the final blood vessel that takes the blood back to the heart from the body, so it has the lowest pressure.

Tip: The gut is another name for the digestive tract or a part of it, e.g. the intestines.

Tip: When you're looking at a diagram of a heart, imagine it's in the body of someone standing opposite you, so the left and right sides are opposite to your left and right.

Arteries, arterioles and veins

Arteries, arterioles and veins have different characteristics, and you need to know why...

Arteries

Arteries carry blood from the heart to the rest of the body. Their walls are thick and muscular and have elastic tissue to stretch and recoil as the heart beats, which helps maintain the high pressure. The inner lining (called the endothelium) is folded, allowing the artery to stretch — this also helps it to maintain high pressure. All arteries carry oxygenated blood except for the pulmonary arteries, which take deoxygenated blood to the lungs.

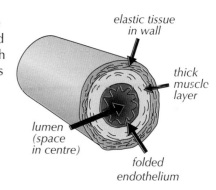

elastic tissue in wall

thick muscle layer

lumen (space in centre)

folded endothelium

Arterioles

Arteries divide into smaller vessels called arterioles. These form a network throughout the body. Blood is directed to different areas of demand in the body by muscles inside the arterioles, which contract to restrict the blood flow or relax to allow full blood flow.

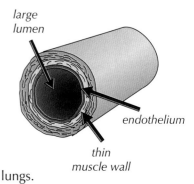

mainly circular muscle

Veins

Veins take blood back to the heart under low pressure. They have a wider lumen than equivalent arteries, with very little elastic or muscle tissue. Veins contain **valves** to stop the blood flowing backwards (see page 178). Blood flow through the veins is helped by contraction of the body muscles surrounding them. All veins carry deoxygenated blood (because oxygen has been used up by body cells), except for the pulmonary veins, which carry oxygenated blood to the heart from the lungs.

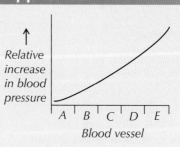

large lumen

endothelium

thin muscle wall

Tip: Arteries are the 'way art' (way out) of the heart, and veins are the 'vey in' (way in).

Exam Tip
An artery stretches to cope with high pressure and then recoils under low pressure — you won't get marks for writing that it contracts and relaxes, or expands.

Tip: The pressure decreases along a blood vessel due to friction.

Practice Question — Application

Q1 The graph on the right shows the relative increase in blood pressure in different blood vessels of a mammal's circulatory system.

Relative increase in blood pressure

A B C D E
Blood vessel

Measurements were taken in the renal artery, the renal vein, an arteriole, the aorta and the vena cava.

Suggest which letter represents each blood vessel.
Explain your choices.

Capillaries

Arterioles branch into capillaries, which are the smallest of the blood vessels. Substances (e.g. glucose and oxygen) are exchanged between cells and capillaries, so they're adapted for efficient diffusion. Capillaries are always found very near cells in exchange tissues (e.g. alveoli in the lungs), so there's a short diffusion pathway. Their walls are only one cell thick, which also shortens the diffusion pathway. There are a large number of capillaries, to increase surface area for exchange. Networks of capillaries in tissue are called **capillary beds**.

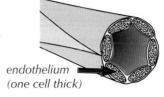

endothelium
(one cell thick)

Tip: Capillaries connect arterioles and venules together at capillary beds. Venules are small blood vessels that connect to veins.

Tissue fluid

Tissue fluid is the fluid that surrounds cells in tissues. It's made from small molecules that leave the blood plasma, e.g. oxygen, water and nutrients. (Unlike blood, tissue fluid doesn't contain red blood cells or big proteins, because they're too large to be pushed out through the capillary walls.) Cells take in oxygen and nutrients from the tissue fluid, and release metabolic waste into it. In a capillary bed, substances move out of the capillaries, into the tissue fluid, by **pressure filtration**.

At the start of the capillary bed, nearest the arteries, the hydrostatic (liquid) pressure inside the capillaries is greater than the hydrostatic pressure in the tissue fluid. This difference in hydrostatic pressure means an overall outward pressure forces fluid out of the capillaries and into the spaces around the cells, forming tissue fluid. As fluid leaves, the hydrostatic pressure reduces in the capillaries — so the hydrostatic pressure is much lower at the venule end of the capillary bed (the end that's nearest to the veins).

Due to the fluid loss, and an increasing concentration of plasma proteins (which don't leave the capillaries), the water potential at the venule end of the capillary bed is lower than the water potential in the tissue fluid. This means that some water re-enters the capillaries from the tissue fluid at the venule end by osmosis (see p. 104 for more on osmosis). Any excess tissue fluid is drained into the **lymphatic system** (a network of tubes that acts a bit like a drain), which transports this excess fluid from the tissues and passes it back into the circulatory system.

Tip: Blood plasma is just the liquid that carries everything in the blood.

Exam Tip
Don't write in the exam that tissue fluid doesn't contain <u>any</u> proteins — it still contains some, just not big ones.

Tip: Pressure filtration is just what it sounds like — filtration happening under pressure. Here it describes the process by which small molecules are filtered out of the capillaries under hydrostatic pressure, forming tissue fluid.

Tip: Pressure is highest at the start of a capillary bed nearest the arterioles — this is caused by the left ventricle contracting and sending the blood out of the heart, through the arteries and arterioles, at high pressure.

Tip: High blood pressure means a high hydrostatic pressure in the capillaries, which can lead to an accumulation of tissue fluid in the tissues.

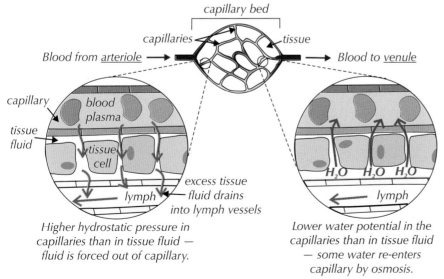

Higher hydrostatic pressure in capillaries than in tissue fluid — fluid is forced out of capillary.

Lower water potential in the capillaries than in tissue fluid — some water re-enters capillary by osmosis.

Figure 4: *The movement of fluid between capillaries, tissue fluid and lymph.*

Practice Questions — Application

Q1 A scientist recorded the hydrostatic pressure of blood and tissue fluid at two points along a capillary bed. The results are shown in the table below.

	Pressure at Point A (kPa)	Pressure at Point B (kPa)
Blood	2	3.5
Tissue fluid	4	2

   a) The direction of fluid movement between blood and tissue fluid changes along the capillary.

      i) Where does fluid move from and to at point B?

      ii) What does the fluid contain at point B?

   b) Suggest where on the capillary bed you would find:

      i) point A   ii) point B

Tip: For Q2, think about how the concentration of protein in the blood affects the water potential of the capillary.

Q2 Albumin is a protein found in the blood. Hypoalbuminemia is a condition where the level of albumin in the blood is very low. It causes an increase in tissue fluid, which can lead to swelling. Explain how hypoalbuminemia causes an increase in tissue fluid.

Practice Questions — Fact Recall

Q1 Why do mammals need a circulatory system?

Q2 Name the two blood vessels that carry blood into the heart.

Q3 Which blood vessel carries deoxygenated blood to the lungs?

Q4 Which blood vessel carries blood to the kidneys?

Q5 Which vessels supply the heart tissue with blood?

Q6 Name the blood vessels A - D shown below.
(The diagrams are not drawn to scale).

Tip: To distinguish between different types of blood vessels, you need to think about how thick the walls need to be for each types and how much muscle there will be in the walls, etc.

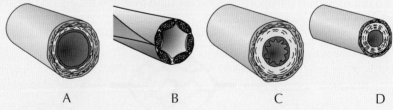

     A   B   C   D

Q7 Describe the structure of an artery.

Q8 What is an arteriole?

Q9 a) Name the blood vessels that have valves in them.

      b) What is the function of these valves?

Q10 Give two ways in which capillaries are adapted for efficient diffusion.

Q11 What is tissue fluid?

Q12 a) Explain the movement of fluid at the arteriole end of a capillary bed.

      b) Explain the movement of water at the venule end of a capillary bed.

4. The Heart

Your heart is responsible for pumping blood all around your body, through your blood vessels. So it's quite important really...

The structure of the heart

Figure 1 below shows the internal structure of the heart. The right side pumps deoxygenated blood to the lungs and the left side pumps oxygenated blood to the whole body. Note — the left and right sides are reversed on the diagram, cos it's the left and right of the person that the heart belongs to.

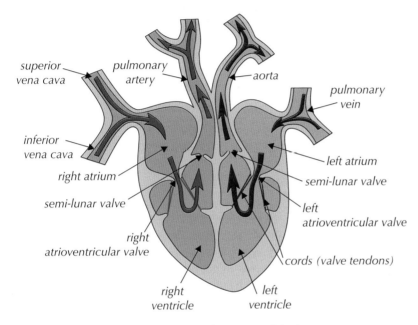

Figure 1: *The internal structure of the heart.*

Each bit of the heart is adapted to do its job effectively.

- The **left ventricle** of the heart has thicker, more muscular walls than the right ventricle — this allows it to contract more powerfully and pump blood all the way around the body. The right side is less muscular so its contractions are only powerful enough to pump blood to the nearby lungs.

- The **ventricles** have thicker walls than the atria therefore they can push blood out of the heart, whereas the atria just need to push blood a short distance into the ventricles.

- The **atrioventricular (AV) valves** link the atria to the ventricles and stop blood flowing back into the atria when the ventricles contract.

- The **semi-lunar (SL) valves** link the ventricles to the pulmonary artery and aorta, and stop blood flowing back into the heart after the ventricles contract.

- The **cords** attach the atrioventricular valves to the ventricles to stop them being forced up into the atria when the ventricles contract.

Learning Objectives:

- Know the gross structure of the human heart.

- Be able to dissect an organ within an animal's mass transport system (Required Practical 5).

- Understand the pressure and volume changes and associated valve movements during the cardiac cycle that maintain a unidirectional flow of blood.

- Be able to analyse and interpret data relating to pressure and volume changes during the cardiac cycle.

Specification Reference 3.3.4.1

Tip: The diagram is a good reminder that veins carry blood <u>in</u>to the heart (vena cava and pulmonary vein) and <u>a</u>rteries carry blood <u>a</u>way from it (pulmonary artery and aorta).

Tip: Right side of the heart = deoxygenated blood (blue). Left side of the heart = oxygenated blood (pink).

Lungs

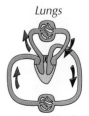

Rest of body

Heart valves

The valves only open one way — whether they're open or closed depends on the relative pressure of the heart chambers. If there's higher pressure behind a valve, it's forced open, but if pressure is higher in front of the valve it's forced shut — see Figure 3. This means that the flow of blood is unidirectional — it only flows in one direction.

Figure 3: *Diagram showing how heart valves open and close.*

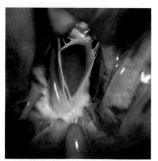

Figure 2: *A heart valve.*

Tip: Remember to carry out a risk assessment before you begin your dissection — be especially careful with sharp dissection tools.

Tip: You're likely to be given a pig or cow's heart to dissect.

Tip: See page 158 for more information on dissections and the tools that you might need to use.

Heart dissection

REQUIRED PRACTICAL **5**

As one of your required practicals you may need to dissect an organ within an animal's mass transport system. If you're lucky enough to get a heart to dissect, this is how you'd do it:

1. Make sure you are wearing a lab coat and lab gloves because heart dissections can be messy.

2. Place the heart you are given on your dissecting tray.

3. Look at the outside of the heart and try to identify the four main vessels attached to it. Feel inside the vessels to help you — remember arteries are thick and rubbery, whereas veins are much thinner.

4. Identify the right and left atria, the right and left ventricles and the coronary arteries. You might be asked to draw a sketch of the outside of the heart and label it.

5. Using a clean scalpel, carefully cut along the lines shown on Figure 5 to look inside each ventricle. You could measure and record the thickness of the ventricle walls and note any differences between them.

6. Next, cut open the atria and look inside them too. Note whether the atria walls are thicker or thinner than the ventricle walls.

7. Then find the atrioventricular valves, followed by the semi-lunar valves. Look at the structure of the valves and see if you can see how they only open one way. Again, you could draw a sketch to show the valves and the inside of the ventricles and atria.

8. Make sure you wash your hands and disinfect all work surfaces once you've completed your dissection.

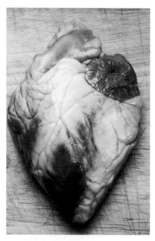

Figure 4: *A heart before dissection. The fat on the outside may make it hard to see the openings of the blood vessels — you might have to find them with your fingers.*

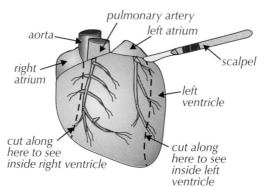

Figure 5: *Diagram showing where to cut heart to examine the ventricles.*

The cardiac cycle

The cardiac cycle is an ongoing sequence of contraction and relaxation of the atria and ventricles that keeps blood continuously circulating round the body. The volume of the atria and ventricles changes as they contract and relax. Pressure changes also occur, due to the changes in chamber volume (e.g. decreasing the volume of a chamber by contraction will increase the pressure of a chamber). The cardiac cycle can be simplified into three stages:

> **Tip:** Cardiac contraction is also called systole, and relaxation is called diastole.

1. Ventricles relax, atria contract

The ventricles are relaxed. The atria contract, decreasing the volume of the chambers and increasing the pressure inside the chambers. This pushes the blood into the ventricles. There's a slight increase in ventricular pressure and chamber volume as the ventricles receive the ejected blood from the contracting atria.

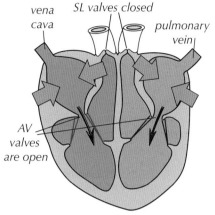

> **Tip:** Contraction of the atria or ventricles is a bit like squeezing a balloon — the size of the balloon decreases and the pressure inside it increases.

2. Ventricles contract, atria relax

The atria relax. The ventricles contract (decreasing their volume), increasing their pressure. The pressure becomes higher in the ventricles than the atria, which forces the atrioventricular (AV) valves shut to prevent back-flow. The pressure in the ventricles is also higher than in the aorta and pulmonary artery, which forces open the semi-lunar (SL) valves and blood is forced out into these arteries.

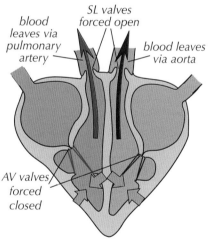

> **Tip:** Remember that if there's a higher pressure in front of a valve it's forced shut and if there's a higher pressure behind a valve it's forced open (see previous page).

3. Ventricles relax, atria relax

The ventricles and the atria both relax. The higher pressure in the pulmonary artery and aorta closes the SL valves to prevent back-flow into the ventricles.

Blood returns to the heart and the atria fill again due to the higher pressure in the vena cava and pulmonary vein. In turn this starts to increase the pressure of the atria. As the ventricles continue to relax, their pressure falls below the pressure of the atria and so the AV valves open. This allows blood to flow passively (without being pushed by atrial contraction) into the ventricles from the atria. The atria contract, and the whole process begins again.

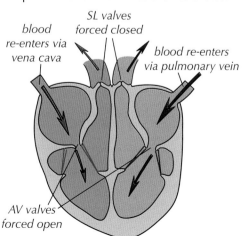

> **Exam Tip**
> When writing about the cardiac cycle in the exam, make sure you always name the valves. You should also make sure you name them in full at least once before abbreviating them.

Interpreting data on the cardiac cycle

You may well be asked to analyse or interpret data about the changes in pressure and volume during the cardiac cycle. Here are two examples of the kind of things you might get:

Tip: Remember that it's the change in volume in a chamber that causes the change in pressure — see previous page.

Example 1

If you get a graph you could be asked questions like this:

When does blood start flowing into the aorta?
At point A, the ventricles are contracting, which increases the pressure inside them. Once the pressure inside the ventricles is higher than that in the atria, the atrioventricular valves shut, forcing blood into the aorta.

Why is ventricular volume decreasing at point B?
The ventricles are contracting, reducing the volume of the chamber.

Are the semi-lunar valves open or closed at point C? Closed.
The ventricles are relaxed and refilling, so the pressure is higher in the pulmonary artery and aorta, forcing the SL valves closed.

Tip: mmHg is a unit of measurement for pressure. It means millimetres of mercury.

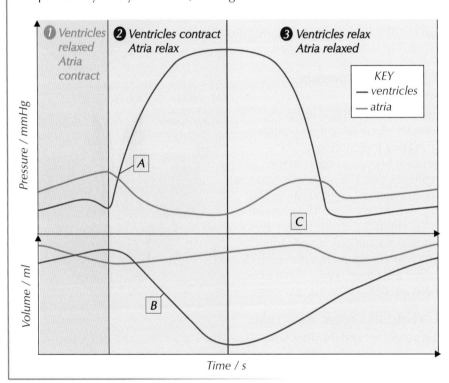

Example 2

Exam Tip
In the exam, the heart might not always be drawn like the one we've shown on the right. Don't let this throw you — just look to see where the valves are and whether they're opened or closed, then answer the questions.

You may have to describe the changes in pressure and volume shown by a diagram, like the one below. In this diagram the AV valves are open. So you know that the pressure in the atria is higher than in the ventricles. So the atria must be contracting because that's what causes the increase in pressure.

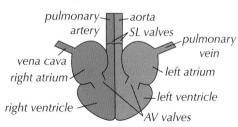

The diagram below shows pressure changes in the cardiac cycle.

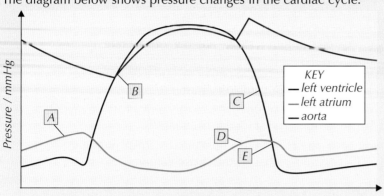

Pressure / mmHg

Time / s

KEY
— left ventricle
— left atrium
— aorta

Q1 Why is the atrial pressure increasing at point A?

Q2 Is the semi-lunar valve open or closed at point B?
Explain your answer.

Q3 Why is the ventricular pressure decreasing at point C?

Q4 Why is the atrial pressure increasing at point D?

Q5 Is the atrioventricular valve open or closed at point E?
Explain your answer.

Tip: The left ventricle has a thicker wall than the right ventricle and so it contracts more forcefully. This means the pressure is higher in the left ventricle (and in the aorta).

Exam Tip
In the exam, if you're given a graph like the one on the left, make sure you read the key carefully so that you don't get the lines mixed up and answer the question incorrectly.

Calculating cardiac output

Examiners love throwing calculations into the exam, and this Topic is no exception. For example, you could be asked to calculate cardiac output (CO).

Cardiac output is the volume of blood pumped by the heart per minute (measured in cm^3 min^{-1}). It's calculated using this formula:

> **cardiac output = stroke volume × heart rate**

- **Heart rate** — the number of beats per minute (bpm).
- **Stroke volume** — the volume of blood pumped during each heartbeat, measured in cm^3.

Exam Tip
You don't need to learn this formula off by heart.

Tip: If you're struggling to remember how to change the subject of a formula, then a formula triangle like this might help:

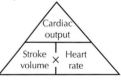

To use a formula triangle, put your finger over the bit of the triangle that corresponds to what you want to find, then read off the correct formula.

Examples — Maths Skills

- Calculate your **cardiac output** if you have a stroke volume of 70 cm^3 and a heart rate of 75 bpm.

  cardiac output = stroke volume × heart rate
  = 70 × 75 = **5250 cm^3 min^{-1}**

- Calculate your **stroke volume** if you have a heart rate of 80 bpm and a cardiac output of 5440 cm^3 min^{-1}.

  stroke volume = $\dfrac{\text{cardiac output}}{\text{heart rate}}$ = $\dfrac{5440}{80}$ = **68 cm^3**

- Calculate your **heart rate** if you have a stroke volume of 68 cm^3 and a cardiac output of 4896 cm^3 min^{-1}.

  heart rate = $\dfrac{\text{cardiac output}}{\text{stroke volume}}$ = $\dfrac{4896}{68}$ = **72 bpm**

Practice Questions — Application

The formula for calculating cardiac output is given below.
Use it to answer the questions that follow.

cardiac output = stroke volume × heart rate

Q1 If you have a stroke volume of 61 cm³ and a heart rate of 79 bpm, what is your cardiac output?

Q2 If you have a stroke volume of 72.5 cm³ and a cardiac output of 5075 cm³ min⁻¹, what is your heart rate?

Q3 If you have a heart rate of 75 bpm and a cardiac output of 5175 cm³ min⁻¹, what is your stroke volume?

Practice Questions — Fact Recall

Q1 Which side of the heart pumps deoxygenated blood?

Q2 The diagram on the right shows the heart. Name the structures labelled A to H.

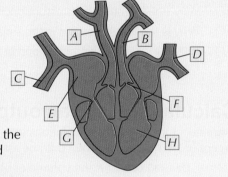

Q3 Why does the left ventricle of the heart have thicker, more muscular walls than the right ventricle?

Q4 a) Name the valves that link the ventricles to the aorta and pulmonary artery.

b) What is the function of these valves?

Q5 What is the cardiac cycle?

Q6 When the atria contract, describe the pressure and volume changes that take place in the atria.

5. Cardiovascular Disease

Your circulatory system keeps you going by constantly supplying all parts of your body with oxygen and glucose for respiration. However, sometimes things can go wrong...

What is cardiovascular disease?

Cardiovascular disease is a general term used to describe diseases associated with the heart and blood vessels. Cardiovascular diseases include aneurysms, thrombosis and myocardial infarction — see next page. Most cardiovascular disease starts with atheroma formation (see below).

Coronary heart disease (CHD) is a type of cardiovascular disease. It occurs when the coronary arteries have lots of atheromas in them, which restricts blood flow to the heart muscle. It can lead to myocardial infarction.

Atheroma formation

The wall of an artery is made up of several layers (see p. 174). The endothelium (inner lining) is usually smooth and unbroken. If damage occurs to the endothelium (e.g. by high blood pressure), white blood cells (mostly macrophages) and lipids (fat) from the blood, clump together under the lining to form fatty streaks.

Over time, more white blood cells, lipids and connective tissue build up and harden to form a fibrous plaque called an atheroma — see Figure 2. This plaque partially blocks the lumen of the artery and restricts blood flow, which causes blood pressure to increase.

Learning Objectives:

- Be able to analyse and interpret data associated with specific risk factors and the incidence of cardiovascular disease.

- Be able to recognise correlations and causal relationships.

- Be able to evaluate conflicting evidence associated with risk factors affecting cardiovascular disease.

Specification Reference 3.3.4.1

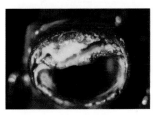

Figure 1: *An atheroma inside an artery.*

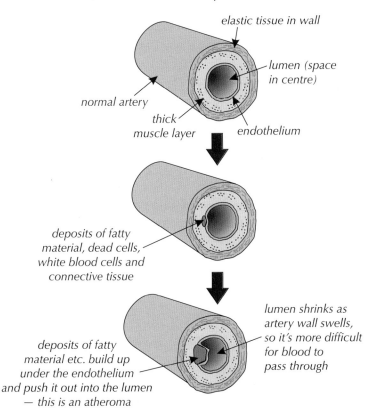

elastic tissue in wall

lumen (space in centre)

normal artery

thick muscle layer

endothelium

deposits of fatty material, dead cells, white blood cells and connective tissue

lumen shrinks as artery wall swells, so it's more difficult for blood to pass through

deposits of fatty material etc. build up under the endothelium and push it out into the lumen — this is an atheroma

Figure 2: *The process of atheroma formation.*

Tip: Some people are more at risk of developing atheromas than others (see pages 185-186 for more).

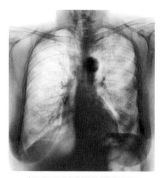

Figure 3: *An x-ray of an aneurysm (red balloon) in the aorta.*

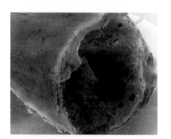

Figure 4: *A blood clot in an artery.*

Tip: You don't need to learn the details of each type of cardiovascular disease, but it will help with interpreting data about them if you understand what is involved in each case.

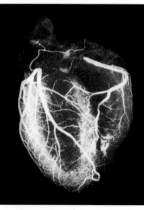

Figure 6: *The coronary arteries.*

Aneurysm

An aneurysm is a balloon-like swelling of the artery. It starts with the formation of atheromas. Atheroma plaques damage and weaken arteries. They also narrow arteries, increasing blood pressure. When blood travels through a weakened artery at high pressure, it may push the inner layers of the artery through the outer elastic layer to form an aneurysm. This aneurysm may burst, causing a haemorrhage (bleeding).

aneurysm

Thrombosis

Thrombosis is the formation of a blood clot. It also starts with the formation of atheromas. An atheroma plaque can rupture (burst through) the endothelium (inner lining) of an artery. This damages the artery wall and leaves a rough surface. Platelets and fibrin (a protein) accumulate at the site of damage and form a **blood clot** (a thrombus). This blood clot can cause a complete blockage of the artery, or it can become dislodged and block a blood vessel elsewhere in the body. Debris from the rupture can cause another blood clot to form further down the artery.

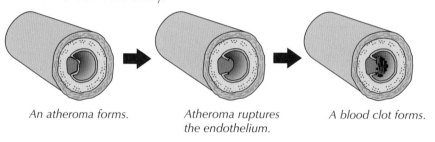

An atheroma forms.   *Atheroma ruptures the endothelium.*   *A blood clot forms.*

Figure 5: *Formation of a blood clot.*

Myocardial infarction (heart attack)

The heart muscle is supplied with blood by the **coronary arteries** — see Figure 6. This blood contains the oxygen needed by heart muscle cells to carry out respiration. If a coronary artery becomes completely blocked (e.g. by a blood clot) an area of the heart muscle will be totally cut off from its blood supply, receiving no oxygen. This causes a myocardial infarction — more commonly known as a heart attack — see Figure 7.

A heart attack can cause damage and death of the heart muscle. Symptoms include pain in the chest and upper body, shortness of breath and sweating. If large areas of the heart muscle are affected complete heart failure can occur, which is often fatal.

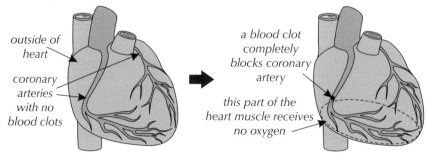

outside of heart

coronary arteries with no blood clots

a blood clot completely blocks coronary artery

this part of the heart muscle receives no oxygen

Figure 7: *How a heart attack is caused.*

Risk factors for cardiovascular disease

There are quite a few things that increase your risk of getting atheromas in your arteries, like smoking or too much salt in your diet. Here are some of the most common risk factors and how they can lead to the development of a myocardial infarction:

Tip: A risk factor is something that increases your chance of developing a disease.

High blood pressure

High blood pressure increases the risk of damage to the artery walls. Damaged walls have an increased risk of atheroma formation, causing a further increase in blood pressure. Atheromas can also cause blood clots to form (see previous page). A blood clot could block flow of blood to the heart muscle, possibly resulting in myocardial infarction (see previous page for details). So anything that increases blood pressure also increases the risk of cardiovascular disease, e.g. being overweight, not exercising and excessive alcohol consumption.

Exam Tip
It's not a good idea to write about high blood pressure 'putting a strain on the heart' — you need to be more technically accurate and write about it increasing the risk of damage to artery walls.

not exercising, overweight etc → high blood pressure → atheroma formation → blood clots → myocardial infarction

Figure 1: *The link between high blood pressure, atheroma formation and myocardial infarction.*

High blood cholesterol and poor diet

If the blood cholesterol level is high (above 240 mg per 100 cm³) then the risk of cardiovascular disease is increased. This is because cholesterol is one of the main constituents of the fatty deposits that form atheromas. Atheromas can lead to increased blood pressure and blood clots, which could cause a myocardial infarction.

A diet high in **saturated fat** is associated with high blood cholesterol levels. A diet high in **salt** also increases the risk of cardiovascular disease because it increases the risk of high blood pressure.

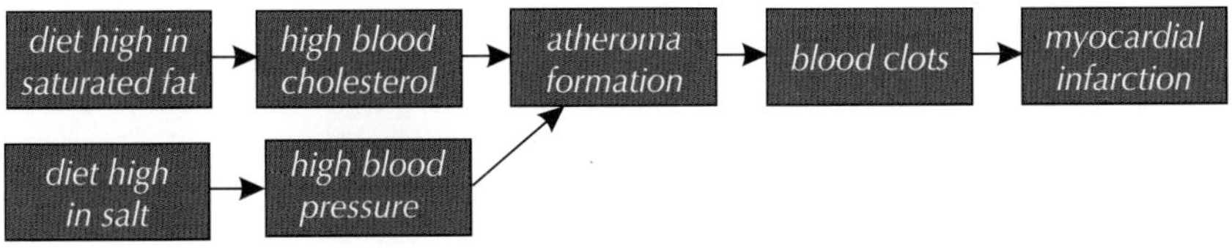

Exam Tip
Don't refer to atheromas 'furring up arteries' — they are fibrous plaques (containing fatty material) that narrow the lumen of arteries.

diet high in saturated fat → high blood cholesterol → atheroma formation → blood clots → myocardial infarction

diet high in salt → high blood pressure

Figure 2: *The link between a diet high in saturated fat or salt, atheroma formation and myocardial infarction.*

Cigarette smoking

Both carbon monoxide and nicotine, found in cigarette smoke, increase the risk of cardiovascular disease and myocardial infarction.

Carbon monoxide combines with haemoglobin and reduces the amount of oxygen transported in the blood, and so reduces the amount of oxygen available to tissues. If the heart muscle doesn't receive enough oxygen it can lead to a heart attack.

Smoking also decreases the amount of antioxidants in the blood — these are important for protecting cells from damage. Fewer antioxidants means cell damage in the coronary artery walls is more likely, and this can lead to atheroma formation.

Tip: Cardiovascular disease doesn't just affect the heart. For example, a blood clot in an artery in the brain can cause a stroke.

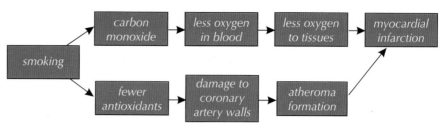

Figure 3: The link between smoking, atheroma formation and myocardial infarction.

Tip: Other common risk factors for cardiovascular disease include obesity, a lack of physical activity, ethnic background (people of South Asian or African Caribbean background may have a greater risk of certain forms of CVD), age (risk increases with age) and sex (men are more at risk than women).

Reducing the risk

Most of these factors are within our control — a person can choose to smoke, eat fatty foods, etc. However, some risk factors can't be controlled, such as having a genetic predisposition to coronary heart disease or having high blood pressure as a result of another condition, e.g. some forms of diabetes. Even so, the risk of developing cardiovascular disease can be reduced by removing as many risk factors as you possibly can.

Interpreting data on risk factors and cardiovascular disease

Take a look at the following example of the sort of study you might see in your exam.

Exam Tip
Make sure you read any information you're given about a study really carefully — it will help you to interpret data from the study and decide how much confidence you can have in any conclusions made (see next page).

┌─ **Example — LDL cholesterol level** ──────────

Figure 4 shows the results of a study involving 27 939 American women. The LDL cholesterol level was measured for each woman. These women were then followed for an average of 8 years and the occurrence of cardiovascular events (e.g. heart attack, surgery on coronary arteries) or death from cardiovascular diseases was recorded. The relative risk of a cardiovascular event, adjusted for other factors that can affect cardiovascular disease, was then calculated.

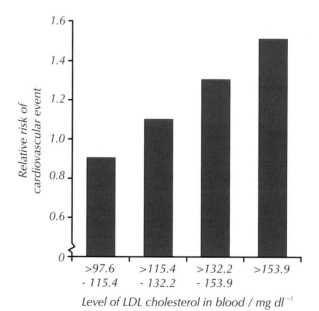

Figure 4: Graph showing the relationship between the level of LDL cholesterol in the blood and the relative risk of cardiovascular event.

Here are some of the things you might be asked to do:

1. **Describe the data** — The relative risk of a cardiovascular event increases as the level of LDL cholesterol in the blood increases, from 0.9 at $> 97.6 – 115.4$ mg dl^{-1} to 1.5 at > 153.9 mg dl^{-1}.

2. **Draw conclusions** — The graph shows a positive correlation between the relative risk of a cardiovascular event and the level of LDL cholesterol in the blood.

3. **Check any conclusions are valid** — Make sure any conclusions match the data, e.g.

   - This data only looked at women — no males were involved, so you can't say that this trend is true for everyone.

   - You can't say that a high LDL cholesterol level is correlated with an increased risk of heart attacks, because the data shows all first cardiovascular events, including surgery on coronary arteries.

   - Also, you can't conclude that a high LDL cholesterol level caused the increased relative risk of a cardiovascular event — there may be other reasons for the trend.

4. **Other things to think about** — A large sample size was used (27 939). Data based on large samples is better than data based on small samples. This is because a large sample is more representative of the whole population (i.e. it shares more of the various characteristics of the population).

Tip: There's more on correlation and cause on page 15.

Tip: The way in which information is collected can also be important. Some studies rely on the results of questionnaires (e.g. asking people how many cigarettes they smoke). Questionnaires can be unreliable as people can tell fibs or give inaccurate information.

Conflicting evidence

You might also have to evaluate conflicting evidence associated with risk factors affecting cardiovascular disease. E.g. one study might conclude that a factor isn't a health risk, whereas another study might conclude that the same factor is a health risk.

If two studies have produced conflicting results, think about why that might be. Was it to do with study design? Was one study based on a small sample size? Did both studies take into account other risk factors (variables) that could have affected the results? Knowing whether both studies used similar groups can be helpful, e.g. same age, gender, etc.

Sometimes, the only way to resolve the problem of conflicting evidence is to carry out more studies and collect more results. Results need to be reproduced by other scientists before they're accepted.

Practice Question — Application

Q1 In a US study, a computer model was used to predict how interventions to reduce some CHD risk factors could affect the number of new cases of CHD per year. The results are shown in the graph on the next page. The results for reducing salt intake are based on the highest estimates from the study.

Tip: Remember, CHD stands for coronary heart disease.

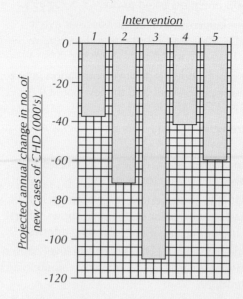

Tip: You need to be really careful when reading complex graphs — make sure you pay attention to the key and axes, so that you know exactly what the graph is showing you.

Tip: An intervention to reduce a risk factor could be a change in diet or lifestyle.

Tip: BMI (body mass index) is the relationship between weight and height — it's used as a measure of obesity.

a) Describe the effect that reducing salt intake by 1 g per day could have on the number of new cases of CHD per year in the US.

b) How many fewer new cases of CHD could there be by reducing BMI by 5% in obese adults, compared to reducing tobacco use/exposure by 50%?

c) Use evidence from the graph to suggest which intervention the US public should be encouraged to carry out and why.

d) i) Describe the trend shown on the graph between reducing salt intake and the number of new cases of CHD per year.

   ii) Explain this trend.

Practice Questions — Fact Recall

Q1 What is an atheroma?

Q2 Give two effects an atheroma has on the artery it's in.

Q3 a) Explain how high blood pressure leads to an increased risk of cardiovascular disease.

   b) Give three things that can cause an increase in blood pressure.

Q4 a) Give two examples of risk factors for cardiovascular disease that can be controlled.

   b) Give an example of a risk factor for cardiovascular disease that can't be controlled.

6. Transport in Plants — Xylem

Plants are pretty clever when it comes to transporting water. They can take it up from their roots to their leaves against the force of gravity. Let's see how they manage that...

Learning Objectives:

- Know that xylem is the tissue that transports water in the stem and leaves of plants.
- Understand the cohesion-tension theory of water transport in the xylem.
- Be able to dissect an organ within a plant's mass transport system (Required Practical 5).

Specification Reference 3.3.4.1 and 3.3.4.2

Types of tissue involved in mass transport in plants

- **Xylem** tissue transports water and mineral ions in solution. These substances move up the plant from the roots to the leaves.

- **Phloem** tissue transports organic substances like sugars (also in solution) both up and down the plant — there's more about the phloem on pages 193-196.

Xylem and phloem are mass transport systems (see page 139) — they move substances over large distances.

Structure of the xylem

Xylem vessels are the part of the xylem tissue that actually transports the water and ions. Xylem vessels are very long, tube-like structures formed from dead cells (vessel elements) joined end to end. There are no end walls on these cells, making an uninterrupted tube that allows water to pass up through the middle easily.

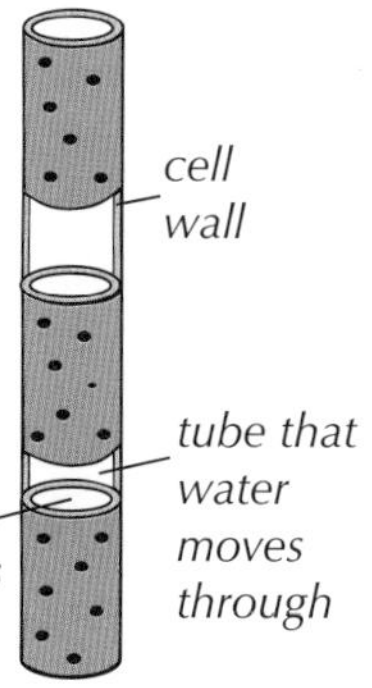

Figure 1: A xylem vessel with internal detail showing.

cell wall

tube that water moves through

no end wall between cells

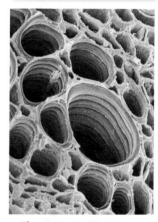

Figure 2: An SEM image of xylem vessels.

Water movement up a plant

Water moves up a plant against the force of gravity, from roots to leaves. This can be explained by the combined action of cohesion and tension.

Cohesion and tension

1. Water evaporates from the leaves at the 'top' of the xylem. This is a process called **transpiration** (see next page).

2. This creates tension (suction), which pulls more water into the leaf.

3. Water molecules are cohesive (they stick together, see page 63) so when some are pulled into the leaf others follow. This means the whole column of water in the xylem, from the leaves down to the roots, moves upwards.

4. Water then enters the stem through the roots.

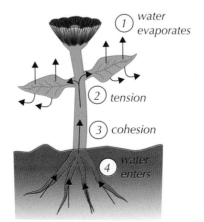

① water evaporates

② tension

③ cohesion

④ water enters

Figure 3: Water movement up a plant.

Tip: This is called the cohesion-tension theory of water transport.

Tip: Water movement up a plant increases as the transpiration rate increases — see next page.

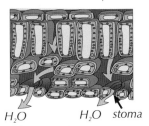

H_2O H_2O *stoma*

Figure 4: *Cross-section of a leaf showing how water moves out during transpiration.*

Tip: Transpiration's really a side effect of photosynthesis — the plant needs to open its stomata to let in CO_2 so that it can produce glucose, but this also lets water out.

Tip: Transpiration rate isn't exactly the same as water uptake by a plant — some water is used in reactions (e.g. in photosynthesis) and to support the plant, and some water is produced during respiration.

Tip: You can use a potometer to test the effect of different factors on transpiration rate, e.g. by using a fan to increase air movement or a lamp to increase light intensity, etc.

Tip: If you want to compare water loss from different types of plant, you need to measure the surface area of the leaves because it will vary with type of plant.

Transpiration

Transpiration is the **evaporation** of water from a plant's surface, especially the leaves. Water evaporates from the moist cell walls and accumulates in the spaces between cells in the leaf. When the stomata open (see page 143), it moves out of the leaf down the **water potential gradient** (because there's more water inside the leaf than in the air outside).

Factors affecting transpiration rate

There are four main factors that affect transpiration rate.

1. **Light intensity** — the lighter it is the faster the transpiration rate (i.e. there's a positive correlation between light intensity and transpiration rate). This is because the stomata open when it gets light to let in CO_2 for photosynthesis. When it's dark the stomata are usually closed, so there's little transpiration.

2. **Temperature** — the higher the temperature the faster the transpiration rate. Warmer water molecules have more energy so they evaporate from the cells inside the leaf faster. This increases the water potential gradient between the inside and outside of the leaf, making water diffuse out of the leaf faster.

3. **Humidity** — the lower the humidity, the faster the transpiration rate (i.e. there's a negative correlation between humidity and transpiration rate). If the air around the plant is dry, the water potential gradient between the leaf and the air is increased, which increases transpiration rate.

4. **Wind** — the windier it is, the faster the transpiration rate. Lots of air movement blows away water molecules from around the stomata. This increases the water potential gradient, which increases the rate of transpiration.

Estimating transpiration rate — potometers

A potometer is a special piece of apparatus used to estimate transpiration rates. It actually measures water uptake by a plant, but it's assumed that water uptake by the plant is directly related to water loss by the leaves. You can use it to estimate how different factors affect the transpiration rate.

Here's what you'd do:

1. Cut a shoot underwater to prevent air from entering the xylem. Cut it at a slant to increase the surface area available for water uptake.

2. Assemble the potometer under the water and insert the shoot with the apparatus still under the water, so no air can enter.

3. Remove the apparatus from the water but keep the end of the capillary tube submerged in a beaker of water.

4. Check that the apparatus is watertight and airtight.

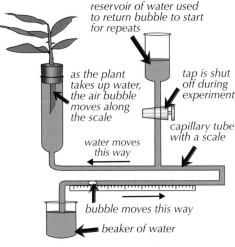

reservoir of water used to return bubble to start for repeats

as the plant takes up water, the air bubble moves along the scale

tap is shut off during experiment

capillary tube with a scale

water moves this way

bubble moves this way

beaker of water

Figure 5: *Diagram showing how to use a potometer.*

5. Dry the leaves, allow time for the shoot to acclimatise and then shut the tap.

6. Remove the end of the capillary tube from the beaker of water until one air bubble has formed, then put the end of the tube back into the water.

7. Record the starting position of the air bubble.

8. Start a stopwatch and record the distance moved by the bubble per unit time, e.g. per hour. The rate of air bubble movement is an estimate of the transpiration rate.

9. Remember, only change one variable (e.g. temperature) at a time. All other conditions (e.g. light intensity, humidity) must be kept constant.

Tip: The air bubble is sometimes called the air-water meniscus.

Tip: To work out the rate of water uptake in mm^3 per minute, you need to measure the distance moved by the bubble per minute <u>and</u> the diameter of the capillary tube.

Practice Questions — Application

A potometer was used to test the effect of temperature on transpiration rate. The test was repeated 3 times. The results are shown in the table.

Temperature (°C)	Distance moved by the bubble in 10 minutes (mm)		
	Test 1	Test 2	Test 3
10	15	12	14
20	19	16	19
30	25	22	23

Q1 a) Calculate the mean result for each temperature.

    b) Plot a graph of the mean results and use it to estimate the distance the bubble would move in ten minutes at 25 °C.

Q2 Describe and explain the results of the experiment.

Exam Tip
Repeats are done to increase precision and help to identify anomalous results.

Tip: For data where the distance moved by the bubble is measured per minute or so, a distance-time graph can be plotted. Then the gradient of the line shows the rate of water uptake.

Plant mass transport dissection

You can look at xylem or phloem in plant tissue (e.g. part of a plant stem) under a microscope, and then draw them. But first you need to dissect the plant and prepare a section of the tissue. You can do this using the following method:

REQUIRED PRACTICAL **5**

┌─ **Example — Looking at the xylem and phloem in a stem** ─

1. Use a scalpel (or razor blade) to cut a cross-section of the stem. Cut the sections as thinly as possible — thin sections are better for viewing under a microscope.

2. Use tweezers to gently place the cut sections in water until you come to use them. This stops them from drying out.

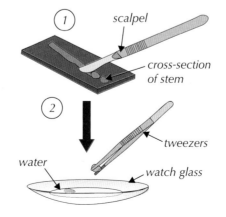

Tip: As with all practicals you do, make sure you have carried out a risk assessment before you begin. Pay particular attention to safety when working with sharp blades and remember you need to wear gloves and eye protection when working with stains.

Tip: You could also dissect part of a leaf or root to look at the xylem and phloem there — the basic method of dissection and preparation is the same.

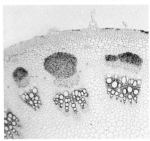

Figure 6: Light micrograph through a stem showing xylem and phloem tissue.

3. Add a drop of water to a microscope slide, add the plant section and carefully add one or two drops of a stain, e.g. toluidine blue O (TBO), and leave for about one minute.

4. Carefully apply a cover slip so you have created a temporary mount (see page 81).

5. When you view the specimen under the microscope, if you've used TBO you should be able to see the xylem cells stained blue-green. The phloem cells and the rest of the tissue should appear pinkish purple.

The arrangement of the xylem and the phloem in a cross-section of a stem (of a non-woody plant) is shown in Figure 7. This should help you understand what you are seeing when you look at your stem section under an optical microscope (see Figure 6).

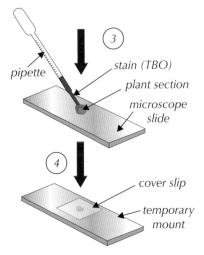
③ *stain (TBO)*
pipette
plant section
microscope slide
④
cover slip
temporary mount

Figure 5: Preparing a cross section of a plant stem for viewing under a microscope.

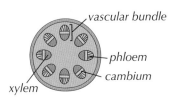
vascular bundle
phloem
cambium
xylem

Figure 7: Cross-section of a non-woody stem.

Practice Questions — Fact Recall

Q1 Which type of plant tissue transports water up the plant from the roots to the leaves?

Q2 Describe and explain how water can move up a plant.

Q3 a) Explain how wind affects transpiration rate.

    b) Give three other factors that affect the rate of transpiration.

Q4 Briefly describe how you could prepare a temporary mount of a stem cross-section for observation of the plant's mass transport systems.

7. Transport in Plants — Phloem

The phloem transports dissolved substances around the plant to where they are needed. Scientists still aren't sure exactly how this movement works, but they do have a hypothesis...

Structure and function of the phloem

Solutes are dissolved substances. Phloem tissue transports organic solutes (mainly sugars like sucrose) round plants. Like xylem, phloem is formed from cells arranged in tubes. Sieve tube elements and companion cells are important cell types in phloem tissue (see Figure 1):

- Sieve tube elements are living cells that form the tube for transporting solutes. They have no nucleus and few organelles, so...

- ...there's a companion cell for each sieve tube element. They carry out living functions for sieve cells, e.g. providing the energy needed for the active transport of solutes.

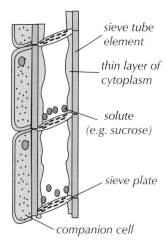

sieve tube element

thin layer of cytoplasm

solute (e.g. sucrose)

sieve plate

companion cell

Figure 1: *Phloem tissue.*

Learning Objectives:

- Know that phloem is the tissue that transports organic substances in plants.

- Know the mass flow hypothesis for the mechanism of translocation in plants.

- Know that ringing and tracer experiments are used to investigate transport in plants.

- Be able to interpret evidence from ringing and tracer experiments, and to evaluate the evidence for and against the mass flow hypothesis.

- Be able to recognise correlations and causal relationships.

Specification Reference 3.3.4.2

What is translocation?

Translocation is the movement of solutes (e.g. amino acids and sugars like sucrose) to where they're needed in a plant. Solutes are sometimes called **assimilates**. It's an energy-requiring process that happens in the phloem.

Translocation moves solutes from 'sources' to 'sinks'. The **source** is where assimilates are produced (so they're at a high concentration there). The **sink** is where assimilates are used up (so they're at a lower concentration there).

┌─ Example ─────────────────────────────────
The source for sucrose is usually the leaves (where it's made), and the sinks are the other parts of the plant, especially the food storage organs and the meristems (areas of growth) in the roots, stems and leaves.
└──

Enzymes maintain a concentration gradient from the source to the sink by changing the solutes at the sink (e.g. by breaking them down or making them into something else). This makes sure there's always a lower concentration at the sink than at the source.

┌─ Example ─────────────────────────────────
In potatoes, sucrose is converted to starch in the sink areas, so there's always a lower concentration of sucrose at the sink than inside the phloem. This makes sure a constant supply of new sucrose reaches the sink from the phloem.
└──

Figure 2: *Phloem vessels in a* Cucurbita *plant. The sieve cells are stained blue and the sieve plates are dark green.*

Tip: Assimilates are substances that become incorporated into the plant tissue.

Exam Tip
Make sure you learn
what the terms 'source'
and 'sink' mean — you
could be tested on them
in the exam.

The mass flow hypothesis

Scientists still aren't certain exactly how the solutes are transported
from source to sink by translocation. The best supported theory is
the mass flow hypothesis (see Figure 3):

1. Source

Active transport is used to actively load the solutes (e.g. sucrose
from photosynthesis) from companion cells into the sieve tubes of
the phloem at the source (e.g. the leaves). This lowers the water
potential inside the sieve tubes, so water enters the tubes by osmosis
from the xylem and companion cells. This creates a high pressure
inside the sieve tubes at the source end of the phloem.

2. Sink

At the sink end, solutes are removed from the phloem to be used up.
This increases the water potential inside the sieve tubes, so water also leaves
the tubes by osmosis. This lowers the pressure inside the sieve tubes.

3. Flow

The result is a pressure gradient from the source end to the
sink end. This gradient pushes solutes along the sieve tubes
towards the sink. When they reach the sink the solutes will
be used (e.g. in respiration) or stored (e.g. as starch).

The higher the concentration of sucrose at the source,
the higher the rate of translocation.

Tip: There's more about
active transport on
page 108.

Tip: Experiments
have shown that some
sucrose is transported
also through the cell
walls of the phloem.

Tip: Companion
cells contain many
mitochondria, which
means they can make
lots of ATP. ATP is
needed to actively load
the solutes into the
phloem at the source.

Tip: There's more
about sieve plates and
companion cells on the
previous page.

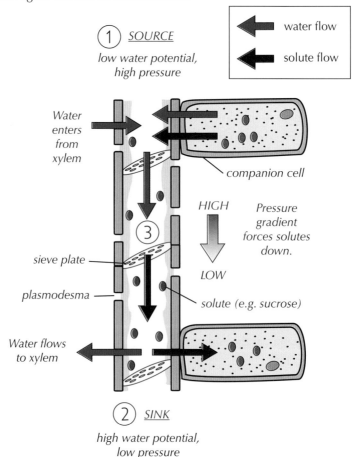

Figure 3: How the mass flow hypothesis works.

Mass flow evidence

There is evidence both for and against mass flow.

Supporting evidence

1. If a ring of bark (which includes the phloem, but not the xylem) is removed from a woody stem, a bulge forms above the ring — see Figure 4. The fluid from the bulge has a higher concentration of sugars than the fluid from below the ring. This is because the sugars can't move past the area where the bark has been removed — this is evidence that there can be a downward flow of sugars.

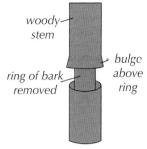

Figure 4: *Diagram to show the effect of removing a ring of bark from a tree.*

2. Pressure in the phloem can be investigated using aphids (they pierce the phloem, then their bodies are removed leaving the mouthparts behind, which allows the sap to flow out... gruesome). The sap flows out quicker nearer the leaves than further down the stem — this is evidence that there's a pressure gradient.

3. A **radioactive tracer** such as radioactive carbon (^{14}C) can be used to track the movement of organic substances in a plant (see below).

4. If a metabolic inhibitor (which stops ATP production) is put into the phloem, then translocation stops — this is evidence that active transport is involved.

Objections

1. Sugar travels to many different sinks, not just to the one with the highest water potential, as the model would suggest.

2. The sieve plates would create a barrier to mass flow. A lot of pressure would be needed for the solutes to get through at a reasonable rate.

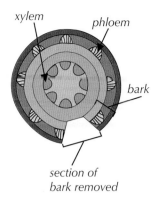

Figure 5: *Diagram to show how the removal of bark removes the phloem but leaves the xylem intact.*

> **Tip:** Sugars are made in the leaves, so that's why there's a downward flow of sugars (from source to sink) in this case.

> **Tip:** The build up of sugars above the ring causes a decrease in water potential, so water moves into the cells — adding to the bulge.

Evidence from radioactive tracers

Translocation of solutes can be modelled in an experiment using radioactive tracers. This can be done by supplying part of a plant (often a leaf) with an organic substance that has a radioactive label, then tracking its movement.

> **Exam Tip**
> You need to be able to 'evaluate' the evidence — so make sure you really know the evidence for and against the mass flow hypothesis.

┌─ **Example** ─────────────────────────────

Carbon dioxide containing the radioactive isotope ^{14}C is used as a radioactive tracer. This radioactively-labelled CO_2 can be supplied to a single leaf by being pumped into a container which completely surrounds the leaf. The radioactive carbon will then be incorporated into organic substances produced by the leaf (e.g. sugars produced by photosynthesis), which will be moved around the plant by translocation.

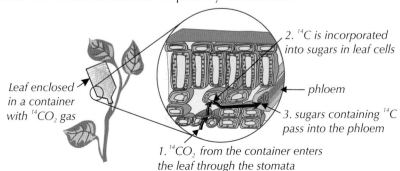

Leaf enclosed in a container with $^{14}CO_2$ gas

2. ^{14}C is incorporated into sugars in leaf cells

phloem

3. sugars containing ^{14}C pass into the phloem

1. $^{14}CO_2$ from the container enters the leaf through the stomata

> **Tip:** Photosynthesis produces glucose. This is converted to sucrose for transport around the plant.

Figure 6: *An autoradiogram showing the fuzzy imprint of a leaf after being given radioactive phosphorus. The black areas show where the radioactive substance is present.*

The movement of these substances can be tracked using a technique called **autoradiography**. To reveal where the radioactive tracer has spread to in a plant, the plant is killed (e.g. by freezing it using liquid nitrogen) and then the whole plant (or sections of it) is placed onto photographic film — wherever the film turns black, the radioactive substance is present (see Figure 6).

The results demonstrate the translocation of substances from source to sink over time — for example, autoradiographs of plants killed at different times show an overall movement of solutes (e.g. products of photosynthesis) from the leaves towards the roots.

Correlation and causal relationships

The data from experiments used to provide evidence for and against mass flow has to be interpreted carefully.

Tip: Looking for correlation from tables is not quite as easy as from graphs but don't panic — if one variable goes up as the other goes up it's a positive correlation. If one variable goes up as the other goes down, it's a negative correlation.

┌─ **Example** ─────────────────────────────────

Scientists carried out a ringing experiment on a particular species of woody plant. A varying amount of bark was left connecting the upper and lower parts of the stems (see below). The plants were left for 24 hours, then the amount of carbohydrate in the plant below the ringing was measured.

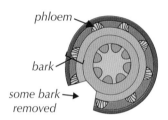

phloem

bark

some bark → removed

Width of bark strip remaining (% of intact stem)	Carbohydrate transported to the lower part of the stem in 24 hours / mg
0	0
10	437
33	609
87	744

Correlation

The results in the table above show a positive correlation — as the width of the bark strip remaining increased, the amount of carbohydrate transported to the lower part of the stem (i.e. below the ringing) also increased.

Conclusions

From the results, you might conclude that removing the bark **caused** a reduction in the amount of carbohydrate transported down the stem. This may be because removing more bark, removes more phloem, which reduces the amount of carbohydrate that can be transported. This provides evidence in support of the mass flow hypothesis because the phloem is transporting carbohydrates down from a source in the leaves to a sink in the roots.

However, you have to be careful when drawing conclusions, especially when there's not much data. The results don't prove that there is a downward flow of sugars in the phloem — there could be other factors affecting the results. For example, it could be that the sugars are actually transported in the xylem, but the xylem tissue was accidently damaged when the bark was removed. The experiment has also been carried out on only one species of plant, so you can't conclude that this would be the case for all plant species.

However, so many studies have now been done on mass flow, that the correlation shown by this experiment is accepted to be a causal relationship, i.e. removing more of a plant's phloem causes less carbohydrate to be transported downwards, towards a plant's roots.

Tip: Correlation and causal relationships come up in lots of topics but the general principles are the same — a correlation between two variables doesn't necessarily mean that one <u>caused</u> the other (see pages 15-16 for more).

Practice Questions — Application

Q1 The diagram on the right shows the translocation of sucrose from the roots (where it was stored as starch) to a sink. This process happens in the spring.

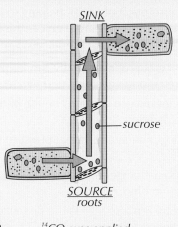

a) Suggest a sink for the sucrose shown on the diagram.

b) Using the mass flow hypothesis:

i) explain why water enters the sieve tubes in the roots,

ii) explain why water leaves the sieve tubes at the sink.

Q2 An experiment was done to investigate translocation in a plant using radioactive carbon dioxide ($^{14}CO_2$). The diagram on the right represents the autoradiography image produced after the experiment. Discuss, using evidence from the diagram, whether or not the experiment provides evidence to support the mass flow hypothesis.

$^{14}CO_2$ was applied to this leaf

Tip: Remember, radioactive substances show up black during autoradiography.

Practice Questions — Fact Recall

Q1 What substances are transported by the phloem?

Q2 Define translocation.

Q3 What is the difference between a source and a sink in a plant?

Q4 Describe one piece of evidence from ringing experiments that supports the mass flow hypothesis.

Q5 Describe one piece of evidence against the mass flow hypothesis.

Section Summary

Make sure you know...

- That during digestion, large molecules, e.g. starch, proteins and lipids, are broken down into smaller molecules by hydrolysis reactions, so that they can be absorbed into the bloodstream.

- That amylase catalyses the breakdown of starch (a polysaccharide).

- That membrane-bound disaccharidases found in cells lining the ileum catalyse the breakdown of disaccharides.

- That lipases catalyse the breakdown of lipids into monoglycerides and fatty acids.

- That bile salts emulsify lipids, increasing the surface area for digestion, and lead to the formation of micelles.

- That peptidases (proteases) catalyse the breakdown of proteins into amino acids.

- That endopeptidases hydrolyse peptide bonds within a protein and exopeptidases hydrolyse bonds at the ends of proteins, removing single amino acids. Membrane-bound dipeptidases are a type of exopeptidase that break down dipeptides into single amino acids.

- That co-transport mechanisms are required for the absorption of monosaccharides, such as glucose.
- The role of micelles in the absorption of lipids, helping to move monoglycerides and fatty acids towards the epithelium, where they can diffuse across the membrane.
- That co-transport mechanisms are required for the absorption of amino acids into the bloodstream.
- That the haemoglobins are a group of chemically similar proteins with a quaternary structure and that they are found in red blood cells, where they are involved in the transport of oxygen.
- That haemoglobin's affinity for oxygen depends on the partial pressure of oxygen (pO_2), loading at high pO_2 and unloading at low pO_2.
- That the saturation of haemoglobin at any partial pressure is shown on an oxyhaemoglobin dissociation curve.
- That the shape of haemoglobin changes once the first oxygen molecule has joined, making it easier for further oxygen molecules to bind.
- That carbon dioxide concentration also affects the dissociation of oxyhaemoglobin, making it dissociate more easily at higher partial pressures of CO_2, which is known as the Bohr effect.
- That different organisms are adapted to their environments by having different types of haemoglobin, which vary in their ability to transport oxygen.
- The general pattern of blood circulation in a mammal, including the names of the coronary arteries and of the blood vessels entering and leaving the heart, lungs and kidneys.
- The structure of arteries, arterioles and veins and how they are related to their functions.
- The structure of capillaries and how capillary beds (networks of capillaries) are adapted for efficient diffusion.
- That hydrostatic pressure at the arteriole end of a capillary bed leads to the formation of tissue fluid and that excess tissue fluid is drained into the lymphatic system for return to the circulatory system.
- The internal structure of the heart — vena cava, pulmonary artery, aorta, pulmonary vein, right atrium, left atrium, semi-lunar valves, atrioventricular valves, cords, right ventricle and left ventricle.
- That the right side of the heart pumps deoxygenated blood and the left side pumps oxygenated blood.
- How to safely dissect a mammalian heart.
- The cardiac cycle, including pressure changes, volume changes and valve movements (which maintain a unidirectional flow of blood).
- How to analyse and interpret data relating to pressure and volume changes during the cardiac cycle.
- That cardiovascular diseases affect the heart and blood vessels and usually involve atheromas, which may lead to aneurysms, thrombosis and myocardial infarction (heart attack).
- How to analyse and interpret data associated with specific risk factors (e.g. high blood pressure, high cholesterol, poor diet and smoking), and the incidence of cardiovascular disease, and how to recognise correlations and causal relationships in any data that is given.
- How to evaluate conflicting evidence associated with risk factors affecting cardiovascular disease.
- That xylem vessels transport water round the plant, i.e. up the roots and stem and to the leaves.
- How cohesion and tension move water up the xylem and how transpiration affects this movement.
- How to dissect an organ within a plant's mass transport system.
- That phloem tissue transports dissolved organic substances, such as sucrose, around the plant.
- That the mass flow hypothesis is a theory that explains translocation in a plant — it involves the creation of a pressure gradient, which pushes solutes from source to sink.
- How ringing experiments (which remove a ring of bark from a woody stem) and radioactive tracer experiments are used to investigate transport in plants.
- How to interpret evidence from ringing and tracer experiments, evaluate the evidence for and against the mass flow hypothesis and recognise correlations and causal relationships in the data given.

Exam-style Questions

1　　　**Figure 1** shows the three main stages of the cardiac cycle.

Figure 1

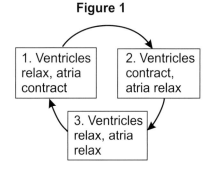

1.1　Explain the pressure change that occurs in the atria in the first stage of the cardiac cycle.

(2 marks)

1.2　Name the valves that connect the atria to the ventricles and describe their function.

(2 marks)

1.3　During stages one and two, are the valves connecting the atria to the ventricles open or closed? Explain your answer(s).

(2 marks)

1.4　During stage three, why does the pressure of the atria increase?

(1 mark)

1.5　Name the vessel in which the blood leaves the right ventricle to travel to the lungs.

(1 mark)

1.6　Suggest how the structure of this vessel is related to its function.

(3 marks)

2　　　A student used a potometer to investigate the effect of light intensity on transpiration rate. Her results are shown in **Figure 2**.

Figure 2

2.1　Using the graph, work out the rate of bubble movement for a light intensity of **1.5 arbitrary units**. Give your answer in mm min⁻¹.

(2 marks)

2.2　Using the cohesion-tension theory, explain the results shown by the graph.

(4 marks)

2.3　Suggest what **negative control** should be used for this investigation.

(1 mark)

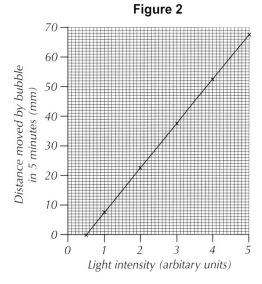

3   A scientist was investigating the link between poor diet and cardiovascular disease. He took 1000 British men, aged 40-60 years old and put them into two groups. One group was given dietary information on how to reduce their risk of cardiovascular disease, e.g. by lowering their saturated fat intake. The other group wasn't given any information. The scientist recorded any deaths from cardiovascular disease over ten years.

3.1   What is cardiovascular disease?

(1 mark)

3.2   What is the name given to the group of men that wasn't given any information?

(1 mark)

3.3   Give **two** ways in which the study could have been improved.

(2 marks)

3.4   It's important to have some fat in the diet to stay healthy.
Explain how dietary fats are digested and absorbed onto the bloodstream.

(3 marks)

4   Cats, pumas and foxes were used in a study to investigate haemoglobin's affinity for oxygen. For each type of animal, blood was taken from a sample that lived at sea level and a sample that lived at high altitude. The pO_2 at which each animal's haemoglobin was 50% saturated was recorded. The results are shown in **Table 1**.

Table 1

Animal	Sea Level (pO_2 / kPa)	High Altitude (pO_2 / kPa)
Cat	3.9	3.0
Puma	4.8	4.1
Fox	3.5	2.5

4.1   Describe the structure of haemoglobin.

(2 marks)

4.2   There is less oxygen at high altitudes than at sea level.
Use evidence from **Table 1** to support this statement.

(3 marks)

5   A fruit grower cut a C-shaped ring in the bark of the trunks of his fruit trees.
He did this so that the branches would receive more nutrients.

5.1   What type of plant tissue involved in mass transport was removed with the bark?

(1 mark)

5.2   Describe how this tissue is involved in mass transport in plants.

(2 marks)

5.3   Explain how the fruit grower's method may result in the trees producing more fruit.

(3 marks)

1. DNA

DNA is stored differently in prokaryotic and eukaryotic cells.

How is DNA stored?

Although the structure of DNA is the same in all organisms, eukaryotic and prokaryotic cells store DNA in slightly different ways. (For a recap on the differences between prokaryotic and eukaryotic cells see pages 68 and 75.)

Eukaryotic cells

Eukaryotic cells contain linear DNA molecules that exist as chromosomes — thread-like structures, each made up of one long molecule of DNA and its associated proteins. Chromosomes are found in the nucleus.

The DNA molecule is really long, so it has to be wound up so it can fit into the nucleus. It's wound around proteins called **histones**. Histone proteins also help to support the DNA. The DNA (and protein) is then coiled up very tightly to make a compact chromosome.

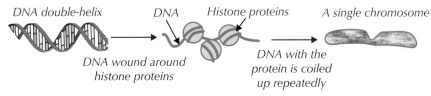

Figure 1: Storage of DNA in eukaryotes.

The mitochondria and chloroplasts in eukaryotic cells also have their own DNA. This is pretty similar to prokaryotic DNA (see below) because it's circular and shorter than DNA molecules in the nucleus. It's not associated with histone proteins.

Prokaryotic cells

Prokaryotes also carry DNA as chromosomes — but the DNA molecules are shorter and circular. The DNA isn't wound around histones — it condenses to fit in the cell by supercoiling.

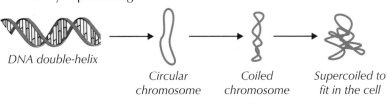

Figure 2: Storage of DNA in prokaryotes.

Practice Questions — Fact Recall

Q1 Describe the structure of a eukaryotic chromosome.

Q2 Describe how DNA in prokaryotic chromosomes differs from DNA in eukaryotic chromosomes.

Learning Objectives:

▪ Know that in the nucleus of eukaryotic cells, DNA molecules are very long, linear and associated with proteins, called histones.

▪ Know that in eukaryotic cells, a DNA molecule together with its associated proteins form a chromosome.

▪ Know that the mitochondria and chloroplasts of eukaryotic cells also contain DNA, which, like the DNA of prokaryotes, is short, circular and not associated with proteins.

▪ Know that in prokaryotic cells, DNA molecules are short, circular and not associated with proteins.

Specification Reference 3.4.1

Tip: Eukaryotic cells include animal and plant cells. Prokaryotic cells are generally bacteria.

- Know that a gene
  is a base sequence
  of DNA that codes
  for the amino
  acid sequence of
  a polypeptide or
  a functional RNA
  (including ribosomal
  RNA and tRNAs).
- Know that a sequence
  of three DNA bases,
  called a triplet, codes
  for a specific amino
  acid.
- Understand the
  concept of the
  genome as the
  complete set of genes
  in a cell and of the
  proteome as the full
  range of proteins
  that a cell is able to
  produce.
- Know that in
  eukaryotes, much
  of the nuclear DNA
  does not code for
  polypeptides. There
  are, for example,
  non-coding multiple
  repeats of base
  sequences between
  genes. Even within
  a gene only some
  sequences, called
  exons, code for amino
  acid sequences.
  Within the gene, these
  exons are separated
  by one or more non-
  coding sequences
  called introns.
- Know that a gene
  occupies a fixed
  position, called a
  locus, on a particular
  DNA molecule.

**Specification
Reference 3.4.1 and 3.4.2**

2. Genes and Chromosomes

*Only a small amount of the DNA in a cell carries genetic information.
The most important parts of a DNA molecule are the genes.*

Genes

DNA contains genes. A gene is a sequence of DNA bases (see page 52) that codes for either a polypeptide or functional RNA (see below). The sequence of amino acids in a polypeptide forms the primary structure of a protein (see page 32).

Different polypeptides have a different number and order of amino acids. It's the order of bases in a gene that determines the order of amino acids in a particular polypeptide. Each amino acid is coded for by a sequence of three bases in a gene called a triplet or codon (see page 209). To make a polypeptide, DNA is first copied into messenger RNA (mRNA). This is the first stage of protein synthesis (see page 204).

Genes that don't code for a polypeptide code for **functional RNA** instead. Functional RNA is RNA molecules other than mRNA, which perform special tasks during protein synthesis, e.g. tRNA (see page 204) and ribosomal RNA (rRNA), which forms part of ribosomes.

The complete set of genes in a cell is known as the cell's **genome** and the full range of proteins that the cell is able to produce is known as its **proteome**.

Non-coding DNA

In eukaryotes, a lot of the nuclear DNA (DNA stored in the nucleus) doesn't code for polypeptides. Some genes don't code for polypeptides at all — they code for functional RNA (see above).

Even genes that do code for polypeptides contain sections that don't code for amino acids. These sections of DNA are called **introns**. There can be several introns within a gene and their purpose isn't known for sure. Introns in eukaryotes are removed during protein synthesis — so they don't affect the amino acid order. Prokaryotic DNA doesn't have introns. All the bits of a gene that do code for amino acids are called **exons**.

Eukaryotic DNA also contains regions of multiple repeats outside of genes. These are DNA sequences that repeat over and over. For example: CCTTCCTTCCTT. These areas don't code for amino acids either, so they're called non-coding multiple repeats.

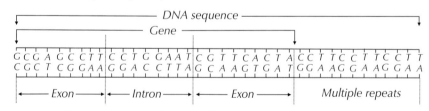

Figure 1: *Diagram showing different types of non-coding DNA.*

Alleles

A gene can exist in more than one form. These forms are called alleles. The order of bases in each allele is slightly different, so they code for slightly different versions of the same polypeptide.

> **Example**
> The gene that codes for blood type exists as one of three alleles —
> one codes for type O, another for type A and the other for type B.

Homologous chromosomes

In a eukaryotic cell nucleus, DNA is stored as chromosomes. Humans have
23 pairs of chromosomes, 46 in total — two number 1s, two number 2s,
two number 3s, etc. Pairs of matching chromosomes (e.g. the 1s) are called
homologous pairs.

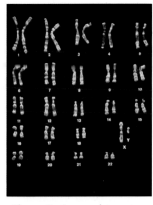

Figure 2: *A complete set of 46 chromosomes from a human male.*

In a homologous pair
both chromosomes are the
same size and have the same
genes, although they could have
different alleles. Alleles coding
for the same characteristic will be
found at the same fixed position
(**locus**) on each chromosome
in a homologous pair. This is
illustrated in Figure 3.

> **Example**
>
>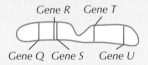
>
> Same size and
> same genes but
> different alleles
>
> Allele for
> type A
>
> Position (locus)
> of gene for
> blood type
>
> Allele for
> type B
>
> **Figure 3:** *Diagram showing a pair of homologous chromosomes.*

Practice Questions — Application

Q1 The diagram on the right shows the
position of five genes on a chromosome.
Draw the homologous chromosome.

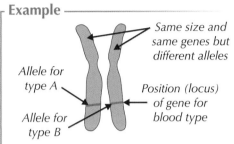

Gene R   Gene T

Gene Q   Gene S   Gene U

Q2 The diagram below shows the sequence of a short stretch of DNA:

Gene
ACTGTAT CGTATCGC TGATCGA TGCTCG ATGTCTA GCGCGCGCGC
| Exon | Intron | Exon | Intron | Exon |

Tip: Don't get confused
between introns and
exons. Just remember
— **IN**trons **IN**terrupt the
exons, which code for
protein.

   a) Write down the base sequence that actually determines the order
of amino acids in the protein.
   b) How many bases long is the region of multiple repeats?
   c) Write down the base sequence that is repeated in the multiple
repeat region.

Practice Questions — Fact Recall

Q1 What is a gene?
Q2 How many DNA bases code for one amino acid?
Q3 What is a cell's genome?
Q4 What is a cell's proteome?
Q5 Name two types of non-coding DNA.
Q6 Name the sections within genes that code for amino acids.
Q7 What is an allele?
Q8 Alleles for the same characteristic can be found at a particular fixed
point on a chromosome. What is the name given to this fixed point?

Tip: There's more on transcription and translation on p. 205-208. There's more on ribosomes on p. 72.

Tip: mRNA is copied from DNA — so its sequence is complementary to the DNA sequence. See page 52 for more.

3. RNA and Protein Synthesis

There are two types of RNA that play a key role in protein synthesis.

What is protein synthesis?

Protein synthesis is the production of proteins (polypeptides) from the information contained within a cell's DNA. It's also known as polypeptide synthesis. It involves two main stages:

- Transcription — where the DNA code is copied into a molecule called mRNA (see pages 205-206).
- Translation — where the mRNA joins with an organelle called a ribosome and the code it carries is used to synthesise a protein (see pages 207-208).

RNA

Remember, RNA is a single polynucleotide strand and it contains uracil (U) as a base instead of thymine (see page 53). Uracil always pairs with adenine during protein synthesis. RNA isn't all the same though — there are different types. You need to know about mRNA and tRNA.

Messenger RNA (mRNA)

mRNA is made during transcription. It carries the genetic code from the DNA to the ribosomes, where it's used to make a protein during translation. mRNA is a single polynucleotide strand. In mRNA, groups of three adjacent bases are usually called **codons** (they're sometimes called triplets or base triplets).

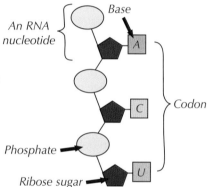

Figure 1: The structure of mRNA.

Transfer RNA (tRNA)

tRNA is involved in translation. It carries the amino acids that are used to make proteins to the ribosomes. tRNA is a single polynucleotide strand that's folded into a clover shape. Hydrogen bonds between specific base pairs hold the molecule in this shape. Every tRNA molecule has a specific sequence of three bases at one end called an anticodon. It also has an amino acid binding site at the other end.

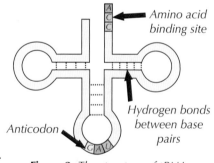

Figure 2: The structure of tRNA.

Practice Questions — Fact Recall

Q1 What role does mRNA play in protein synthesis?

Q2 What is an mRNA codon?

Q3 What does 'mRNA' stand for?

Q4 What does 'tRNA' stand for?

4. Transcription and Translation

Proteins are synthesised (made) using the instructions in DNA.
Protein synthesis involves transcription and translation.

Transcription

During transcription an mRNA copy of a gene is made from DNA.
In eukaryotic cells, transcription takes place in the nucleus. Prokaryotes
don't have a nucleus, so transcription takes place in the cytoplasm.
Here's how transcription happens:

1. RNA polymerase attaches to the DNA

Transcription starts when **RNA polymerase**
(an enzyme) attaches to the DNA
double-helix at the beginning of a gene.

The hydrogen bonds between the two
DNA strands in the gene break,
separating the strands, and the DNA
molecule uncoils at that point, exposing
some of the bases. One of the strands is
then used as a template to make an
mRNA copy — see Figure 1.

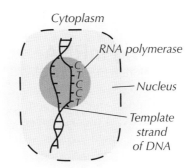

Cytoplasm

RNA polymerase

Nucleus

Template strand of DNA

Figure 1: *RNA polymerase attaches to the DNA double-helix.*

2. Complementary mRNA is formed

The RNA polymerase lines up free RNA
nucleotides alongside the exposed
bases on the template strand. The free
bases are attracted to the exposed bases.
Specific, complementary base pairing
(see p. 52) means that the mRNA strand
ends up being a **complementary copy**
of the DNA template strand (except
the base T is replaced by U in RNA).
Once the RNA nucleotides have paired
up with their specific bases on the
DNA strand, they're joined together by
RNA polymerase, forming an mRNA
molecule — see Figure 2.

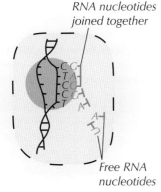

RNA nucleotides joined together

Free RNA nucleotides

Figure 2: *A complementary mRNA molecule starts to form.*

3. RNA polymerase moves down the DNA strand

The RNA polymerase moves
along the DNA, separating the
strands and assembling the
mRNA strand. The hydrogen
bonds between the uncoiled
strands of DNA re-form once
the RNA polymerase has passed
by and the strands coil back into
a double-helix — see Figure 3.

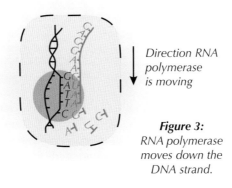

Direction RNA polymerase is moving

Figure 3:
RNA polymerase moves down the DNA strand.

Learning Objectives:

- Know that
  transcription is the
  production of mRNA
  from DNA.

- Recall the role of RNA
  polymerase in joining
  mRNA nucleotides.

- Know that in
  eukaryotes,
  transcription results
  in the production of
  pre-mRNA. This is
  then spliced to form
  mRNA.

- Know that, in
  prokaryotes,
  transcription results
  directly in the
  production of mRNA
  from DNA.

- Know that translation
  is the production of
  polypeptides from the
  sequence of codons
  carried by mRNA.

- Understand the roles
  of ribosomes, tRNA
  and ATP in translation.

  **Specification
  Reference 3.4.2**

Tip: Free RNA
nucleotides aren't
attached to anything
— they're just floating
freely in the nucleus.

Tip: Complementary
RNA nucleotides bind to
each DNA triplet and a
complementary mRNA
strand forms.

DNA
triplet A T C

codon U A G
on mRNA

Tip: mRNA acts as a messenger by carrying genetic information between DNA and the ribosomes — that's how it gets its name.

Tip: Stop signals are particular base triplets, see page 209 for more.

Tip: Remember, introns are the bits of a gene that don't code for anything and exons are the bits that do — see page 202.

Tip: The pre-mRNA strand shown here is complementary to the DNA template strand that it's been transcribed from:

C G C U C ...
G C G A G ...

4. RNA polymerase reaches stop signal

When RNA polymerase reaches a particular sequence of DNA called a **stop signal**, it stops making mRNA and detaches from the DNA.

In eukaryotes, mRNA moves out of the nucleus through a nuclear pore and attaches to a ribosome in the cytoplasm, where the next stage of protein synthesis takes place (see next page).

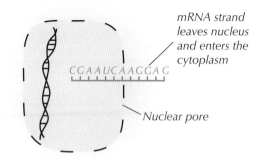

mRNA strand leaves nucleus and enters the cytoplasm

CGAAUCAAGGAG

Nuclear pore

Figure 4: *mRNA leaves the nucleus.*

Editing mRNA

Transcription produces different products in eukaryotes and prokaryotes. In eukaryotes, the introns and exons are both copied into mRNA during transcription. mRNA strands containing introns and exons are called **pre-mRNA**. A process called **splicing** then occurs — introns are removed and the exons joined together — forming mRNA strands (see Figure 5). This takes place in the nucleus. The mRNA then leaves the nucleus for the next stage of protein synthesis (translation).

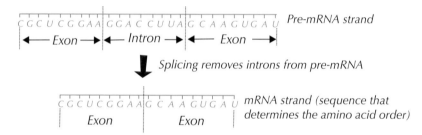

Figure 5: *Pre-mRNA is spliced to produce mRNA.*

In prokaryotes, mRNA is produced directly from the DNA — without splicing taking place. There's no need for splicing because there are no introns in prokaryotic DNA.

Practice Questions — Application

Q1 α–amanitin is a deadly toxin produced by some mushrooms. It works by inhibiting RNA polymerase. What effect will this have on protein synthesis? Explain your answer.

Q2 Part of the DNA sequence of a gene is shown below.

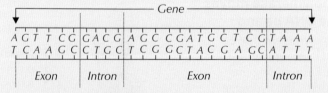

a) A molecule of pre-mRNA is transcribed using the blue strand as a template. Write down the sequence of this pre-mRNA molecule.

b) The pre-mRNA molecule is spliced to produce mRNA. How many amino acids would this mRNA strand code for?

Translation

Translation is the second stage of protein synthesis. In both eukaryotes and prokaryotes, translation occurs at the ribosomes in the cytoplasm. During translation, amino acids are joined together to make a polypeptide chain (protein), following the sequence of codons carried by the mRNA.
Here's how it works:

The mRNA attaches itself to a ribosome and transfer RNA (tRNA) molecules carry amino acids to it. ATP provides the energy needed for the bond between the amino acid and the tRNA molecule to form.

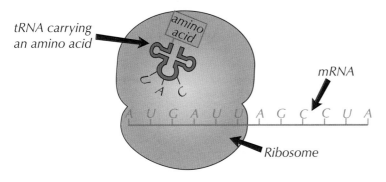

Figure 6: *mRNA (turquoise) attached to a bacterial ribosome.*

A tRNA molecule (carrying an amino acid), with an anticodon that's complementary to the first codon on the mRNA, attaches itself to the mRNA by complementary base pairing. A second tRNA molecule attaches itself to the next codon on the mRNA in the same way.

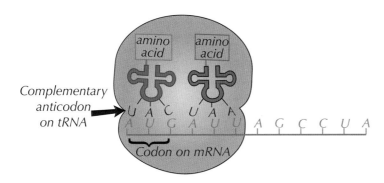

The two amino acids attached to the tRNA molecules are joined by a peptide bond. The first tRNA molecule moves away, leaving its amino acid behind.

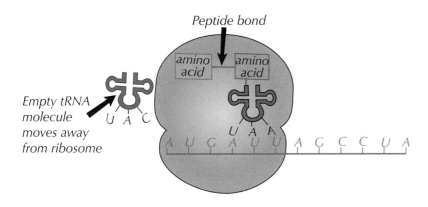

A third tRNA molecule binds to the next codon on the mRNA. Its amino acid binds to the first two and the second tRNA molecule moves away. This process continues, producing a chain of linked amino acids (a polypeptide chain), until there's a stop signal (see next page) on the mRNA molecule.

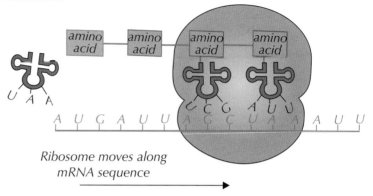

Ribosome moves along mRNA sequence

The polypeptide chain (protein) then moves away from the ribosome and translation is complete.

Practice Questions — Application

Tip: A mutation is any change to the DNA base sequence. See page 221 for more.

Q1 Diamond-Blackfan anaemia is an inherited condition caused by one of several gene mutations. The mutations can affect the function of the proteins that make up ribosomes. What effect could this have on protein synthesis? Explain your answer.

Q2 An error occurs during transcription that accidentally inserts a stop signal into the middle of an mRNA sequence. What effect could this have on the protein that is eventually produced? Explain your answer.

Practice Questions — Fact Recall

Q1 Name the two stages of protein synthesis and state where each one takes place in eukaryotes.

Q2 a) What is RNA polymerase?

b) In which stage of protein synthesis is it involved?

Q3 Why is the mRNA that's produced from a DNA template always a complementary copy of the DNA?

Q4 Explain why eukaryotic mRNA gets spliced.

Q5 Why does prokaryotic mRNA not undergo splicing?

Q6 Describe the function of tRNA.

Q7 What role does ATP play in translation?

Tip: Don't get confused between mRNA and tRNA... Take another look at page 204 if you need a recap.

Q8 Explain how tRNA molecules pair up with mRNA during protein synthesis.

Q9 What type of bond joins two amino acids together?

5. The Genetic Code and Nucleic Acids

Learning Objectives:

- Know that the genetic code is universal, non-overlapping and degenerate.

- Be able to relate the base sequence of nucleic acids to the amino acid sequence of polypeptides, when provided with suitable data about the genetic code.

- Be able to interpret data from experimental work investigating the role of nucleic acids.

Specification Reference 3.4.1 and 3.4.2

The genetic code is pretty important — it encodes the information in genes and these determine what we look like, how we develop and much, much more. Which is probably why the examiners expect you to know all about the genetic code...

What is the genetic code?

The genetic code is the sequence of base triplets (codons) in mRNA which code for specific amino acids. In the genetic code, each base triplet is read in sequence, separate from the triplet before it and after it. Base triplets don't share their bases — the code is **non-overlapping**.

─ **Examples** ─────────────────────────

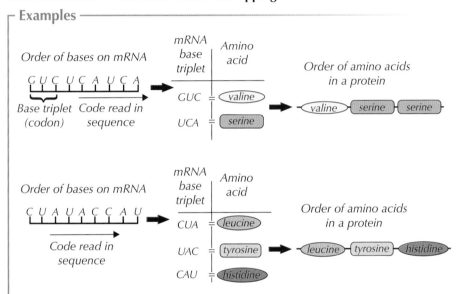

Figure 1: *Examples to explain how the non-overlapping genetic code works.*

The genetic code is also **degenerate** — there are more possible combinations of triplets than there are amino acids (20 amino acids but 64 possible triplets). This means that some amino acids are coded for by more than one base triplet, e.g. tyrosine can be coded for by UAU or UAC. Not all triplets code for amino acids though. For example, some triplets are used to tell the cell when to stop production of a protein — these are called stop signals. They're found at the end of the mRNA. E.g. UAG is a stop signal. (There are also start signals at the start of the mRNA which tell the cell when to start protein production, but these code for a specific amino acid called methionine.)

The genetic code is also **universal** — the same specific base triplets code for the same amino acids in all living things. E.g. UAU codes for tyrosine in all organisms.

Interpreting data on nucleic acids

You might have to interpret information on nucleic acids in the exam. The examples on the next page show you the sorts of data you might get given and the things you might be asked to do.

Tip: The same genetic code is found in all organisms that are found on Earth. This provides indirect evidence for evolution, as it suggests that the code might have been preserved from a common ancestor of all living organisms.

The mRNA codons for some amino acids are given in the table on the right.

mRNA codon	Amino acid
UCU	Serine
CUA	Leucine
UAU	Tyrosine
GUG	Valine
GCA	Alanine
CGC	Arginine

You might be asked to give the DNA sequence for amino acids...

Because mRNA is a complementary copy of the DNA template, the DNA sequence for each amino acid is made up of bases that would pair with the mRNA sequence. The DNA sequence is shown in the table below.

mRNA codon	Amino acid	DNA sequence
UCU	Serine	AGA
CUA	Leucine	GAT
UAU	Tyrosine	ATA
GUG	Valine	CAC
GCA	Alanine	CGT
CGC	Arginine	GCG

Tip: When interpreting data on nucleic acids remember that DNA contains T and RNA contains U.

Tip: You could also be asked to work out the amino acids from a given DNA sequence and a table.

...or to give the tRNA anticodons from mRNA codons...

tRNA anticodons are complementary copies of mRNA codons, so you can work out the tRNA anticodon from the mRNA codon:

mRNA codon	tRNA anticodon
UCU	AGA
CUA	GAU
UAU	AUA
GUG	CAC
GCA	CGU
CGC	GCG

Tip: You might be asked to name the amino acid coded for by a tRNA anticodon using a table like the one at the top of the page.

...or to write the amino acid sequence for a section of mRNA

To work out the sequence of amino acids from some mRNA, you need to break the genetic code into codons and then use the information in the table to work out what amino acid they code for.

<u>mRNA:</u> CUAGUGCGCUAUUCU

<u>Codons:</u> CUA   GUG   CGC   UAU   UCU

<u>Amino acids:</u> Leucine   Valine   Arginine   Tyrosine   Serine

Tip: You might have to work out the sequence of some mRNA from a sequence of amino acids and a table.

Practice Questions — Application

The table on the right shows some mRNA codons and the amino acids they code for.

Q1 Using the table, give the mRNA codons for the following amino acid sequence:

Tyr - Phe - Gln - Ile - Ala - His

Q2 Give the DNA base sequence that would code for the following amino acid sequence:

Met - Phe - Gln - Gln - Ala - Tyr - Ile

mRNA codon	Amino Acid
UUU	Phe
UAC	Tyr
CAA	Gln
GCG	Ala
AUG	Met
CAU	His
AUA	Ile

Q3 Give the tRNA anticodons for the following mRNA codons:

AUGCAUAUACAUUUCAA

Q4 Write down the amino acid sequence that would be produced from the following tRNA anticodons:

AAAGUUUAUGUACGCAUG

Q5 The DNA base sequence below codes for the amino acid sequence beneath it. Neither is complete. Fill in the blanks, using the information in the table to help you.

DNA: GTA - __ - __ - AAA - ATG - __ - GTA

Amino acid: His - Ala - Ile - Phe - ____ - Gln - __

Tip: The amino acids given in the table are abbreviations — e.g. 'Phe' is short for Phenylalanine.

Tip: To answer Q2, don't jump straight into working out the DNA base sequence. You've got to find the complementary mRNA codon from the table first.

Tip: It's easy to make a mistake if you misread one of the letters in the table, so double-check your answers to make sure you've got it right.

Interpreting experimental data on nucleic acids

In the exam you might have to interpret data from experiments done to investigate nucleic acids and their role in protein synthesis.

Example

To investigate how two new drugs affect nucleic acids and their role in protein synthesis, bacteria were grown in normal conditions for a few generations, then moved to media containing the drugs. After a short period of time, the concentration of protein and complete strands of mRNA in the bacteria were analysed. The results are shown in Figure 2.

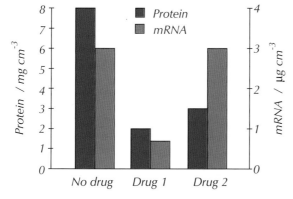

Figure 2: Bar chart to show mRNA and protein concentration in the presence and absence of drugs.

Exam Tip
You don't need to learn this example — it's just here to show you the sort of thing you might get in the exam.

Figure 2 on the previous page shows that both mRNA and protein concentration were lower in the presence of drug 1 compared to the no-drug control. This suggests that drug 1 affects the production of full length mRNA, so there's no mRNA for protein synthesis during translation.

mRNA production in the presence of drug 2 was unaffected, but less protein was produced — 3 mg cm^{-3} compared to 8 mg cm^{-3}. This suggests that drug 2 interferes with translation. mRNA was produced, but less protein was translated from it.

Further tests to establish the nature of the two drugs were carried out. Drug 1 was found to be a ribonuclease (an enzyme that digests RNA). This could explain the results of the first experiment — most strands of mRNA produced by the cell would be digested by drug 1, so couldn't be used in translation to make proteins.

Drug 2 was found to be a single-stranded, clover-shaped molecule capable of binding to the ribosome. Again, this helps to explain the results from the first experiment — drug 2 could work by binding to the ribosome, blocking tRNAs from binding to it and so preventing translation.

Practice Questions — Application

A chemical called puromycin is believed to affect the development of rapid respiration in a freshly cut potato slice, by either affecting the synthesis of proteins or nucleic acids. In an experiment, potato slices were kept in various concentrations of puromycin for 24 hours. Nucleic acid synthesis was monitored by radioactively tagging uracil and then measuring its uptake. Protein synthesis was monitored by radioactively tagging leucine and then measuring its uptake. Afterwards the percentage inhibition of the development of respiration, leucine uptake and uracil uptake were calculated. The results are shown in the table below.

Puromycin concentration (mol/l)	% inhibition of the development of respiration	% inhibition of leucine uptake	% inhibition of uracil uptake
Control	-	-	-
0.6×10^{-4}	33	32	19
1.0×10^{-4}	49	55	31
2.0×10^{-4}	76	73	55
4.0×10^{-4}	97	93	79

Q1 Suggest why uracil was the only base that was radioactively tagged.

Q2 Describe the results shown in the table for the four different concentrations of puromycin used.

Q3 Do the results show that puromycin has a greater effect on nucleic acid synthesis or protein synthesis?

Practice Questions — Fact Recall

Q1 The genetic code is described as 'non-overlapping'. What does this mean?

Q2 What is meant by the term 'start signal' in mRNA?

Q3 The same base triplets code for the same amino acids in all living things. What word is used to describe this feature of the genetic code?

Section Summary

Make sure you know...

- How DNA is stored as chromosomes in eukaryotes and prokaryotes. In eukaryotes, long, linear DNA molecules are wound around proteins called histones and then coil up to form compact chromosomes, which are stored in the nucleus. In prokaryotes, DNA molecules are shorter and circular. They condense by supercoiling and aren't associated with histone proteins.

- That the DNA in mitochondria and chloroplasts in eukaryotic cells is similar to prokaryotic DNA in its structure.

- That genes are base sequences of DNA that code for a polypeptide or a functional RNA.

- That a sequence of three DNA bases, known as a triplet (or codon), codes for one amino acid in a polypeptide.

- That a cell's genome is the complete set of genes in the cell and a cell's proteome is the full range of proteins that the cell is able to produce.

- That much of the nuclear DNA in eukaryotic cells doesn't code for polypeptides. Even within genes that code for polypeptides, only the exons code for amino acids. Two types of non-coding DNA in eukaryotes are introns (within genes) and multiple repeats (between genes).

- That alleles are different versions of the same gene and that alleles coding for the same characteristic are found at the same position (locus) on each chromosome in a homologous pair.

- That mRNA (messenger RNA) is made of a single polynucleotide strand and tRNA (transfer RNA) is made of a single polynucleotide strand folded into a clover shape.

- That transcription is the first stage of protein synthesis and involves the production of an mRNA copy of a gene from DNA.

- That during transcription, DNA strands separate and the enzyme RNA polymerase lines up free RNA nucleotides and joins them together to form an mRNA strand.

- That transcription in prokaryotes results in the direct production of mRNA from DNA. In eukaryotes, transcription produces pre-mRNA.

- That pre-mRNA contains introns. These non-coding introns are removed by splicing to form mRNA — this leaves only exons present in the mRNA.

- That translation is the second stage of protein synthesis in which amino acids are joined together by ribosomes to make a polypeptide strand (protein) based on the order of codons in mRNA.

- That tRNA molecules carry amino acids to the ribosomes during translation.

- That ATP is needed to provide the energy for the bond formation between the amino acid and the tRNA molecule to form, allowing the tRNA to carry the amino acid during translation.

- That the genetic code is universal (the same base pairs code for the same amino acids in all living things), non-overlapping (codons do not share triplets) and degenerate (there are more possible combinations of triplets than there are amino acids).

- How to relate the base sequence of nucleic acids to the amino acid sequence of the polypeptides that they code for.

- How to interpret experimental data relating to the role of nucleic acids (e.g. data from the investigation of transcription and/or translation).

Exam-style Questions

1 A species of bacteria has a gene that codes for the production of a blue-coloured antibiotic.

1.1 Describe the role of RNA polymerase in the transcription of a gene sequence.

(2 marks)

1.2 The mRNA for the gene coding for the antibiotic is the same length as its DNA. Explain how and why this might be different for a eukaryotic gene.

(3 marks)

2 Researchers have been studying the genetic code of a gene with the aim of developing a treatment for a particular genetic disease.

2.1 What is the genetic code?

(1 mark)

2.2 The genetic code is described as universal and degenerate. Explain what these terms mean.

(2 marks)

The genetic disease is caused by the production of a specific enzyme. Part of the enzyme's amino acid sequence is shown below.

Glycine — Histidine — Alanine — Proline — Histidine

Table 1 shows the DNA sequence for some amino acids.

Table 1

Amino acid	DNA sequence
Valine	CAG
Proline	GGA
Glutamine	GTT
Histidine	GTG
Glycine	CCT
Serine	TCG
Alanine	CGT

2.3 Use **Table 1** to give the tRNA anticodons for the amino acid sequence shown above.

(2 marks)

2.4 Describe how the structure of tRNA differs from mRNA.

(3 marks)

The researchers are exploring a possible treatment for the genetic disease that would involve disrupting the process of translation.

2.5 Name the organelle that mRNA attaches to for translation to take place.

(1 mark)

2.6 Give a detailed description of tRNA's role in translation.

(4 marks)

1. Meiosis and Genetic Variation

Most cells in the body contain exactly the same genetic information. The one major exception to this rule is the gametes — the cells involved in sexual reproduction.

Diploid body cells

Normal body cells have the **diploid number** (**2n**) of chromosomes — meaning each cell contains two of each chromosome (a pair), one from the mum and one from the dad.

The chromosomes that make up each pair are the same size and have the same genes, although they could have different versions of those genes (called alleles). These pairs of matching chromosomes are called **homologous pairs** — see page 203. Humans have 23 homologous pairs and so 46 chromosomes in total. Therefore the diploid number for humans is 46.

Gametes and sexual reproduction

Gametes are the sperm cells in males and egg cells in females. Gametes have a **haploid (n) number** of chromosomes — they only contain one copy of each chromosome in a homologous pair. The haploid number for humans is 23.

In sexual reproduction two gametes join together at fertilisation to form a zygote, which divides and develops into a new organism.

Fertilisation

At fertilisation, a haploid sperm fuses with a haploid egg, making a cell with the normal diploid number of chromosomes (see Figure 1). Half these chromosomes are from the father (the sperm) and half are from the mother (the egg).

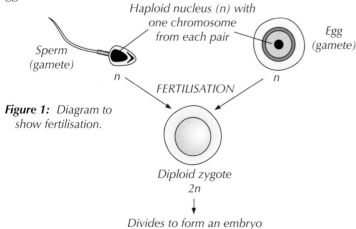

Haploid nucleus (n) with one chromosome from each pair

Sperm (gamete)

Egg (gamete)

n

n

FERTILISATION

Figure 1: *Diagram to show fertilisation.*

Diploid zygote 2n

↓

Divides to form an embryo

During sexual reproduction, any sperm can fertilise any egg — fertilisation is random. Random fertilisation produces zygotes with different combinations of chromosomes to both parents. This mixing of genetic material in sexual reproduction increases genetic diversity within a species (there's more on genetic diversity on page 224).

Learning Objectives:

- Be able to explain how the random fertilisation of haploid gametes increases genetic variation within a species.

- Know that meiosis produces daughter cells that are genetically different from each other.

- Know that in meiosis, two nuclear divisions usually result in the formation of four haploid daughter cells from a single diploid parent cell.

- Know that genetically different daughter cells result from independent segregation in meiosis.

- Know that crossing over results in further genetic variation among daughter cells.

- Be able to complete diagrams showing the chromosome content of cells after the first and second meiotic divisions, when given the chromosome content of the parent cell.

- Be able to recognise where meiosis occurs when given information about an unfamiliar life cycle.

- Be able to explain the different outcomes of mitosis and meiosis.

Specification Reference 3.4.3

Meiosis

Meiosis is a type of cell division. It takes place in the reproductive organs of multicellular, eukaryotic organisms. Cells that divide by meiosis are diploid to start with, but the cells that are formed from meiosis are haploid — the chromosome number halves. Meiosis in humans and other mammals produces gametes directly. In other organisms (e.g. some insects and plants) it produces haploid cells which later divide by mitosis to become gametes. Without meiosis, you'd get double the number of chromosomes when the gametes fused. Not good. The process of meiosis is summarised in Figure 4.

Tip: All the different chromosome-related terms can get a bit confusing — this diagram might help:

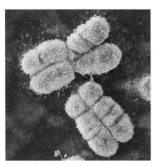

Double-armed chromosome

Centromere

One chromatid *Sister chromatids*

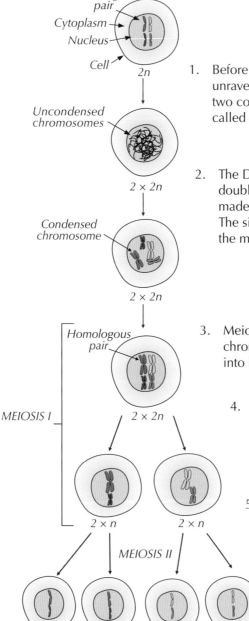

1. Before meiosis starts, the DNA unravels and replicates so there are two copies of each chromosome, called **chromatids**.

2. The DNA condenses to form double-armed chromosomes, each made from two sister chromatids. The sister chromatids are joined in the middle by a **centromere**.

3. Meiosis I (first division) — the chromosomes arrange themselves into homologous pairs.

4. These homologous pairs are then separated, halving the chromosome number.

5. Meiosis II (second division) — the pairs of sister chromatids that make up each chromosome are separated (the centromere is divided).

6. Four haploid cells that are genetically different from each other are produced.

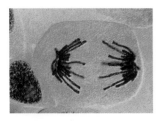

Figure 2: *Condensed double-armed chromosomes.*

Tip: Remember, in the first division, the homologous pairs separate. In the second division, the chromatids separate.

Figure 3: *Chromatids separating during meiosis II.*

Figure 4: *Diagram showing the different stages of meiosis in a diploid cell with four chromosomes.*

Creating genetic variation in gametes

There are two main events during meiosis that lead to genetic variation:

1. Crossing over of chromatids

During meiosis I, homologous chromosomes come together and pair up. The chromatids twist around each other and bits of chromatids swap over. The chromatids still contain the same genes but now have a different combination of alleles — see Figure 5.

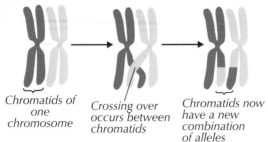

Chromatids of one chromosome

Crossing over occurs between chromatids

Chromatids now have a new combination of alleles

Figure 5: *Crossing over.*

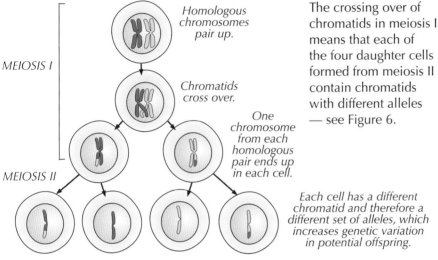

Homologous chromosomes pair up.

Chromatids cross over.

One chromosome from each homologous pair ends up in each cell.

MEIOSIS I

MEIOSIS II

Each cell has a different chromatid and therefore a different set of alleles, which increases genetic variation in potential offspring.

The crossing over of chromatids in meiosis I means that each of the four daughter cells formed from meiosis II contain chromatids with different alleles — see Figure 6.

Figure 6: *Crossing over in meiosis.*

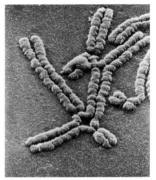

Figure 7: *Electron micrograph showing crossing over occurring in cells.*

> **Tip:** Crossing over is also known as recombination.

2. Independent segregation of chromosomes

Each homologous pair of chromosomes in your cells is made up of one chromosome from your mum (maternal) and one chromosome from your dad (paternal). When the homologous pairs are separated in meiosis I, it's completely random which chromosome from each pair ends up in which daughter cell. So the four daughter cells produced by meiosis have completely different combinations of those maternal and paternal chromosomes (see Figure 8). This is called independent segregation (separation) of the chromosomes. This 'shuffling' of chromosomes leads to genetic variation in any potential offspring.

> **Tip:** In any diploid species there are 2^n possible combinations of maternal and paternal chromosomes (where n is the number of homologous pairs). This means that in humans (which have 23 homologous pairs) there are 2^{23} or 8 388 608 possible combinations of chromosomes.

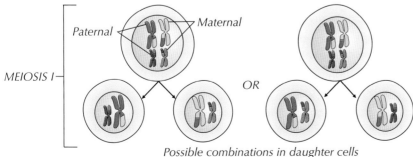

Paternal   Maternal

MEIOSIS I

OR

Possible combinations in daughter cells

Figure 8: *Independent segregation of chromosomes.*

Life cycles

In the exams, you might need to spot when meiosis happens in an organism with a life cycle you haven't seen before, e.g. an insect or plant. Just remember that in any organism, meiosis is needed for sexual reproduction because it produces daughter cells (usually gametes) with half the number of chromosomes of the parent cell.

Tip: The malaria parasite is a single-celled eukaryotic organism called a protist. Prokaryotes don't divide by meiosis or reproduce sexually.

Tip: Compare the number of chromosomes in the parent and daughter cells — if they <u>halve</u>, the cell must have undergone meiosis.

Tip: Different species have different numbers of chromosomes, so '2n' and 'n' represent different numbers in different species. E.g. in mosquitoes 2n = 14. In humans 2n = 46.

Tip: Zygotes in humans divide by mitosis, not by meiosis. Don't let this put you off. The important thing here is what's happening to the chromosome number.

Tip: Meiosis doesn't produce gametes directly in the mosquito life cycle. It still produces haploid cells though.

--- Example ---

The stages in the life cycle of the malaria parasite are shown in Figure 9.

When and where does meiosis take place in the parasite's life cycle?

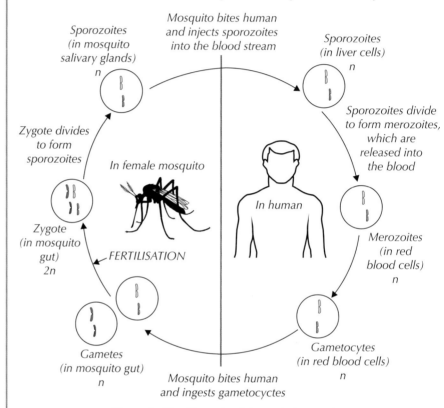

Figure 9: The life cycle of the malaria parasite.

- Only the zygote of the malarial parasite is diploid (2n). All the other stages of its life cycle are haploid (n).

- The chromosome number only halves when the diploid zygote divides in the mosquito's gut to form haploid sporozoites. In all the other divisions in the parasite's life cycle, the chromosome number stays the same — a haploid cell forms another haploid cell, e.g. haploid sporozoites divide (by mitosis) to form haploid merozoites.

- So only the zygote divides by meiosis and it only happens in the mosquito's gut.

- Fertilisation of the gametes (sexual reproduction) also takes place in the mosquito's gut.

You might also be told how many chromosomes are in a parent cell, then asked to complete diagrams showing how many chromosomes will be in the daughter cells after the first and second divisions of meiosis. Remember that the chromosome number is halved during the first division.

Outcomes of mitosis and meiosis

You may remember mitosis from pages 84-85. It's part of the cell cycle — the process multicellular organisms use to grow and divide. Mitosis and meiosis have different outcomes. These are shown in Figure 10.

	Outcomes:		
Mitosis	Produces cells with the same number of chromosomes as the parent cell.	Daughter cells are genetically identical to each other and to the parent cell.	Produces two daughter cells.
Meiosis	Produces cells with half the number of chromosomes as the parent cell.	Daughter cells are genetically different from one another and the parent cell.	Produces four daughter cells.

Figure 10: *Table comparing outcomes in mitosis and meiosis.*

You need to be able to explain the different outcomes of mitosis and meiosis. They're different because mitosis only involves one division (which separates the sister chromatids) whereas meiosis has two divisions (which separate the homologous pairs and then the sister chromatids). There's no pairing or separating of homologous chromosomes in mitosis, and so no crossing over or independent segregation of chromosomes. This produces genetically identical daughter cells — unlike meiosis.

Practice Questions — Application

Q1 The diagram below shows two homologous chromosomes. The red cross marks a point at which crossing over can occur. Draw the chromosomes as they would be if crossing over occurred at this point.

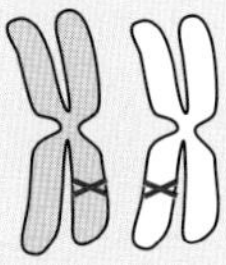

Q2 The diagram below shows a cell that contains three pairs of homologous chromosomes. Draw a viable gamete that could be produced by this cell after meiosis.

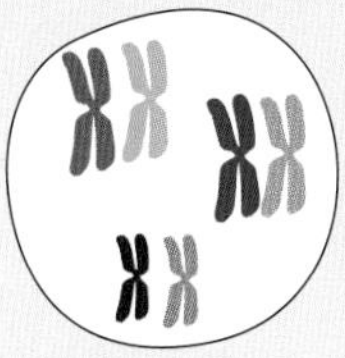

Q3 For each of the following cells state what stage the cell is at in meiosis. Choose from: before meiosis I, between meiosis I and II, or after meiosis II. Give a reason for each answer.

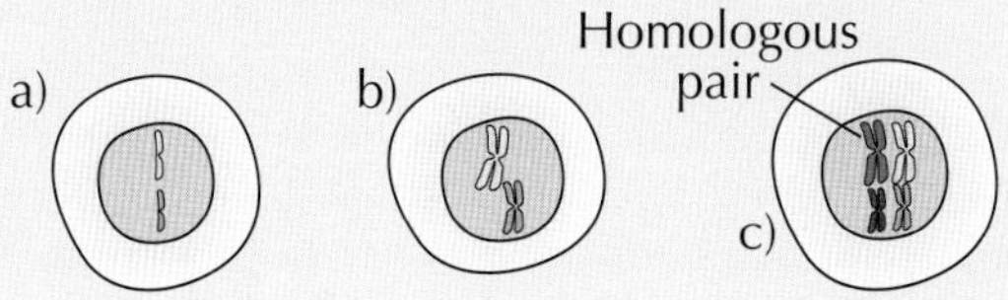

a) b) Homologous pair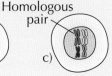
c)

Exam Tip
Make sure you know what the chromosomes look like in each stage of meiosis.

Exam Tip
Examiners just love
a good graph — so
make sure you practise
interpreting them.

Q4 The graph below shows the average DNA content of a group of cells that are undergoing meiosis:

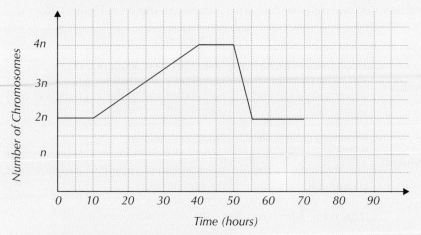

a) Describe what is happening:
   i) between 10 hours and 40 hours.
   ii) between 40 hours and 50 hours.
   iii) between 50 and 55 hours.

b) Sketch a line on the graph to show what is likely to happen to the DNA content of the cell between 70 and 95 hours.

Practice Questions — Fact Recall

Q1 Are the following haploid or diploid:
   a) normal body cells?   b) gametes?   c) zygotes?

Q2 Outline what happens in: a) meiosis I.   b) meiosis II.

Q3 a) What are the two main events in meiosis that lead to genetic variation?
   b) Describe how each of these processes works.

Q4 Give three differences in the outcomes of mitosis and meiosis.

2. Mutations

Sometimes things don't quite go as they're supposed to in cell replication — gene mutations and mutations in the number of chromosomes can occur.

Gene mutations

Gene mutations involve a change in the DNA base sequence of chromosomes. The types of errors that can occur include:

- Substitution — one base is substituted with another, e.g. ATGCCT becomes ATTCCT (G is swapped for T).

- Deletion — one base is deleted, e.g. ATGCCT becomes ATCCT (G is removed).

The order of DNA bases in a gene determines the order of amino acids in a particular protein (see p. 202). If a mutation occurs in a gene, the sequence of amino acids it codes for (and the protein formed) could be altered:

Example

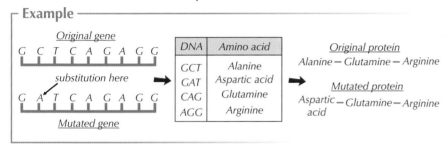

Effects of mutations

The degenerate nature of the genetic code (see page 209) means that some amino acids are coded for by more than one DNA triplet (e.g. tyrosine can be coded for by TAT or TAC in DNA). This means that not all substitution mutations will result in a change to the amino acid sequence of the protein — some substitutions will still code for the same amino acid.

Example

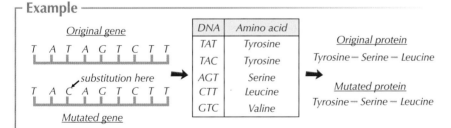

Substitution mutations won't always lead to changes in the amino acid sequence, but deletions will — the deletion of a base will change the number of bases present, which will cause a shift in all the base triplets after it.

Example

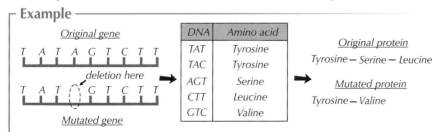

Learning Objectives:

- Know that gene mutations involve a change in the base sequence of chromosomes.

- Know that gene mutations can arise spontaneously during DNA replication and include base deletion and base substitution.

- Understand that due to the degenerate nature of the genetic code, not all base substitutions cause a change in the sequence of encoded amino acids.

- Know that mutagenic agents can increase the rate of gene mutation.

- Know that mutations in the number of chromosomes can arise spontaneously by chromomere non-disjunction during meiosis.

Specification Reference 3.4.3

Tip: Remember, three DNA bases (a triplet) code for one amino acid.

Tip: Errors can also be caused by insertion, duplication, addition and translocation of bases. You'll learn more about these if you go on to take Year 2 of A-level Biology.

Mutagenic agents

Tip: X-rays and gamma rays are examples of ionising radiation.

Mutations occur spontaneously, e.g. when DNA is misread during replication. But some things can cause an increase in the rate of mutations — these are called mutagenic agents. Ultraviolet radiation, ionising radiation, some chemicals and some viruses are examples of mutagenic agents. Mutagenic agents increase the probability of a mutation occurring.

Example — Maths Skills

The **chance** of something happening is the possibility that it will occur. **Probability** is a measure of how likely events are to happen. In maths, the probability of any event happening has to be between 0 (the event is impossible) and 1 (the event is certain).

There is always a chance of gene mutations occurring. However, under normal circumstances, the probability of a mutation occurring at any particular point is very low. This probability is increased by exposure to mutagenic agents, such as ultraviolet radiation. You can't predict where exactly in the DNA the mutation will occur, but the likelihood of a mutation occurring somewhere is increased when an organism is exposed to UV radiation.

Tip: Mutations are always random — only the rate of mutation is affected by mutagenic agents.

Chromosome mutations

In humans, when meiosis works properly, all four daughter cells will end up with 23 whole chromosomes — one from each homologous pair (1 to 23). But sometimes meiosis goes wrong and the cells produced contain variations in the numbers of whole chromosomes or parts of chromosomes. E.g. two cells might have 23 whole chromosomes, one each of 1 to 23, but the other two might get a bit muddled up, one having two chromosome 6's and the other no chromosome 6. This is called chromosome mutation and is caused by errors during meiosis. Chromosome mutations lead to inherited conditions because the errors are present in the gametes (the hereditary cells). One type of chromosome mutation is called **chromosome non-disjunction** — it's a failure of the chromosomes to separate properly.

Tip: Non-disjunction leading to Down's syndrome can occur in meiosis I, as shown in Figure 2, or in meiosis II.

Example

Down's syndrome is caused by a person having an extra copy of chromosome 21 (or sometimes an extra copy of part of chromosome 21). Non-disjunction means that chromosome 21 fails to separate properly during meiosis, so one cell gets an extra copy of 21 and another gets none. When the gamete with the extra copy fuses to another gamete at fertilisation, the resulting zygote will have three copies of chromosome 21 (see Figure 2).

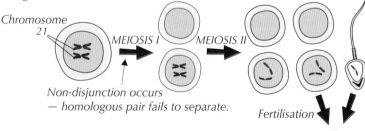

Figure 2: Chromosome non-disjunction in meiosis I leading to Down's syndrome.

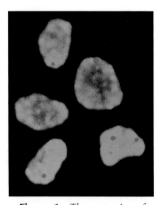

Figure 1: Three copies of chromosome 21 (pink) are seen in each of the cell nuclei (blue) of a fetus.

Practice Questions — Application

Q1 The diagram on the right shows part of a
gene sequence that has been mutated.

a) Describe the mutation that has
occurred.

b) Using the table on the right, give the
amino acid sequences of the original
and mutated genes.

c) The diagram below shows the
mutation of a different gene sequence.
Explain why the mutation results in
the same amino acid sequence.

Original gene
CTTGAGTAC

Mutated gene
CTTAGTAC

DNA	Amino acid
TAT	Tyrosine
TAC	Tyrosine
GAA	Glutamic acid
GAG	Glutamic acid
AGT	Serine
CTT	Leucine
TTT	Phenylalanine

Tip: You'll need to use
the table in Q1 to help
you answer part c) too.

Original gene   *Mutated gene*
TATAGTGAG   TACAGTGAG

Q2 Edwards' syndrome is caused by a person having an extra copy
of chromosome 18.

a) Name the event that occurs during meiosis, which causes a
person to have an extra copy of a chromosome.

b) Explain how this event could lead to a person having an
extra copy of chromosome 18.

c) Complete the diagram below showing what would happen
if the event took place during meiosis II and explain what
briefly what it shows.

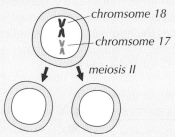

chromsome 18

chromsome 17

meiosis II

Practice Questions — Fact Recall

Q1 What are gene mutations?

Q2 Which type of gene mutations will always lead to a change in the
amino acid sequence?

Q3 a) What effect do mutagenic agents have on mutations?

b) Give an example of a mutagenic agent.

Learning Objectives:

- Know that genetic diversity is the number of different alleles of genes in a population.

- Understand that genetic diversity is a factor enabling natural selection to occur.

Specification Reference 3.4.4

3. Genetic Diversity

Meiosis generates genetic diversity, but it isn't the only thing that affects it.

What is genetic diversity?

Remember, there can be different versions of a single gene — these are called alleles (see page 202). Alleles code for different versions of characteristics, e.g. blonde hair or brown hair. **Genetic diversity** is the number of different alleles of genes in a species or population. A large number of different alleles in a population means a large variety of different characteristics (e.g. blonde, brown, red or black hair) and a high genetic diversity.

Genetic diversity is important — if a population has low genetic diversity, it might not be able to adapt to a change in the environment and the whole population could be wiped out by a single event (e.g. a disease). Genetic diversity within a population is increased by:

- Mutations in the DNA forming new alleles. Some of these can be advantageous, whilst others lead to problems (see page 87).

- Different alleles being introduced into a population when individuals from another population migrate into it and reproduce. This is known as gene flow.

Genetic diversity is what allows natural selection to occur (see page 226) because some characteristics are more advantageous than others.

Tip: All members of a species have the same genes. Diversity only occurs in the form of different alleles of those genes.

Genetic bottlenecks

A genetic bottleneck is an event that causes a big reduction in a population, e.g. when a large number of organisms within a population die before reproducing. This reduces the number of different alleles in the **gene pool** and so reduces genetic diversity. The survivors reproduce and a larger population is created from a few individuals — see Figure 1.

Tip: The gene pool is the complete range of alleles in a population.

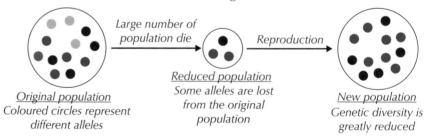

Original population
Coloured circles represent different alleles

Reduced population
Some alleles are lost from the original population

New population
Genetic diversity is greatly reduced

Figure 1: *Diagram illustrating the effect of genetic bottlenecks.*

--- Example ---

Northern elephant seals were hunted by humans in the late 1800s. Their original population was reduced to around 50 seals who have since produced a population of around 170 000. This new population has very little genetic diversity compared to the southern elephant seals, which have not suffered such a reduction in numbers.

The founder effect

The founder effect describes what happens when just a few organisms from a population start a new colony and there are only a small number of different alleles in the initial gene pool (see Figure 3 on the next page).

Figure 2: *Northern elephant seals in California.*

The frequency of each allele in the new colony might be very different to the frequency of those alleles in the original population — for example, an allele that was rare in the original population might be more common in the new colony. This may lead to a higher incidence of genetic disease.

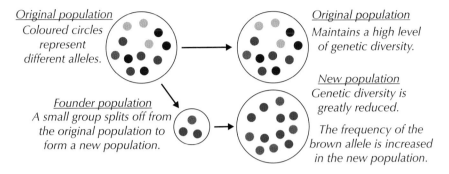

Figure 3: *Diagram illustrating the founder effect.*

Tip: The brown allele in Figure 3 could represent a genetic disorder. It's easy to see why the founder effect can lead to an unusually high incidence of a certain genetic disorder, if the allele for it is present in the founding population.

The founder effect can occur as a result of migration leading to geographical separation or if a new colony is separated from the original population for another reason, such as religion.

Example

The Amish population of North America are all descended from a small number of Swiss who migrated there. The population shows little genetic diversity. They have remained isolated from the surrounding population due to their religious beliefs, so few new alleles have been introduced. The population has an unusually high incidence of certain genetic disorders.

Practice Question — Application

Q1 Flowers of a plant species can be purple, pink or white. Each colour is coded for by a different allele. The graphs below show the frequencies of these alleles in two populations of the plant species.

a) Based on this information alone, which population is more genetically diverse? Explain your answer.

b) Explain how a genetic bottleneck could have led to the allele frequencies shown in Population 2.

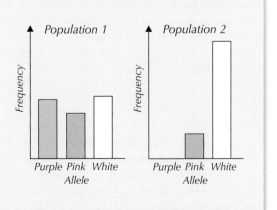

Practice Questions — Fact Recall

Q1 What is genetic diversity?

Q2 Give two ways in which genetic diversity within a population can be increased.

- Understand the principles of natural selection in the evolution of populations.

- Know that random mutation can result in new alleles of a gene.

- Know that many mutations are harmful but, in certain environments, the new allele might benefit its possessor, leading to increased reproductive success.

- Understand that the advantageous allele is inherited by members of the next generation and that over many generations, the new allele increases in frequency in the population.

- Be able to use unfamiliar information to explain how selection produces changes within a population of a species.

- Know that natural selection results in species that are better adapted to their environment and that adaptations may be anatomical, physiological or behavioural.

- Understand that adaption and selection are major factors in evolution and contribute to the diversity of living organisms.

Specification Reference 3.4.4

4. Natural Selection

Variation gives some organisms an advantage over others. Natural selection increases the proportion of the advantageous alleles within a population.

The process of natural selection

Randomly-occurring mutations sometimes result in a new allele being formed. This can be harmful, which usually means that the mutated allele quickly dies out. However, some mutations can produce alleles that are beneficial to an organism (e.g. a protein is produced that works better than the original), helping the organism to survive in certain environments.

When the allele codes for a characteristic that increases the chances of an organism surviving, its frequency within the population can increase. This process is known as **natural selection**. Here's how it works:

1. Not all individuals are as likely to reproduce as each other. In other words, there's **differential reproductive success** in a population — individuals that have an allele that increases their chance of survival are more likely to survive, reproduce and pass on their genes (including the beneficial allele), than individuals with less advantageous alleles.

2. This means that a greater proportion of the next generation inherits the beneficial allele.

3. They, in turn, are more likely to survive, reproduce and pass on their genes.

4. So the frequency of the beneficial allele in the population increases from generation to generation.

5. Over generations this leads to **evolution** as the advantageous alleles become more common in the population.

Evolution is the gradual change in species over time. It has led to the huge diversity of living organisms on Earth. Adaptation and selection are both key factors in evolution.

> **Example**
>
> In 1810 a herd of caribou were taken from the Arctic to an area with a warmer climate. In 1810 the average fur length was 3.5 cm. In 1960 it was 2.1 cm. This change can be explained by natural selection:
>
>
>
> **Figure 1:** *Grazing caribou.*
>
> - There is variation in fur length in the population of caribou — mutations in the fur length gene mean some caribou have an allele for shorter fur and some have an allele for longer fur.
>
> - Caribou with shorter fur will be better adapted to the warmer climate as they'll be less likely to overheat. These caribou will be more likely to survive, reproduce and pass on their genes (including the allele for shorter fur) than caribou with the allele for longer fur.
>
> - This means that a greater proportion of the next generation will inherit the allele for shorter fur, so the frequency of this allele will increase from generation to generation.
>
> - Over many generations this leads to evolution, as the advantageous allele for short fur becomes more common in the population.

Types of adaptations

Natural selection leads to organisms becoming better adapted to their environment. **Adaptations** are features that help organisms to survive in their environment. They can be behavioural, physiological or anatomical.

Tip: Organisms that are well adapted to their environment have a <u>selective advantage</u> over less-well adapted organisms.

1. Behavioural adaptations

These are ways an organism acts that increase its chance of survival.

--- Examples ---
- Possums sometimes 'play dead' — if they're being threatened by a predator they play dead to escape attack. This increases their chance of survival.
- Scorpions dance before mating — this makes sure they attract a mate of the same species, increasing the likelihood of successful mating.

Figure 2: When American possums feel threatened, they 'play dead' to escape attack.

2. Physiological adaptations

These are processes inside an organism's body that increase its chance of survival.

--- Examples ---
- Brown bears hibernate — they lower their rate of metabolism (all the chemical reactions taking place in their body) over winter. This conserves energy, so they don't need to look for food in the months when it's scarce — increasing their chance of survival.
- Some bacteria produce antibiotics — these kill other species of bacteria in the area. This means there's less competition, so they're more likely to survive.

Figure 3: An otter's streamlined body helps it to move easily through water.

3. Anatomical (structural) adaptations

These are structural features of an organism's body that increase its chance of survival.

--- Examples ---
- Otters have a streamlined shape — making it easier to glide through the water. This makes it easier for them to catch prey and escape predators, increasing their chance of survival.
- Whales have a thick layer of blubber (fat) — this helps to keep them warm in the cold sea. This increases their chance of survival in places where their food is found.

Practice Questions — Application

Q1 There are many different species of rat snake, all found in different habitats and with slightly different colourings. The black rat snake lives in wooded habitats and has a dark, brown-black colouring (see Figure 4).

Describe how natural selection could explain the evolution of a rat snake with black colouring in a wooded habitat.

Figure 4: A black rat snake climbing up a tree.

Q2 DDT is a chemical insecticide that was first used to kill malaria-carrying mosquitos around the time of WWII. In the 1950s, DDT-resistant mosquitos began to appear in areas of widespread DDT use.

Describe how DDT-resistance became widespread in some mosquito populations.

Q3 Killer whales are commonly found in the cold seas around the Arctic and Antarctic. Like all whales, they are mammals. They can't breathe underwater, so have to hold their breath while they dive. They live and hunt in groups called pods, eating a varied diet of fish, seals, sea lions and other whales. Killer whales dive to catch their prey and can reduce their heart rate by up to half whilst diving. A thick layer of blubber (fat) under the whales' skin gives them a smooth, rounded shape.

Using the information given above:

a) Name one behavioural, one physiological and one anatomical adaptation of the killer whale to its environment.

b) For each adaptation, explain how it helps the killer whale to survive.

Practice Questions — Fact Recall

Q1 Describe the role of random mutations in natural selection.

Q2 Describe how natural selection increases the frequency of advantageous alleles in a population.

Q3 What is an adaptation?

Q4 Explain what is meant by the term 'physiological adaptations'.

5. The Effects of Selection

Natural selection affects different populations in different ways, leading to different allele frequencies...

Types of selection

Natural selection alters allele frequency in a population — see page 226. Directional selection and stabilising selection are types of natural selection that affect allele frequency in different ways.

1. Directional selection

Directional selection is where individuals with alleles for characteristics of an extreme type are more likely to survive and reproduce. This could be in response to an environmental change.

┌─ **Example — Bacteria evolving antibiotic resistance** ────────

Some individuals in a bacterial population have alleles that give them resistance to an antibiotic. The population is exposed to the antibiotic, killing bacteria without the resistance allele.

The resistant bacteria survive and reproduce without competition, passing on the allele that gives antibiotic resistance to their offspring. After some time, most organisms in the population will carry the antibiotic resistance allele — see Figure 1.

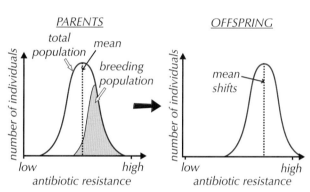

Figure 1: *Graphs to show directional selection in bacteria.*

2. Stabilising selection

Stabilising selection is where individuals with alleles for characteristics towards the middle of the range are more likely to survive and reproduce. It occurs when the environment isn't changing, and it reduces the range of possible characteristics.

┌─ **Example — Human birth weight** ────────

Humans have a range of birth weights. Very small babies are less likely to survive — they have a high surface area to volume ratio, which means they find it hard to maintain their body temperature. This puts pressure on their respiratory and cardiac systems, which can be fatal.

Very large babies are less likely to survive too. Giving birth to large babies can be difficult because their large size makes it harder for them to fit through the mother's pelvis. This can lead to complications for both mother and child.

Conditions are most favourable for medium-sized babies — so the weight of human babies tends to shift towards the middle of the range — see Figure 2 on the next page.

Learning Objectives:

- Understand the process of directional selection, exemplified by antibiotic resistance in bacteria.
- Understand the process of stabilising selection, exemplified by human birth weights.
- Be able to interpret data relating to the effects of selection in producing change within populations.

Specification Reference 3.4.4

Tip: Bacteria can also evolve resistance to other chemicals that are designed to kill them, e.g. antiseptics.

Exam Tip
Make sure you learn both of the examples on this page for the exams.

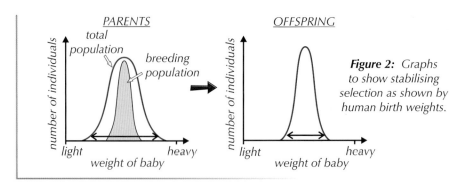

Figure 2: Graphs to show stabilising selection as shown by human birth weights.

Interpreting data on the effects of selection

You might be asked to interpret data on selection in the exam.

─ **Example** ─

A population of rabbits has varying fur length. Longer fur helps to keep the rabbits warmer. The graph below shows how the average fur length of the rabbits changed over a period of six years, which had particularly cold winters. The bars span the difference between the shortest and longest fur lengths recorded.

Describe what the data shows:
Over the first two years the average fur length is about 21 mm. However, the average length gradually increases from 21 mm to 24 mm. This shows directional selection.

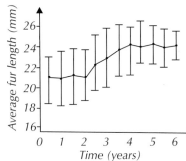

Suggest a possible cause:
The rabbits with the longer fur are more likely to survive the cold winters than the short-furred rabbits. This makes them more likely to reproduce and, when they do, they pass on the allele for longer fur to the next generation. Over time, the allele for longer fur becomes more common in the population and the average fur length of the rabbits increases.

Practice Question — Application

Q1 The graph on the right shows how the average mass in an isolated population of wolves changed over a period of 8 years. The vertical bars span the difference between the lightest and heaviest wolves. The wolves lived in a snowy habitat.

a) Is this an example of directional or stabilising selection? Give a reason for your answer.

b) Suggest why these changes occurred in the population of wolves.

Practice Questions — Fact Recall

Q1 What is directional selection?

Q2 Bacteria evolving antibiotic resistance is an example of directional selection. Explain why.

6. Investigating Selection

You can carry out practical investigations into the effects of antimicrobial substances (substances that kill microorganisms, e.g. antibiotics, antiseptics or disinfectants) on microbes. These investigations should show you whether the microbes have evolved resistance to these substances or not.

Learning Objective:

- Be able to use aseptic techniques to investigate the effect of antimicrobial substances on microbial growth (Required Practical 6).
  Specification Reference 3.4.4

Testing the effects of antibiotics

REQUIRED PRACTICAL 6

Antibiotics are medicines that are designed to kill bacteria. This makes them a type of **antimicrobial substance**. You can investigate the effects of different antibiotics on bacterial growth using the following method. The whole investigation must be carried out using **aseptic techniques**. These are explained on the next page. Read them through before you begin.

1. The bacteria you will use are likely to have been grown in a liquid broth (a mixture of distilled water, bacterial culture and nutrients).

2. Take a wire inoculation loop that's been sterilised in a Bunsen burner flame (see next page) and use it to transfer the bacteria from the broth to an agar plate — this is a Petri dish containing agar jelly. Spread the bacteria over the plate using the loop.

3. Place sterile paper discs soaked with different antibiotics spaced apart on the plate. Various concentrations of antibiotics should be used. You also need to add a negative control disc soaked only in sterile water.

4. Tape a lid onto the Petri dish (without completely sealing it), invert, and incubate the plate at about 25°C for 48 hours. This allows the bacteria to grow, forming a 'lawn'. Anywhere the bacteria can't grow can be seen as a clear patch in the lawn of bacteria. This is called an **inhibition zone**.

5. The size of an inhibition zone tells you how well an antibiotic works. The larger the zone, the more the bacteria were inhibited from growing.

> **Tip:** Make sure you carry out a full risk assessment before you carry out this practical. It's also really important that you understand how to use aseptic techniques properly before you start.

> **Tip:** A negative control is not expected to have any effect on the experiment — see page 2 for more.

> **Tip:** Don't completely seal the Petri dish with tape before incubation — it will prevent oxygen from entering the dish, which may encourage the growth of anaerobic disease-causing bacteria. Don't open the dish after incubation.

--- Example ---

Figure 1 shows an agar plate after it has been incubated with paper discs soaked in the antibiotics meticillin, tetracycline and streptomycin.

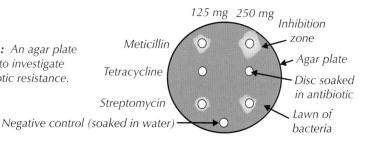

Figure 1: *An agar plate used to investigate antibiotic resistance.*

125 mg 250 mg
Meticillin
Tetracycline
Streptomycin
Negative control (soaked in water)
Inhibition zone
Agar plate
Disc soaked in antibiotic
Lawn of bacteria

- The tetracycline discs have no inhibition zones, so the bacteria are resistant to tetracycline up to 250 mg.

- The streptomycin discs have small inhibition zones, with the zone at 250 mg slightly larger than the one at 125 mg. So streptomycin inhibits the growth of some of the bacteria.

- The meticillin discs have the largest inhibition zones, so meticillin inhibits the growth of most of the bacteria.

- The negative control has no inhibition zone, which shows that the other results must be due to the presence of the antibiotics, not the paper disc.

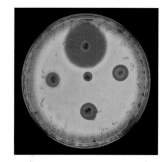

Figure 2: *A bacterial culture plate with clear inhibition zones where an antibiotic has stopped the bacteria from growing.*

A similar method can be used to test the effects of antiseptics or disinfectants on microbial growth — just replace the paper discs soaked in antibiotics with discs soaked in antiseptics or disinfectants.

Aseptic techniques

Aseptic techniques are used to prevent contamination of cultures by unwanted microorganisms. This is important because contamination can affect the growth of the microorganism that you're working with. It's also important to avoid contamination with disease-causing microbes that could make you ill. When carrying out the investigation on the previous page or any other investigation involving microorganisms, you need to use the following aseptic techniques:

- Disinfect work surfaces before you start work to minimise contamination. Disinfect them again once you've finished.

- Work near a Bunsen flame. Hot air rises, so any microbes in the air should be drawn away from your culture.

- Sterilise the wire inoculation loop before and after each use by passing it through a hot Bunsen burner flame for 5 seconds. This will kill any microbes on the loop.

- Briefly flame the neck of the glass container of broth just after it's opened and just before it's closed — this causes air to move out of the container, preventing unwanted organisms from falling in.

- Sterilise all glassware before and after use, e.g. in an autoclave (a machine which steams equipment at high pressure).

Figure 3: *An inoculation loop being sterilised in a Bunsen burner flame.*

Practice Question — Application

Q1 Turbidity is a measure of the cloudiness of a liquid. The more bacteria in a liquid, the cloudier it will be. A scientist grew some bacteria in a liquid broth. She then measured the turbidity of samples of the bacteria over time to see how an antibiotic affected growth. The results are shown below. The antibiotic (diluted in sterile water) was added at 4 hours.

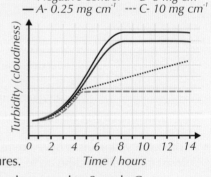

a) Suggest what the negative control might be and explain why it's used.

b) Describe two aseptic techniques that the scientist would need to carry out in the preparation of the broth.

c) Explain the importance of aseptic techniques when working with microbial cultures.

d) Describe and explain what has happened to Sample C.

Practice Questions — Fact Recall

Q1 Give three examples of antimicrobial substances.

Q2 What substances would be present in a bacterial broth?

Q3 a) What is an inhibition zone?

    b) What does an inhibition zone tell you?

Q4 Describe how to sterilise a wire inoculation loop before and after use.

Section Summary

Make sure you know:

- That haploid gametes fuse at fertilisation to produce a diploid cell called a zygote.
- How the random fertilisation of gametes during sexual reproduction increases genetic diversity.
- That the process of meiosis involves two divisions — meiosis I (in which the homologous pairs separate) and meiosis II (in which the sister chromatids separate).
- That meiosis results in the formation of four haploid daughter cells from a single diploid parent cell and that the daughter cells are all genetically different from each other.
- How crossing over between homologous chromosomes in meiosis I leads to genetic variation among daughter cells.
- How independent segregation of homologous chromosomes in meiosis I results in the formation of genetically different daughter cells.
- How to recognise where meiosis occurs when given information about an unfamiliar life cycle.
- How to complete diagrams showing the chromosomal content of cells after meiosis I and meiosis II, when given the chromosome content of the parent cell.
- Why mitosis and meiosis have different outcomes.
- That gene mutations involve a change in the DNA base sequence of chromosomes.
- That gene mutations may involve base deletion or base substitution and that these can affect the sequence of amino acids coded for and therefore the protein that is produced.
- Why the degenerate nature of the genetic code means that not all substitutions result in a change in amino acid sequence in the protein, though deletions will.
- That gene mutations arise spontaneously during DNA replication.
- That the rate of mutation can be increased by mutagenic agents, such as ultraviolet radiation.
- That chromosome non-disjunction during meiosis can cause mutations in the number of chromosomes in a cell.
- That genetic diversity is the number of different alleles of genes in a species or population.
- That alleles introduced from other populations or by mutations can increase genetic diversity and that genetic bottlenecks and the founder effect can reduce genetic diversity.
- That random mutations can result in new alleles of a gene, which could be harmful or beneficial.
- That in the process of natural selection, individuals possessing an advantageous allele are more likely to survive, reproduce and pass on their genes to the next generation and that this process leads to an increase in frequency of the advantageous allele in a population over many generations.
- Why adaptation and selection are major factors in evolution and contribute to the diversity of living organisms.
- That natural selection results in species that are better adapted to their environment and that these adaptations may be anatomical, physiological or behavioural.
- How directional selection in bacteria results in a shift in the mean towards antibiotic resistance.
- How stabilising selection causes human birth weights to shift towards the middle of the range.
- How to interpret data relating to the effect of selection in producing change within populations.
- How to use aseptic techniques to investigate the effect of antimicrobial substances on microbial growth (Required Practical 6) — e.g. testing the effects of antibiotics on bacterial growth.

Exam-style Questions

1   **Figure 1** shows the life cycle of a moss species.

Figure 1

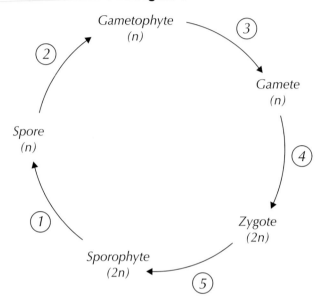

1.1   At which point(s) in **Figure 1** is meiosis occurring?
       Give a reason for your answer.

(2 marks)

1.2   What is happening at point **4** of **Figure 1**? Give a reason for your answer.

(2 marks)

       Genetic diversity in one population of this moss species is very low.

1.3   Suggest **one** reason why genetic diversity in this population may be low.

(1 mark)

1.4   Give **two** ways that genetic diversity could be increased
       in a population of this moss species.

(2 marks)

2   **Figure 2** shows two chromosomes during meiosis I.

2.1   Name the event taking place in **Figure 2**.

(1 mark)

Figure 2

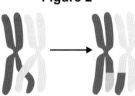

2.2   The event shown in **Figure 2** increases genetic
       variation in potential offspring. Name another event
       that takes place during meiosis that has the same effect
       and explain how this event increases genetic variation.

(3 marks)

3　　Mitosis and meiosis are both types of cell division.
Explain the different outcomes of mitosis and meiosis.

(6 marks)

4　　Species of *Streptomyces* bacteria are naturally found in soil, along with many other types of bacteria. They produce a wide range of clinically useful antibiotics including tetracycline-based antibiotics.

4.1　Use your knowledge of evolution by natural selection to explain how tetracycline-producing *Streptomyces* species may have become common in the population.

(4 marks)

4.2　Species of *Streptomyces* also possess tet-resistance genes that protect them from the effects of tetracycline. For example, the *tetA* genes are responsible for pumping tetracycline out of cells, thereby protecting cells from its harmful effects.

State whether tet-resistance is an example of directional or stabilising selection. Give a reason for your answer.

(1 mark)

Tet-resistance is now found in a number of other species of bacteria. Scientists investigated the link between the use of antibiotics in cattle feed and the tetracycline resistance of *E. coli* samples isolated from the cattle. The samples were grown on agar plates and then tested for resistance to tetracycline.

The results are shown in **Figure 3**.

Figure 3

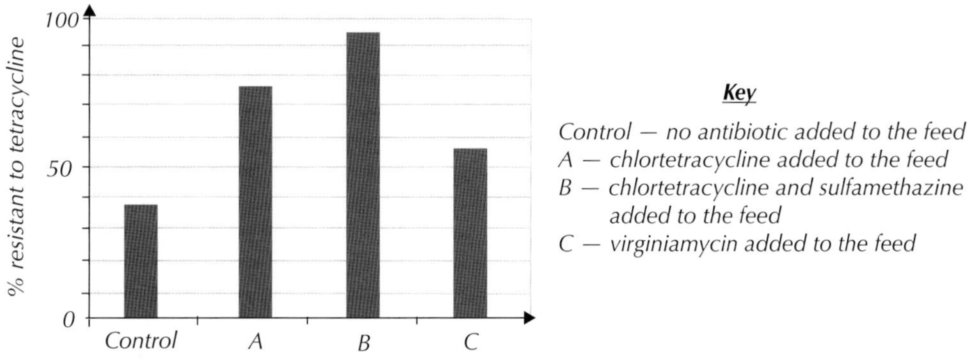

Key

Control — no antibiotic added to the feed
A — chlortetracycline added to the feed
B — chlortetracycline and sulfamethazine
　　added to the feed
C — virginiamycin added to the feed

4.3　Suggest **two** factors the scientists should have considered when selecting cattle for the experiment.

(2 marks)

4.4　Explain why the bacteria in the control sample were taken from cattle that had no antibiotics added to their feed.

(1 mark)

4.5　What conclusions can be drawn from the results of the study?

(3 marks)

Learning Objectives:

- Know that a phylogenetic classification system attempts to arrange species into groups based on their evolutionary origins and relationships. It uses a hierarchy in which smaller groups are placed within larger groups, with no overlap between groups. Each group is called a taxon (plural taxa).

- Know that one hierarchy comprises the taxa: domain, kingdom, phylum, class, order, family, genus and species.

- Know that two organisms belong to the same species if they are able to produce fertile offspring.

- Know that each species is universally identified by a binomial consisting of the name of its genus and species, e.g. *Homo sapiens*.

Specification Reference 3.4.5

1. Classification of Organisms

Scientists group related organisms together to make them easier to study. This is classification.

Phylogeny

Phylogeny is the study of the evolutionary history of groups of organisms. Phylogeny tells us who's related to whom and how closely related they are.

All organisms have evolved from shared common ancestors (relatives). This can be shown on a **phylogenetic tree** like the one in Figure 1.

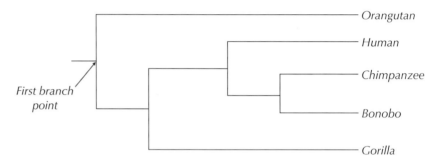

First branch point

— Orangutan
— Human
— Chimpanzee
— Bonobo
— Gorilla

Figure 1: *Phylogenetic tree of the Hominidae family.*

This tree shows the relationship between members of the Hominidae family (great apes and humans). The first branch point represents a common ancestor of all the family members. This ancestor is now extinct. Orangutans were the first group to diverge (evolve to become a different species) from this common ancestor.

Each of the following branch points represents another common ancestor from which a different group diverged. Gorillas diverged next, then humans, closely followed by bonobos and chimpanzees.

Closely related species diverged away from each other most recently. E.g. humans and chimpanzees are closely related, as they diverged very recently. You can see this because their branches are close together.

Taxonomy

Taxonomy is the science of classification. It involves naming organisms and organising them into groups. This makes it easier to identify and study them. Scientists now take into account phylogeny when classifying organisms, and group organisms according to their evolutionary relationships.

There are eight levels of groups used to classify organisms. These groups are called **taxa**. Each group is called a taxon. The groups are arranged in a **hierarchy**, with the largest groups at the top and the smallest groups at the bottom. Organisms can only belong to one group at each level in the hierarchy — there's no overlap.

Figure 2: *Chimps and gorillas are closely related.*

Organisms are first sorted into three large groups (or taxa) called domains — the Eukarya, Bacteria and Archaea. Related organisms in a domain are then sorted into slightly smaller groups called kingdoms, e.g. all animals are in the animal kingdom. More closely related organisms from that kingdom are then grouped into a phylum, then grouped into a class, and so on down the eight levels of the hierarchy. This is illustrated in Figure 3.

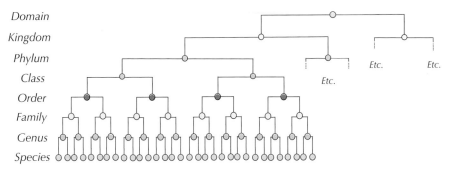

Domain
Kingdom
Phylum
Class
Order
Family
Genus
Species

Etc. *Etc.*
Etc.
Etc.

Figure 3: *A diagram illustrating the taxonomic groups used in classification.*

Example — the classification of humans

Domain = *Eukarya*, Kingdom = *Animalia*, Phylum = *Chordata*,
Class = *Mammalia*, Order = *Primates*, Family = *Hominidae*,
Genus = *Homo*, Species = *sapiens*.

As you move down the hierarchy, there are more groups at each level but fewer organisms in each group. The organisms in each group also become more closely related. The hierarchy ends with **species** — the groups that contain only one type of organism (e.g. humans). A species is a group of similar organisms able to reproduce to give fertile offspring.

Example

If a female horse breeds with a male horse of the same species their offspring will be fertile. But if a female horse breeds with a male donkey their offspring (known as a mule) will be infertile. Because horses and donkeys can't reproduce to give fertile offspring, they're classified as separate species.

Scientists constantly update classification systems because of discoveries about new species and new evidence about known organisms (e.g. DNA sequence data — see page 241).

The binomial system

The nomenclature (naming system) used for classification is called the binomial system — all organisms are given one internationally accepted scientific name in Latin that has two parts.

The first part of the name is the genus name and has a capital letter. The second part is the species name and begins with a lower case letter. Names are always written in italics (or they're underlined if they're handwritten).

Examples

Humans are *Homo sapiens* — The genus is *Homo* and the species is *sapiens*.
Dogs are *Canis familiaris* — The genus is *Canis* and the species is *familiaris*.
Cats are *Felis catus* — The genus is *Felis* and the species is *catus*.

Exam Tip
You need to learn the names and order of the groups (taxa). If you're struggling to remember the order, try this mnemonic...

<u>D</u>emanding <u>K</u>ids <u>P</u>refer <u>C</u>hips <u>O</u>ver <u>F</u>loppy <u>G</u>reen <u>S</u>pinach.

Tip: You need to learn the definition of a species.

Tip: You'll often see the genus shortened to just the first letter. E.g. *E. coli* is short for *Escherichia coli* — *Escherichia* is the genus and *coli* is the species.

Exam Tip
The plural of genus is genera. You'll see this sometimes in exams.

Tip: Some species have the same genus name and species name, e.g. *Bison bison* (which is commonly known as a... erm, bison). Imaginative.

Giving organisms a scientific name enables scientists to communicate about organisms in a standard way, which helps to avoid the confusion of using common names.

Example

Americans call a type of bird cockatoos and Australians call them flaming galahs, but it's the same bird. If the correct scientific name is used — *Eolophus roseicapillus* — there's no confusion.

Practice Questions — Application

Q1 The diagram below shows a simplified phylogenetic tree for the phylum Chordata:

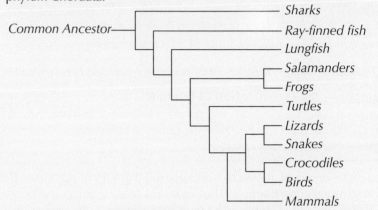

Tip: It might surprise you that some organisms are closely related — but just because you can't see a similarity in their features doesn't mean the phylogenetic tree is wrong.

a) Which group was first to diverge from the common ancestor?

b) Are frogs more closely related to salamanders or turtles?

c) To which other group are:

   (i) birds most closely related?

   (ii) snakes most closely related?

Q2 Donkeys are part of the phylum Chordata.
The binomial name for a donkey is *Equus asinus*.

Complete the table below for the classification of the donkey.

Taxon	
	Eukarya
Kingdom	Animalia
Class	Mammalia
Order	Perrisodactyla
Family	Equidae

Practice Questions — Fact Recall

Q1 How does a phylogenetic classification system attempt to arrange organisms into groups?

Q2 What is the naming system used in biological classification called?

2. Classification Using Courtship Behaviour

Learning Objectives:
- Know that courtship behaviour is a necessary precursor to successful mating.
- Understand the role of courtship in species recognition.

Specification Reference 3.4.5

Similar species don't only look similar — they also behave in a similar way. This means that behaviour can also be used to help classify species. Courtship behaviour can be particularly useful when classifying species.

What is courtship behaviour?

Courtship behaviour is carried out by organisms to attract a mate of the right species. It can be fairly simple or quite complex.

┌─ Examples ──────────────────────────────

Simple Courtship behaviours:

- Releasing a chemical — e.g. male bumble bees produce chemicals called pheromones to attract female bumble bees to their territory.

- Using sound — e.g. male red deer make a roaring noise to attract a mate.

- Visual displays — e.g. the great tit will attract a mate by puffing out its chest to show off its black stripe.

Complex Courtship behaviours:

- Dancing — e.g. blue-footed boobies perform a complex dance which involves lifting up their feet to show off the blue colour (see Figure 1).

- Building — e.g. bowerbirds construct bowers (shelters) made of leaves, twigs, flowers, shells, stones and whatever else the male can find (see Figure 2).

Figure 1: The dance of the blue-footed booby.

Courtship behaviours can be performed by either the male or the female or may sometimes involve both sexes.

Using courtship behaviour to classify species

Courtship behaviour is species specific — only members of the same species will do and respond to that courtship behaviour. This allows members of the same species to recognise each other, preventing interbreeding and making reproduction more successful (as mating with the wrong species won't produce fertile offspring).

Figure 2: A male bowerbird constructing a bower.

┌─ Examples ──────────────────────────────

- Fireflies give off pulses of light. The pattern of flashes is specific to each species.

- Crickets make sounds that are similar to Morse code, the code being different for different species.

- Male peacocks show off their colourful tails. This tail pattern is only found in peacocks (see Figure 3).

- Male butterflies use chemicals to attract females. Only those of the correct species respond.

Because of this specificity, courtship behaviour can be used to classify organisms. The more closely related species are, the more similar their courtship behaviour.

Figure 3: A male peacock displaying his tail feathers.

Practice Questions — Application

Male fireflies give off pulses of light to attract females. To investigate this, 10 fireflies were caught and the pattern of light pulses that they used was observed. The table below shows the results:

Firefly	Pattern of pulses produced
1	xx-xx-xx-xx
2	xxx-x-xxx-x-xxx
3	x-xx-xxx-x-xx-xxx
4	xxx-xxx-xxx
5	x-x-x-x-x-x
6	xx-xx-xx-xx
7	x-xx-x-xx-x-xx
8	xx-xx-xx-xx
9	xxx-xxx-xxx
10	x-xx-xxx-x-xx-xxx

Key:
x = flash of light
- = no light

Q1 What do the patterns of light pulses they produce suggest about fireflies 4 and 9?

Q2 How many different species of firefly were caught in total?

Q3 Are fireflies 1 and 3 likely to be closely related or distantly related? Explain your answer.

Q4 Firefly 2 was later found to belong to a family of fireflies that all start their display with three pulses of light. Are any of the other fireflies likely to belong to the same family?

Practice Questions — Fact Recall

Q1 What is courtship behaviour?

Q2 Why can courtship behaviour be used to classify species?

3. Classification Using DNA or Proteins

Classifying organisms according to their evolutionary relationships (see page 236) isn't easy, but advances in DNA and molecular technology are helping us to classify organisms more accurately.

Clarifying evolutionary relationships

New or improved technologies can result in new discoveries being made and the relationships between organisms being clarified. This can lead to classification systems being updated. Technologies that have been useful for clarifying evolutionary relationships include:

Genome sequencing

Advances in genome sequencing have meant that the entire base sequence of an organism's DNA can be determined. The DNA base sequence of one organism can then be compared to the DNA base sequence of another organism, to see how closely related they are. Closely related species will have a higher percentage of similarity in their DNA base sequence, e.g. humans and chimps share around 94%, humans and mice share about 86%.

--- Example ---

Genome sequencing has clarified the relationship between skunks and members of the Mustelidae family (e.g. weasels and badgers). Skunks were classified in the Mustelidae family until their DNA sequence was revealed to be significantly different to other members of that family. So they were reclassified into the family Mephitidae.

Comparing amino acid sequence

Proteins are made of amino acids. The sequence of amino acids in a protein is coded for by the base sequence in DNA (see p. 202). Related organisms have similar DNA sequences and so similar amino acid sequences in their proteins.

--- Example ---

Cytochrome C is a short protein found in many species. The more similar the amino acid sequence of cytochrome C in two different species, the more closely related the species are likely to be.

Immunological comparisons

Similar proteins will also bind the same antibodies.

--- Example ---

If antibodies to a human version of a protein are added to isolated samples from some other species, any protein that's like the human version will also be recognised (bound) by that antibody.

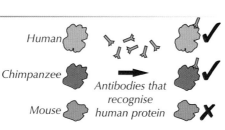

Human

Chimpanzee

Mouse

Antibodies that recognise human protein

Learning Objectives:

- Appreciate that advances in genome sequencing and immunology help to clarify evolutionary relationships between organisms.

- Be able to interpret data relating to similarities and differences in the base sequences of DNA and in the amino acid sequences of proteins to suggest relationships between different organisms within a species and between species.

Specification Reference 3.4.5 and 3.4.7

Tip: See page 202 for more on the DNA base sequence.

Tip: See page 117 for more on antibodies binding to proteins.

Tip: Proteins that bind antibodies will often form a precipitate (solid mass) in solution. The more antibodies the protein binds, the more precipitate will form — so the amount of precipitate can be used to determine how similar two proteins are.

Interpreting data

You might be given data on DNA and protein similarities to interpret in your exam. Don't panic. Just look at what's in front of you and think logically.

Here are a few examples of the type of thing you might get:

Example 1

The table below shows the % similarity of DNA using DNA sequence analysis between several species of bacteria.

Species A and B have a higher percentage of DNA in common with each other than they do with either species C or D. This means that A and B are more closely related to each other than they are to either C or D.

	Species A	Species B	Species C	Species D
Species A	100%	86%	42%	44%
Species B	86%	100%	51%	53%
Species C	42%	51%	100%	49%
Species D	44%	53%	49%	100%

Example 2

Tip: You can also compare DNA base sequences to determine relationships between organisms of the <u>same species</u>. Again, the more similarities there are, the more closely related the two organisms are likely to be.

The diagram below shows the DNA sequence for gene X in three different species.

Species A: ATTGTCTGATTGGTGCTAGTCGTCGATGCTAGGATCG

Species B: ATTGT<u>A</u>TGATTGGTGCTAGTCG<u>G</u>CGATGCTAGGATCG

Species C: ATTG<u>A</u><u>TT</u>GA<u>AA</u>GG<u>A</u>GCTA<u>C</u>TCGT<u>A</u>GAT<u>ATA</u>AGGA<u>GGT</u>

There are 13 differences between the base sequences in species A and C, but only 2 differences between the base sequences in species A and B. This suggests that species A and B are more closely related than A and C.

Example 3

Tip: 'Val', 'Ser', 'Phe' and 'Glu' are short for the names of the amino acids.

The diagram below shows the amino acid sequences of a certain protein from three different species.

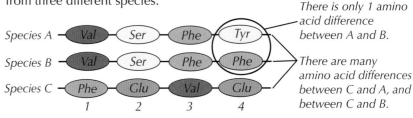

There is only 1 amino acid difference between A and B.

There are many amino acid differences between C and A, and between C and B.

You can see that the amino acid sequences from species A and B are very similar. The sequence from species C is very different to any of the other sequences. This suggests that species A and B are more closely related.

Practice Questions — Application

Q1 The amino acid sequence of the insulin protein was determined for humans, horses and chickens. When this was done, it was found that horse insulin was more similar to human insulin than chicken insulin. What do these results suggest?

Q2 The graph below illustrates the sequence of a small stretch of DNA in 3 different species:

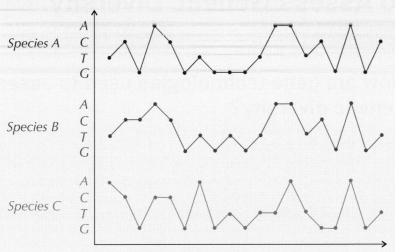

Tip: The distance along the gene sequence on the diagram is given as 'bp' — base pairs.

Distance along gene sequence (bp)

a) Using the graph, write down the base sequence for this stretch of DNA in each of the three species.

b) In how many places do the base sequences of species A and B differ?

c) In how many places do the base sequences of species A and C differ?

d) Is species A more closely related to species B or species C? Explain your answer.

e) To which of the two species is species C most closely related? Explain your answer.

Q3 Antibodies against a protein from species X were fluorescently labelled and mixed with cells from three other species. Any unbound antibody was then washed away and the level of remaining fluorescence was recorded.

Species	Relative fluorescence after washing
A	0.2
B	10.5
C	2.1

Tip: Antibodies are often linked to a fluorescent protein (e.g. GFP). This allows the antibodies to be detected once they have bound to a protein.

Use the results table above to determine which species is most closely related to species X. Explain your choice.

■ Know that estimates
of genetic diversity
within, or between
species, can be made
by comparing:

  ■ the frequency
  of measurable
  or observable
  characteristics

  ■ the base sequence
  of DNA

  ■ the base sequence
  of mRNA

  ■ the amino acid
  sequence of the
  proteins encoded by
  DNA and mRNA.

■ Be able to appreciate
that gene technology
has caused a change
in the methods of
investigating genetic
diversity — inferring
DNA differences
from measurable
or observable
characteristics has
been replaced by
direct investigation of
DNA sequences.

**Specification
Reference 3.4.7**

Tip: DNA is copied into
mRNA in order to make
a protein — see pages
205-206.

4. Using Gene Technologies to Assess Genetic Diversity

*Gene technologies haven't just helped in the clarification of evolutionary
relationships, they've also changed how genetic diversity is assessed.*

How are gene technologies used to assess genetic diversity?

You might remember from page 224, that genetic diversity is the number of
different alleles in a population.

Early estimates of genetic diversity were made by looking at the
frequency of measurable or observable characteristics in a population, e.g.
the number of different eye colours in a population and the number of
people with each particular eye colour. Since different alleles determine
different characteristics (see page 224) a wide variety of each characteristic
in a population indicates a high number of different alleles — and so a high
genetic diversity. However gene technologies have now been developed that
allow us to measure genetic diversity directly:

┌─ **Examples** ──────────────────────────────

■ Different alleles of the same gene will have slightly different DNA
base sequences. Comparing the DNA base sequences of the same
gene in different organisms in a population allows scientists to find
out how many alleles of that gene there are in that population.

■ Different alleles will also produce slightly different mRNA base
sequences, and may produce proteins with slightly different amino
acid sequences, so these can also be compared.

These new technologies can be used to give more accurate estimates of
genetic diversity within a population (or species) than can be made just by
looking at the frequency of observable characteristics. They also allow the
genetic diversity of different species to be compared more easily.

Practice Question — Application

Q1 The colour and pattern of the shells of the snail species *Cepaea
nemoralis* is controlled by several genes, each of which has several
alleles. A scientist interested in the species thinks that there may
be more genetic diversity in the genes controlling shell colour
and pattern in populations of snails from warmer climates, than in
populations of snails from colder climates.

a) Describe and explain how comparing the DNA sequences
of individuals from different populations could be used to test
this theory.

b) Before gene technologies like this became available,
how was genetic diversity estimated?

Practice Question — Fact Recall

Q1 What are the advantages of using gene technologies rather than
traditional methods to assess genetic diversity in a population?

5. Investigating Variation

Sometimes it's helpful to know whether variations in a population are primarily due to genetics or the environment. The next few pages are all about how variation is studied and how data on variation is analysed.

Causes of variation

Variation is the differences that exists between individuals. There's variation between species and within species.

Variation can be caused by genetic factors. Different species have different genes, which causes variation between species. Individuals of the same species have the same genes, but different alleles (versions of genes) — this causes variation within a species.

Variation within a species can also be caused by differences in the environment, e.g. climate, food, lifestyle.

Most variation within a species is caused by a combination of genetic and environmental factors. E.g. genes determine how tall an organism can grow, but nutrient availability affects how tall the organism actually grows.

Population samples

When studying variation within a species, you usually only look at a sample of the population, not the whole thing. For most species it would be too time-consuming or impossible to catch all the individuals in the group. So samples are used as models for the whole population.

Random sampling

Because sample data will be used to draw conclusions about the whole population, it's important that it accurately represents the whole population and that any patterns observed are tested to make sure they're not due to chance.

To make sure the sample isn't **biased**, it should be random. For example, if you were looking at plant species in a field you could pick random sample sites by dividing the field into a grid and using a random number generator to select coordinates — see Figure 1.

Learning Objectives:

- Know that quantitative investigations of variation within a species involve:
  - collecting data from random samples
  - calculating a mean value of the collected data and the standard deviation of that mean
  - interpreting mean values and their standard deviations.
  Specification Reference 3.4.7

Tip: Variation <u>between</u> species is known as <u>inter</u>specific variation. Variation <u>within</u> a species is known as <u>intra</u>specific variation.

Tip: A sample is biased if it doesn't represent the population as a whole. For example, if you were looking at the average height of students in a school but only measured the heights of people from one particular class, the sample would be biased.

Tip: A random number generator will give you coordinates at random, e.g. C3, E5, etc. Then you just take your samples from these coordinates.

Non-random sampling

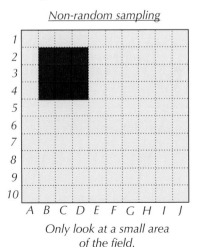

Only look at a small area of the field.

Random sampling

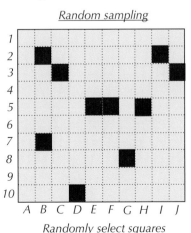

Randomly select squares in the field.

Figure 1: *Diagram to show non-random sampling by picking a small area (left) and random sampling using a random number generator (right).*

To ensure any variation observed in the sample isn't just due to chance, it's important to analyse the results statistically. This allows you to be more confident that the results are true and therefore will reflect what's going on in the whole population. There's more on statistical analysis on page 9.

Mean and standard deviation

You can use the mean and standard deviation to measure how much variation there is in a sample.

Mean

The mean is an average of the values collected in a sample. Find it using this formula:

$$\text{mean} = \frac{\text{total of all the values in your data}}{\text{the number of values in your data}}$$

Tip: When you calculate the mean, check that it's within the range of values that you used in the calculation. If the mean isn't within the range, you know you've calculated it wrong. E.g. the mean here should be between 4 and 9 cm.

Example — Maths Skills

The heights of different seedlings in a group are: 6 cm, 4 cm, 7 cm, 6 cm, 5 cm, 8 cm, 7 cm, 5 cm, 7 cm and 9 cm.

To calculate the mean, add all of the heights together and divide by the number of seedlings:

Mean height = (6 + 4 + 7 + 6 + 5 + 8 + 7 + 5 + 7 + 9) ÷ 10 = 64 ÷ 10
= **6.4 cm**

The mean can be used to tell if there is variation between samples.

Examples

- The mean height of a species of tree in woodland A = 26 m, woodland B = 32 m and woodland C = 35 m. So the mean height varies.
- The mean number of leaves on a clover plant in field X = 3, field Y = 3 and field Z = 3. So the mean number of leaves does not vary.

Most samples will include values either side of the mean, so you end up with a bell-shaped graph — this is called a **normal distribution** (see Figure 2). A normal distribution is symmetrical about the mean.

Tip:
Normal distribution (symmetrical):

Not a normal distribution (skewed):

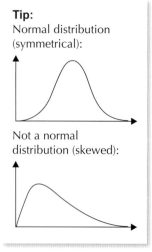

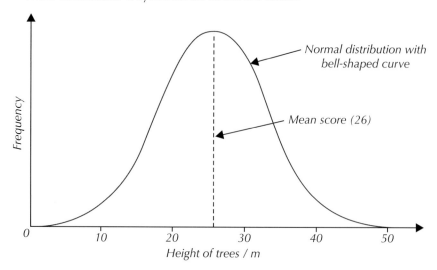

Figure 2: The height of trees in woodland A.

Standard deviation

The standard deviation tells you how much the values in a single sample vary. It's a measure of the spread of values about the mean. Sometimes you'll see the mean written as, for example, 9 ± 3. This means that the mean is 9 and the standard deviation is 3, so most of the values are spread between 6 and 12.

Both of the graphs in Figure 3 show a normal distribution. However, the values in a sample can vary a little or a lot:

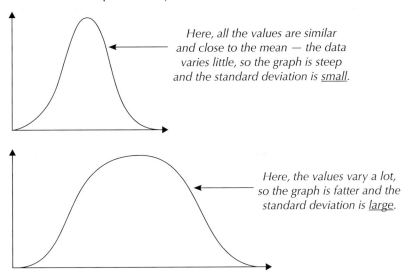

Here, all the values are similar and close to the mean — the data varies little, so the graph is steep and the standard deviation is <u>small</u>.

Here, the values vary a lot, so the graph is fatter and the standard deviation is <u>large</u>.

Figure 3: *A normal distribution curve with a small standard deviation (top) and with a large standard deviation (bottom).*

Example

Height of trees in woodland A:
mean = 26,
standard deviation = 3

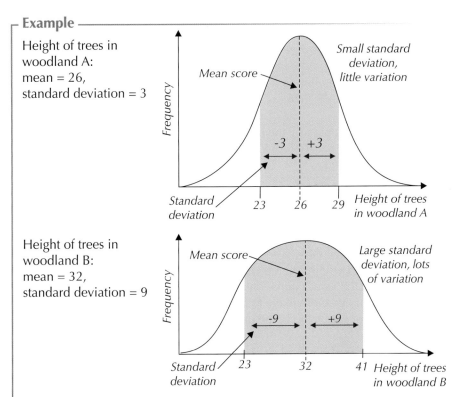

Height of trees in woodland B:
mean = 32,
standard deviation = 9

So the trees are generally taller in woodland B but there's a greater variation in height, compared to woodland A.

Calculating standard deviation

Figure 4 shows the formula for finding the standard deviation of a group of values:

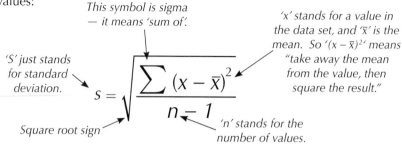

This symbol is sigma — it means 'sum of'.

'x' stands for a value in the data set, and 'x̄' is the mean. So '(x − x̄)²' means "take away the mean from the value, then square the result."

'S' just stands for standard deviation.

$$S = \sqrt{\frac{\sum (x - \bar{x})^2}{n - 1}}$$

Square root sign

'n' stands for the number of values.

Figure 4: *Explanation of the formula for standard deviation.*

Exam Tip
You won't be asked to calculate standard deviation in your written exams, but it's helpful to know how to do it for when you're analysing data in class or doing practical investigations.

Tip: Standard deviation (S) can also be represented by the Greek letter sigma: 'σ'.

Example — Maths Skills

The table shows the height of four different trees in a forest. To find the standard deviation:

- Write out the equation:

$$S = \sqrt{\frac{\sum (x - \bar{x})^2}{n - 1}}$$

Tree	Height (m)
A	22
B	27
C	26
D	29

- Work out the mean height of the trees, $\bar{x}$:

  $(22 + 27 + 26 + 29) \div 4 = \mathbf{26}$

- Work out $(x - \bar{x})^2$ for each value of x. For each tree height in the table, you need to take away the mean, then square the answer:

  A: $(22 - 26)^2 = (-4)^2 = \mathbf{16}$ B: $(27 - 26)^2 = 1^2 = \mathbf{1}$
  C: $(26 - 26)^2 = 0^2 = \mathbf{0}$ D: $(29 - 26)^2 = 3^2 = \mathbf{9}$

- Add up all these numbers to find $\sum (x - \bar{x})^2$:

  $16 + 1 + 0 + 9 = \mathbf{26}$

- Divide this number by the number of values, n, minus 1. Then take the square root to get the answer:

  $26 \div 3 = 8.66...$
  $\sqrt{8.66...} = \mathbf{2.9 \text{ to 2 s.f.}}$

Standard deviation is one method of calculating the dispersion of data. Another method of calculating dispersion is by looking at the range — see page 5. This is simply the difference between the highest and lowest figures in the data. Standard deviation is more useful than the range because it takes into account all the values in the data set, whereas the range only uses two. This makes the range more likely to be affected by an anomalous result (an unusually high or low value in the data set) than standard deviation.

Using standard deviation to draw error bars

Standard deviations can be plotted on a graph or chart of mean values using **error bars**. Error bars extend one standard deviation above and one standard deviation below the mean (so the total length of an error bar is twice the standard deviation). The longer the bar, the larger the standard deviation and the more spread out the sample data is from the mean — see Figure 5.

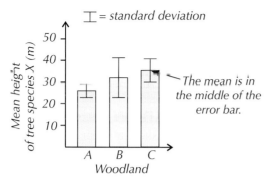

$\perp$ = standard deviation

The mean is in the middle of the error bar.

Figure 5: *An example of a graph with standard deviation error bars.*

Tip: The smaller the error bars, the smaller the standard deviation and the less the data in the sample varies.

Practice Questions — Application

Q1 The graph below shows the wing spans of two different species of bird, both of which live in the same area of woodland.

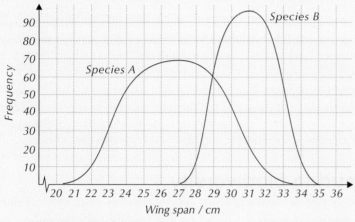

a) i) Describe the data.

ii) Which species shows a greater variation in wing span? Explain your answer.

b) How much longer is species B's mean wing span than species A's? Give your answer as a percentage.

Q2 The table on the right shows the length of five rainbow boa snakes measured by conservationists investigating the effect of habitat loss on the well-being of the species.

Using the formula below, calculate the standard deviation of this data.

$$s = \sqrt{\frac{\sum (x - \bar{x})^2}{n - 1}}$$

Snake	length (cm)
A	177
B	182
C	190
D	187
E	191

Exam Tip
Always show your working in calculation questions. You could pick up marks for using the correct method, even if your final answer is wrong.

Practice Questions — Fact Recall

Q1 How do you calculate the mean?

Q2 What shape is the graph of a data set with a normal distribution?

Q3 What does standard deviation measure?

- Know that biodiversity can relate to a range of habitats, from a small local habitat to the Earth.
- Understand that species richness is a measure of the number of different species in a community.
- Know that an index of diversity describes the relationship between the number of species in a community and the number of individuals in each species.
- Be able to calculate an index of diversity (*d*) from the formula:

$$d = \frac{N(N-1)}{\sum n(n-1)}$$

where *N* = total number of organisms of all species and *n* = total number of organisms of each species.

Specification Reference 3.4.6

Tip: A species is a group of similar organisms able to reproduce to give fertile offspring (see page 237).

Tip: The number of species in a community and the abundance of each species is also known as the species diversity.

6. Biodiversity

Biodiversity is important — the higher the biodiversity in an ecosystem, the healthier that ecosystem is.

Terms you need to know

Before you can sink your teeth into the real meat of biodiversity, there are a few definitions you need to know:

- **Biodiversity** is the variety of living organisms in an area.
- A **habitat** is the place where an organism lives, e.g. a rocky shore or field.
- A **community** is all the populations of different species in a habitat.

Levels of biodiversity

Biodiversity can be considered at a range of scales from the local to the global:

- Local biodiversity — you could consider the variety of different species living in a small habitat that's local to you, e.g. a pond or meadow, or even your back garden. Some habitats will be more biodiverse than others.
- Global biodiversity — you could also consider the variety of species on Earth. Recent estimates put the total number of species on Earth at about 8.7 million. Biodiversity varies in different parts of the world — it is greatest at the equator and decreases towards the poles.

Measuring biodiversity

Biodiversity can be measured using species richness or an index of diversity.

Species richness is a measure of the number of different species in a community — which makes it a simple measure of biodiversity. It can be worked out by taking random samples of a community (see page 245) and counting the number of different species.

However, the number of different species in a community isn't the only thing that affects biodiversity. The population sizes of those species do too. Species that are in a community in very small numbers shouldn't be treated the same as those with bigger populations. This is where an index of diversity comes in.

An **index of diversity** is another way of measuring biodiversity. It's calculated using an equation that takes both the number of species in a community (species richness) and the abundance of each species (population sizes) into account.

You can calculate an index of diversity (*d*) using this formula:

$$d = \frac{N(N-1)}{\sum n(n-1)}$$

Where...
N = Total number of organisms of all species
n = Total number of organisms of one species
$\sum$ = 'Sum of' (i.e. added together)

The higher the number, the more diverse the area is. If all the individuals are of the same species (i.e. no biodiversity) the index is 1.

Example — Maths Skills

There are 3 different species of flower in this field — a red species, a white and a blue. There are 3 of the red species, 5 of the white and 3 of the blue.

There are 11 organisms altogether, so $N = 11$.

So the species diversity index of this field is:

$$d = \frac{11(11-1)}{3(3-1) + 5(5-1) + 3(3-1)} = \frac{110}{6 + 20 + 6} = \mathbf{3.44} \text{ (3 s.f.)}$$

Tip: When calculating the bottom half of the equation you need to work out the $n(n-1)$ bit for each different species then add them all together.

Example — Maths Skills

A student investigates the diversity of fish species in her local pond. She finds 46 fish of 6 different species. To help her calculate the index of diversity for the pond she draws the following table:

Species	***n*** (total number of organisms in species)	***n* − 1**	***n*(*n* − 1)**
A	1	0	0
B	6	5	30
C	2	1	2
D	15	14	210
E	3	2	6
F	19	18	342
N (total number of all organisms)	46		

She then uses the numbers from the table to calculate the diversity index:

$$d = \frac{N(N-1)}{\Sigma n(n-1)} = \frac{46\,(46-1)}{0 + 30 + 2 + 210 + 6 + 342} = \frac{2070}{590} = \mathbf{3.51} \text{ (3 s.f.)}$$

Tip: If you've got a lot of data, you might find it easier to plug the numbers into a table (as in example 2) to make sure you don't miss any steps.

Tip: $n(n-1)$ just means $n \times (n-1)$.

Tip: To get the figures in the last column in the table, you multiply together the figures in the second and third columns.

Practice Questions — Application

Q1 The table below shows the number of individuals of each species of insect found in two ponds.

Species	Number of individuals found in Pond A	Number of individuals found in Pond B
Damselfly	3	13
Dragonfly	5	5
Stonefly	2	7
Water boatman	3	2
Crane fly	1	18
Pond skater	4	9

Tip: This question continues on the next page.

a) What is the species richness of insects in Pond A?

b) Use the data provided in the table and the formula given below to calculate the index of diversity for:

   i) Pond A

   ii) Pond B

$$d = \frac{N(N-1)}{\sum n(n-1)}$$

where N = total number of all organisms
and n = total number of organisms in one species.

c) Birds and amphibians feed on insects. Which of the two ponds would you expect to have a higher diversity of birds and amphibians? Explain your answer.

Q2 A study was conducted on the trees found in a wood and town. The results are shown in the graph below.

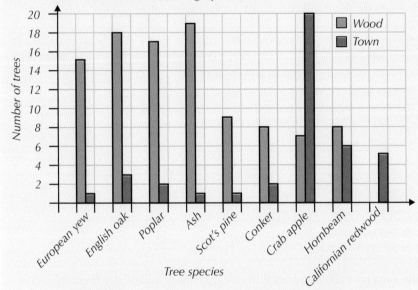

Exam Tip
Don't be thrown if you get asked to calculate species diversity using data from a graph — just read off the values carefully.

a) Use the data in the graph and the formula provided below to calculate the index of diversity for the tree species in:

   i) the wood

   ii) the town

$$d = \frac{N(N-1)}{\sum n(n-1)}$$

where N = total number of all organisms
and n = total number of organisms in one species.

b) The index of diversity gives a better estimate of the diversity of tree species than simply counting the number of species present. Explain why, using data from the graph to support your answer.

Exam Tip
If you've got time at the end of the exam, always go back over any calculation questions and check the answer — it's easy to make a silly mistake somewhere and lose marks.

Practice Questions — Fact Recall

Q1 What is the definition of biodiversity?

Q2 What is a community?

7. Agriculture and Biodiversity

Lots of things humans do can affect biodiversity — including agriculture.

The impact of agriculture on biodiversity

Farmers try to maximise the amount of food they can produce from a given area of land. But many of the methods they use reduce biodiversity:

- Woodland clearance is done to increase the area of farmland. It directly reduces the number of trees and sometimes the number of different tree species. It also destroys habitats, so some species could lose their shelter and food source. This means that species will die or be forced to migrate to another suitable area, further reducing biodiversity.

- Hedgerow removal is also done to increase the area of farmland by turning lots of small fields into fewer large fields. This reduces biodiversity for the same reasons as woodland clearance.

- Pesticides are chemicals that kill organisms (pests) that feed on crops. This reduces diversity by directly killing the pests. Also, any species that feed on the pests will lose a food source, so their numbers could decrease too.

- Herbicides are chemicals that kill unwanted plants (weeds). This reduces plant diversity and could reduce the number of organisms that feed on the weeds.

- Monoculture is when farmers have fields containing only one type of plant (see Figure 2). A single type of plant reduces biodiversity directly and will support fewer organisms (e.g. as a habitat or food source), which further reduces biodiversity.

> **Example**
>
> A study carried out over several decades found that the diversity of insect species in the UK fell during years when agricultural practices were intensified and when large areas of land were given over to growing cereals. This was correlated with a fall in the diversity of birds that fed on the insects.

Conservation schemes

Agriculture is one way of producing the resources we need from the environment — we need it to produce food and fibres for clothing, as well as some medicines and fuels. Biodiversity helps maintain the environment. It provides us with new sources of food and medicines, and it benefits agriculture, e.g. a wide variety of insects help to pollinate crops. So there needs to be a balance between agriculture and biodiversity. Conservationists try to achieve this through **conservation schemes**.

> **Examples**
>
> - Giving legal protection to endangered species.
> - Creating protected areas such as SSSIs (Sites of Special Scientific Interest) and AONBs (Areas of Outstanding Natural Beauty). These restrict further development, including agricultural development.
> - The Environmental Stewardship Scheme encourages farmers to conserve biodiversity, e.g. by replanting hedgerows and leaving margins around fields for wild flowers to grow.

Figure 1: *Spraying herbicide on crops.*

Figure 2: *A monoculture field containing a single crop.*

Tip: We need to make sure we produce enough food to feed our growing population, as well as conserving biodiversity.

Analysing the effect of agriculture on biodiversity

Exam Tip
Don't worry — you won't be expected to calculate a correlation coefficient in your written exams. You are expected to know <u>when</u> <u>to use</u> this type of test for statistical analysis though, and you could be asked to <u>interpret the</u> <u>results</u> of the test — see next page for more.

If you need to work out whether there's a correlation between two variables or not (or how strongly two variables are correlated), you can calculate the **Spearman's rank correlation coefficient** (r_s). This is a type of correlation coefficient and an example of a statistical test (see page 9). It uses the formula:

$$r_s = 1 - \frac{6\sum d^2}{n(n^2 - 1)}$$

where 'd' is the 'difference in rank between data pairs' and 'n' is the total number of data pairs

The result of the test is a number between -1 and +1. If the figure is -1, then there is a perfect negative correlation between the two variables. If the figure is +1, then there's a perfect positive correlation. The closer the figure is to 0, the weaker the correlation is. It'll all become clear with an example...

Example — Maths Skills

Tip: A positive correlation means that as one variable increases, so does the other. A negative correlation means that as one variable increases, the other decreases. See page 15 for more.

A team of biologists investigated the effect of repeated pesticide applications on the number and abundance of different insect species found on an area of crops. They applied pesticides once a month over a 6 month period. They measured the index of diversity for the test area seven days after each pesticide application. The table on the right shows their results.

Number of pesticide applications	Index of Diversity
0	4.89
1	4.19
2	3.80
3	3.12
4	3.26
5	2.36
6	1.92

Tip: A data pair consists of the two corresponding figures for each variable. E.g. 0 pesticide applications and an index of diversity of 4.89 make up one data pair.

1. First, rank both sets of data, keeping the data pairs together. The highest value for each variable is given the rank of 1, the second highest value is ranked 2, etc.

Number of pesticide applications	Rank	Index of Diversity	Rank
0	7	4.89	1
1	6	4.19	2
2	5	3.80	3
3	4	3.12	5
4	3	3.26	4
5	2	2.36	6
6	1	1.92	7

2. Then work out the difference in rank between the two values in each data pair (d) and square it to calculate d^2.

Number of pesticide applications	Rank	Index of Diversity	Rank	Difference between ranks (d)	d^2
0	7	4.89	1	6	36
1	6	4.19	2	4	16
2	5	3.80	3	2	4
3	4	3.12	5	1	1
4	3	3.26	4	1	1
5	2	2.36	6	4	16
6	1	1.92	7	6	36

3. Now count the number of data pairs (n). There are 7 data pairs here, so $n = 7$.

4. Now you can put all this information into the Spearman's rank formula:

$$r_s = 1 - \frac{6\sum d^2}{n(n^2-1)} = 1 - \frac{6\ (36+16+4+1+1+16+36)}{7\ (7^2-1)}$$

$$= 1 - \frac{6 \times 110}{7 \times 48} = 1 - \frac{660}{336}$$

$$= \mathbf{-0.964}\ \text{(3 s.f.)}$$

Because the figure is negative and close to -1, this suggests that there is a strong negative correlation between the number of applications of pesticides and the diversity index.

Once you've got your result, you need to find out if it's statistically significant or not. First, you need to come up with a **null hypothesis**. A null hypothesis always suggests that there is no correlation between the factors you're investigating — even if you expect that there will be some correlation. So the null hypothesis for the example above could be "there is no correlation between the number of applications of pesticides over a 6 month period and the biodiversity of the test area".

The result of the Spearman's rank test allows you to decide whether the null hypothesis can be rejected. To determine whether the null hypothesis can be rejected, you consult a table of **critical values** (see Figure 3).

The result is compared to the critical value at p = 0.05, which corresponds to n for the data you're looking at (in this case, 7). This value represents the point at which the correlation you're investigating would occur 95 out of 100 times, so there's only a 5% chance that the correlation is down to chance. You can reject the null hypothesis if the result of your test is higher than this value. If your result is a negative number, you ignore the minus sign when comparing it to the critical value. In this example, the Spearman's rank correlation coefficient (0.964) is higher than the relevant critical value, so the null hypothesis can be rejected. The result is statistically significant and the positive correlation is unlikely to be due to chance.

n	p = 0.05
7	0.786
8	0.738
9	0.700
10	0.648
11	0.618
12	0.587

Figure 3: A table of critical values for the Spearman's rank test.

Tip: You usually come up with the null hypothesis before you start your investigation — but we've explained how to calculate the correlation coefficient first here for clarity.

Tip: When you're checking your result against the critical value, always make sure that you use the right critical value for the number of data pairs that you've investigated.

Tip: If your result is not statistically significant, it means it could just be down to chance.

Practice Question — Application

Q1 A group of scientists were investigating the effect of the number of different types of crop being grown in a field on the field's biodiversity. They calculated the index of diversity for 8 different 0.5 km² fields, each with a different number of types of crop growing in them. Their results are shown in the table on the right.

Number of Crop Types	Index of Diversity
1	1.87
2	2.24
3	2.71
4	3.18
5	4.01
6	3.59
7	4.44
8	4.97

a) Using the formula on the right, calculate the Spearman's rank correlation coefficient for this data.

$$r_s = 1 - \frac{6\sum d^2}{n(n^2-1)}$$

b) Does the result suggest a positive or negative correlation?

c) Using the table of critical values in Figure 3 above, determine whether the null hypothesis "there is no correlation between the number of different types of crop growing in a field and its biodiversity" should be accepted or rejected.

Q1 Many farmers clear woodland and remove hedgerows from their land. Explain:
  a) why this is done.
  b) how these practices can reduce biodiversity.

Q2 Why does there need to be a balance between agriculture and conservation?

Section Summary

Make sure you know...

- That scientists take into account phylogeny (the evolutionary history and relationships of organisms) when classifying organisms.
- That the classification system consists of a hierarchy — larger groups are divided into smaller groups, and there is no overlap between groups.
- The eight levels of groups (taxa) used to classify organisms — domain, kingdom, phylum, class, order, family, genus and species.
- That a species is defined as a group of similar organisms able to reproduce to give fertile offspring.
- That every organism is given a two-part scientific name using the binomial naming system. The first part of the name is the genus the organism belongs to and the second part is the species. This naming system allows every organism to be universally identified.
- That courtship behaviour is carried out to attract a mate of the right species.
- That courtship behaviour is species specific, so it can be used to help classify organisms.
- That advances in genome sequencing and immunology have helped clarify evolutionary relationships between organisms.
- How to interpret data on DNA or protein similarities and use this to suggest relationships between different organisms.
- How early estimates of genetic diversity were made by comparing the number of different observable characteristics in a population.
- That the use of gene technologies has changed the way we investigate genetic diversity and estimates can now be made by comparing the base sequence of DNA, the base sequence of mRNA or the amino acid sequence of the proteins encoded by DNA and mRNA.
- How variation can be investigated using random sampling, mean values and standard deviations.
- How to interpret mean values and standard deviations.
- That biodiversity can be considered on a range of scales — from local to global.
- That species richness is a measure of the number of different species in a community and so is a simple measure of biodiversity.
- That an index of diversity is also a measure of biodiversity and that it takes into account both species richness and population size.
- How to calculate an index of diversity from given data.
- How farming can reduce biodiversity (e.g. through woodland clearance, pesticides, herbicides, hedgerow removal, competition and monoculture).
- Why it's important that there's a balance between agriculture and conservation.
- When to use a correlation coefficient (Spearman's rank) and how to compare the result to a table of critical values to determine its significance.

Exam-style Questions

1   Songbirds use elaborate songs to attract a mate.
This is a type of courtship behaviour.

1.1   Explain **one** way in which courtship behaviour makes organisms more likely to mate successfully.

(2 marks)

The graphs in **Figure 1** illustrate a mating song from three different songbirds. The arrows on the graphs show the beginnings of each phrase. Each phrase is made up of a series of notes and is repeated multiple times to make a song:

Figure 1

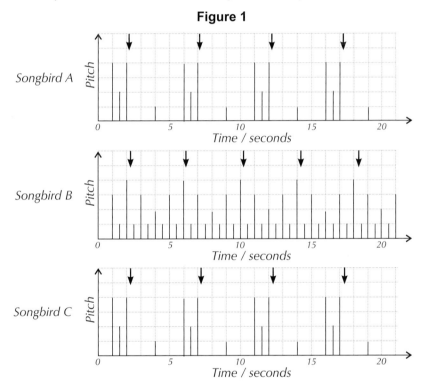

1.2   Calculate the number of phrases sung each minute by songbird B.

(1 mark)

1.3   What can you conclude about the classification of songbird A and songbird C from the data in **Figure 1**? Explain your answer.

(2 marks)

1.4   A scientist thinks there may be a relationship between the pitch of a songbird's song and its body size. She records the body size and song pitch of songbird B and 50 individuals of the same species.

What statistical test could she carry out on her results to determine whether there is a relationship between song pitch and body size? Explain your answer.

(2 marks)

2   The RuBisCo gene is found in all plants. When a new species of plant is being classified, this gene is often compared with the gene in other species to determine evolutionary relatedness.

2.1   Explain why the RuBisCo gene is useful for determining relationships between plant species.

(1 mark)

2.2   Evolutionary relationships could also be determined by comparing the RuBisCo protein itself. Describe **one** way in which proteins from two different organisms could be used to determine evolutionary relationships.

(2 marks)

3   A team of students have investigated plant biodiversity on two farms.
To do so, they calculated an index of diversity.
Species richness can also be used to measure biodiversity.

3.1   Explain why an index of diversity is a more accurate way of measuring biodiversity than species richness.

(2 marks)

Table 1

Table 1 shows the number of individuals of different plant species found in a single hedgerow on each farm.

Plant Species	Farm A	Farm B
A	3	12
B	6	2
C	9	4
D	7	6
E	11	3
F	11	0

3.2   Calculate the index of diversity for the hedgerow on each farm using the equation provided below.

$$d = \frac{N(N-1)}{\sum n(n-1)}$$

where, N = total number of all organisms
and n = total number of organisms in one species.

(4 marks)

3.3   One of the farms grows organic crops and does not use chemical herbicides. Which farm is this most likely to be? Explain your answer.

(2 marks)

3.4   Many organic farms use biological pesticides. These include introducing organisms that prey on the pests that eat crops. The students behind the first study want to investigate the impact of biological pesticides on insect species diversity in farm hedgerows.

Suggest a control the students might use in their investigation.

(1 mark)

The government offers grants to farmers to maintain their hedgerows.

3.5   Suggest **one** advantage to farmers of removing hedgerows from their land.

(1 mark)

3.6   Suggest what impact hedgerow removal could have on insect biodiversity on the farm. Explain your answer.

(3 marks)

4   A group of scientists is trying to develop a new strain of wheat that grows successfully in an area of Africa with low rainfall. They begin by testing two different species.

To compare them, the scientists take a random sample of plants from each species. The plants are grown in the same environment and the scientists monitor how long each plant can survive without water. The results are shown in **Figure 2**.

Figure 2

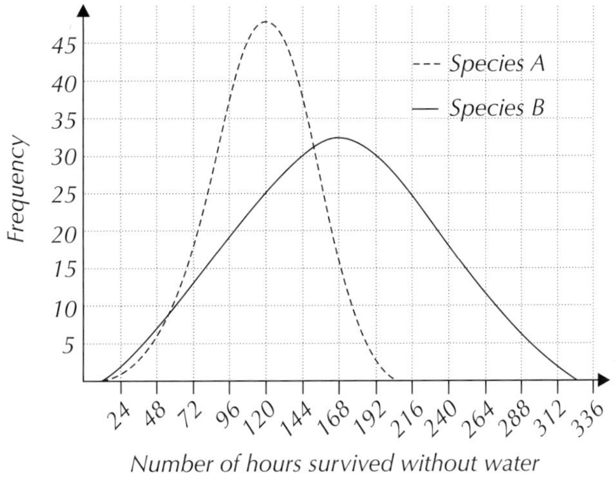

Number of hours survived without water

4.1   Evaluate the method used by the scientists to obtain their results.

(4 marks)

4.2   The scientists must choose one species to take to Africa for further testing.
Discuss the reasons for and against selecting **species B**.
Use data from **Figure 2** to support your answer.

(2 marks)

The scientists try to increase survival of their chosen species by inserting two genes for drought-resistance from other plants. The results are shown in **Table 2**.

Table 2

Gene	Mean no. days survived without water (± standard deviation)
X	20 (±4.3)
Y	26 (±1.2)
X and Y combined	24 (±5.4)

4.3   Based on the data in **Table 2**, which gene(s) should the scientists introduce into their chosen plant? Explain your answer.

(1 mark)

Exam Help

1. The Exams

You'll take two exams as part of AS Biology. Everything you need to know about them is summarised below.

It seems obvious, but if you know exactly what will be covered in each of the exams, how much time you'll have to do them and how they'll be structured, you can be better prepared. So let's take a look at the ins and outs of the exams you'll be facing for AS Biology...

How are the exams structured?

AQA AS Biology is examined in two papers that are each worth 50% of the total marks.

Paper	Total marks	Time	Topics assessed
1	75	1 hour 30 minutes	1, 2, 3, 4 & relevant Practical Skills
2	75	1 hour 30 minutes	1, 2, 3, 4 & relevant Practical Skills

- Paper 1 has 65 marks' worth of short answer questions and 10 marks' worth of comprehension questions.
- Paper 2 has 65 marks' worth of short answer questions and 10 marks' worth of extended response questions.

Solving problems in a practical context

In the exams, you'll get plenty of questions set in a 'practical context'. As well as answering questions about the methods used or the conclusions drawn (see pages 1-18), you'll need to be able to apply your scientific knowledge to solve problems set in these contexts.

┌─ **Example** ─────────────────

1   A scientist is investigating how the rate of an enzyme-controlled reaction is affected by substrate concentration. The results are shown in **Figure 1**.

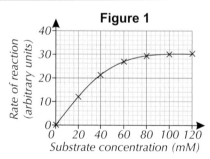

Figure 1

1.1   Suggest why the graph levels off at substrate concentrations higher than 80 mM.

(2 marks)

You should remember from page 39 that once all the enzymes' active sites are full (the saturation point has been reached) adding more substrate won't increase the rate of reaction any further — which is why the rate levels off.

2. Command Words

Command words are just the bits of a question that tell you what to do.

You'll find answering exam questions much easier if you understand exactly what they mean, so here's a brief summary table of the most common command words:

Command word:	What to do:
Give / Name / State	Give a brief one or two word answer, or a short sentence.
Describe	Write about what something's like, e.g. describe the structure of fish gills.
Explain	Give reasons for something.
Suggest	Use your scientific knowledge to work out what the answer might be.
Compare	Give the similarities and differences between two things.
Contrast	Give the differences between two things.
Calculate	Work out the solution to a mathematical problem.
Evaluate	Give the arguments both for and against an issue, or the advantages and disadvantages of something. You also need to give an overall judgement.

Exam Tip
When you're reading exam questions, underline the command words. That way you'll know exactly what type of answer to give.

Exam Tip
If you're answering a longer 'compare' or 'evaluate' question make a mental list of the similarities and differences or pros and cons first, so you know what you want your answer to include before you start writing.

Some questions will also ask you to answer 'using the information/data provided' (e.g. a graph, table or passage of text) or 'with reference to figure X' — if so, you must refer to the information, data or figure you've been given or you won't get the marks. Some questions may also ask you to answer 'using your calculation' — it's the same here, you need to use your answer to a particular calculation, otherwise you won't get the marks.

Not all of the questions will have command words — instead they may just ask a which / what / how type of question.

Exam Tip
Make sure you take a calculator and ruler into both your exams to help you with the calculation questions. A pencil and a spare pen may come in handy as well.

3. Time Management

Time management is really important in your exams — it's no good writing a perfect answer to a 3 mark question if it takes you an hour.

For AS Biology, you get just over a minute per mark in each paper. So, if you get stuck on a short question, sometimes it's worth moving onto another one and then coming back to it if you have time. Bear in mind that you might want to spend a bit longer than a minute per mark on the comprehension and extended response questions.

If you've got any time left once you've finished the paper, hold off on celebrating and have a look back through the questions. You can use the time to go back to any questions you've skipped, check your answers to calculation questions and to make sure you haven't accidentally missed any questions out.

Answers

Topic 1

Topic 1A — Biological Molecules

1. Molecules of Life
Page 20 — Application Question
Q1 Cytochrome c is present in the cells of a wide variety of organisms, suggesting that they could all have descended from a common ancestor.

Page 20 — Fact Recall Questions
Q1 A polymer is a large, complex molecule composed of many monomers joined together.
Q2 A monomer is a small, basic molecular unit that can form a polymer.
Q3 Any two from, e.g. monosaccharides / amino acids / nucleotides.
Q4 A chemical bond is formed between the monomers and a molecule of water is released.
Q5 A hydrolysis reaction.

2. Sugars
Page 23 — Application Questions
Q1 a)

This diagram looks a bit different from other disaccharide diagrams. It's because the OH group needed to form the glycosidic bond is at the top of the galactose molecule rather than the bottom.
b)

Q2 Test 1 — no reducing sugars present, but non-reducing sugars might be present.
Test 2 — non-reducing sugars are present, but reducing sugars are not.
Test 3 — no sugars are present.
Test 4 — reducing sugars are present.
These tests are quite tricky. Think carefully about what sugars have been tested for and what the different colours of the results indicate. Remember that a negative result for a reducing sugar test doesn't rule out non-reducing sugars.

Page 23 — Fact Recall Questions
Q1

Q2 glycosidic
Q3 water
Q4 a) glucose and glucose
b) glucose and fructose
c) glucose and galactose
Q5 Add Benedict's reagent to a test sample and heat it in a water bath that's been brought to the boil. Look at the colour of the sample for the result. A positive result would be a coloured precipitate (green, orange, yellow or brick red, depending on the concentration of the reducing sugar) and a negative result would be blue.

3. Polysaccharides
Page 24 — Application Questions
Q1

Q2 a)

b)

Page 26 — Fact Recall Questions
Q1 monosaccharide
Q2 a) starch
b) glycogen
Q3 a) insoluble
b) It doesn't affect water potential so it doesn't cause water to enter cells by osmosis, which would make them swell.
Q4 a) A — amylopectin, B — amylose
b) It has lots of side branches, which means the enzymes that break amylopectin down can get to the glycosidic bonds easily. This means glucose can be released quickly when it is needed.
Q5 a) cellulose
b) Cellulose is made from long, unbranched chains of β-glucose. These are joined by hydrogen bonds to form microfibrils. Microfibrils are very strong, which means they provide support/strength/rigidity in a cell wall.

Q6

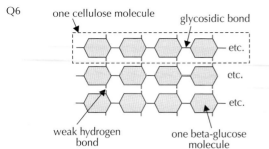

one cellulose molecule

glycosidic bond

etc.

etc.

etc.

weak hydrogen bond

one beta-glucose molecule

Q7 Use the iodine test — add iodine dissolved in potassium iodide solution to a test sample. Look at the colour of the sample for the result. A positive result would be dark blue-black and a negative result would be a browny-orange colour.

4. Lipids

Pages 29–30 — Application Questions

Q1

O
‖
C—C—H
| | |
OH   H

Q2 a) propanoic acid = CH_3CH_2
palmitic acid = $CH_3(CH_2)_{14}$
stearic acid = $CH_3(CH_2)_{16}$
oleic acid = $CH_3(CH_2)_7CH=CH(CH_2)_7$

b)

H
|
H—C—O—C—C—C—H
|
H—C—O—C—C—C—H
|
H—C—O—C—C—C—H
|
H

c) oleic acid

Page 30 — Fact Recall Questions

Q1 A molecule of glycerol and three fatty acids.
Q2 A saturated fatty acid doesn't have any double bonds between its carbon atoms, an unsaturated fatty acid does.
Q3 A — phosphate group, B — glycerol, C — ester bond, D — fatty acid/hydrocarbon tail
Q4 Because they contain lots of chemical energy and they're insoluble in water.
Q5 Phospholipid heads are hydrophilic and their tails are hydrophobic, so they form a double layer with their heads facing out towards the water on either side. This makes the centre of the membrane bilayer hydrophobic, so water-soluble substances can't easily pass through it.
Q6 a) lipids / fats / oils
b) The student should shake the test substance with ethanol for about a minute, before pouring the solution into water. A milky emulsion will appear if the result is positive.

5. Proteins

Page 32 — Application Question

Q1 a) E.g.

CH₃   CH₃
H   O   H   CH
| ‖ | |
H₂N—C—C—N—C—COOH
| |
H   H

b) E.g.

CH₃   O   H   H
| ‖ | |
H₂N—C—C—N—C—COOH
| |
H   H

c) E.g.

CH₃   CH₃
H   O   H   CH₃   O   H   CH
| ‖ | | ‖ | |
H₂N—C—C—N—C—C—N—C—COOH
| | |
H   H   H

Page 34 — Application Questions

Q1 Orange juice and goat's milk.
Q2 As a control.
Q3 a) The liquid needs to be alkaline for the test to work.
b) Not added any/enough sodium hydroxide solution.

Page 34 — Fact Recall Questions

Q1 Amino acids
Q2 A chain of more than two amino acids joined together.
Q3

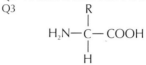

R
|
H₂N—C—COOH
|
H

Q4 Condensation
Q5 Peptide
Q6 Hydrogen bonds, ionic bonds and disulfide bridges.
Q7 Structural proteins are made of long polypeptide chains lying parallel to each other with cross links between them. This makes them physically strong.
Q8 a) sodium hydroxide solution
b) copper(II) sulfate solution
c) It would be purple.

6. Enzymes

Page 37 — Fact Recall Questions

Q1 extracellular
Q2 a) B
b) The activation energy needed for the reaction with the presence of an enzyme.
Q3 Activation energy is needed to start a chemical reaction. The activation energy is often provided as heat. With the presence of an enzyme, the activation energy required to start a reaction is lowered. Therefore not as much heat is needed, so the reaction can take place at lower temperatures than it could do without an enzyme.
Q4 In the lock and key model the active site has a fixed shape that is complementary to the substrate, but in the induced fit model the active site has to change shape slightly to allow the substrate to bind tightly.
Q5 The enzyme's tertiary structure.
Q6 An enzyme can only bind with a substrate that has a complementary shape to its active site.

7. Factors Affecting Enzyme Activity
Page 41 — Application Questions
Q1 a) i) C — the enzyme is still active at 80 °C.
This means the bacteria can live at very high
temperatures and therefore is hyperthermophilic.
ii) A — the enzyme is active at temperatures between
0 and 17 °C. This means the bacteria can live at very
cold temperatures, so is psychrotrophic.
b) A — The enzyme would become denatured at
temperatures over 17 °C, so the enzyme activity would
be reduced to zero.
B — There would be some enzyme activity but the rate
of reaction would gradually decrease until temperatures
of around 70 °C were reached. At this point the enzyme
would be denatured and there would be no further
enzyme activity at higher temperatures.
C — There would be an increasing amount of enzyme
activity. The rate of reaction would gradually increase as
the temperature increased.
Q2 a) A — The rate of reaction is higher in relation to the
hydrogen peroxide concentration. This is because there
are more catalase molecules present, which means
the hydrogen peroxide molecules will collide more
frequently with the active sites.
b) The curves flatten out at the saturation point. All the
active sites are full, so increasing the hydrogen peroxide
concentration won't increase the rate of reaction any
further.
Q3 The initial rate of reaction is fastest at pH 5. The graph
eventually reaches a plateau at pH 5 because all the
substrate is used up. At pH 3, the enzyme's tertiary structure
is disrupted and the shape of its active site is altered, so the
reaction is slower and the graph doesn't reach a plateau
because it takes longer for all the substrate to be used up.

Page 43 — Application Questions
Q1 Ethanol has a similar shape to methanol. This means it will
act as a competitive inhibitor, binding to the active site of
alcohol dehydrogenase and blocking methanol molecules.
This means lower levels of methanol will be hydrolysed so
the toxic product (formaldehyde) won't build up to fatal
levels.

Q2

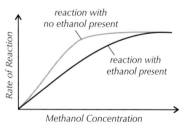

Methanol Concentration

Your curve should be lower than the rate of reaction without
any ethanol present. The reaction won't stop completely as
some of the methanol molecules will still bind with the active
sites. The plateau should be later as the reaction won't reach
its maximum rate until the methanol concentration is much
higher. The curve should start at zero.

Page 43 — Fact Recall Questions
Q1 At higher temperatures the molecules have more kinetic
energy, so they move faster. This makes the substrate
molecules more likely to collide with the enzymes' active
sites. The energy of these collisions also increases, which
means each collision is more likely to result in a reaction.
Q2 A very high temperature makes the enzyme's molecules
vibrate more. This vibration breaks some of the bonds/
hydrogen bonds and ionic bonds that hold the enzyme in
shape. The active site changes shape and the enzyme and
substrate no longer fit together. The enzyme is denatured.
Q3 The bonds that hold the enzyme in shape are broken. This
alters the shape of the active site meaning it is no longer a
complementary shape to the substrate. The enzyme can't
catalyse the reaction.
Q4 e.g. pH
Q5 The point at which all active sites are occupied by substrate
molecules.
Q6 The rate of reaction stays constant. All active sites are
occupied so increasing the substrate concentration has no
effect.
Q7 At first, increasing the enzyme concentration increases
the rate of the reaction. This is because the more enzyme
molecules there are in a solution, the more likely a substrate
molecule is to collide with an active site and form an
enzyme-substrate complex. The rate of reaction continues
to increase until the substrate concentration becomes a
limiting factor. At this point the rate of the reaction levels
off.
Q8 a) Away from the active site.
b) At the active site.
Q9 A non-competitive inhibitor molecule binds to the enzyme
away from the active site. Its presence alters the shape of
the active site meaning that substrate molecules can no
longer bind here. This prevents enzyme activity.

8. Enzyme-Controlled Reactions
Page 47 — Application Questions

Q1

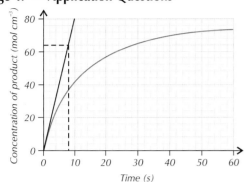

change in y ÷ change in x = 64 mol cm^{-3} ÷ 8 s
= 8 mol cm^{-3} s^{-1}

(accept answers between 6.5 mol cm^{-3} s^{-1} and 10 mol cm^{-3} s^{-1})
Tangents are tricky things to draw — there'll usually be a small range of acceptable answers that will get the mark.

Q2 a) Any two from: e.g. temperature, pH, enzyme concentration
    b)

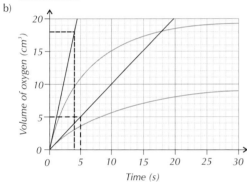

2 mol dm^3 — change in y ÷ change in x = 18 cm^3 ÷ 4 s
= 4.5 cm^3 s^{-1}
(accept answers between 3.3 cm^3 s^{-1} and 5 cm^3 s^{-1})
1 mol dm^3 — change in y ÷ change in x = 5 cm^3 ÷ 5 s
= 1 cm^3 s^{-1}
(accept answers between 0.8 cm^3 s^{-1} and 1.3 cm^3 s^{-1})
So 2 mol dm^3 : 1 mol dm^3 = **4.5 : 1**
Your answer depends on the values calculated for the tangents — it should fall between 6.25 : 1 and 2.5 : 1.
See page 7 for help on calculating ratios.

Page 47 — Fact Recall Question

Q1 E.g. set up boiling tubes containing the same volume and concentration of hydrogen peroxide. To keep the pH constant, add equal volumes of a suitable buffer solution to each boiling tube. Fill a measuring cylinder with water, turn it upside down and place it in a trough of water. Feed a delivery tube attached to a bung into the measuring cylinder. Put each boiling tube in a water bath set to a different temperature (e.g. 10 °C, 20 °C, 30 °C and 40 °C) along with another tube containing catalase. Wait 5 minutes before moving onto the next step so the enzyme gets up to temperature. Use a pipette to add the same volume and concentration of catalase to each boiling tube. Then quickly attach the bung and delivery tube. Record how much oxygen is produced in the first minute (60 s) of the reaction. Use a stopwatch to measure the time. Repeat the experiment at each temperature three times, and use the results to find the mean volume of oxygen produced. Calculate the mean rate of reaction at each temperature by dividing the volume of oxygen produced by the time taken (i.e. 60 s).

Exam-style Questions — pages 49-50

1.1 Sucrose is made from a fructose molecule *(1 mark)* and a glucose molecule *(1 mark)* which are joined by a glycosidic bond *(1 mark)* formed during a condensation reaction *(1 mark)*.

1.2

H   H   CH$_2$OH   H
     O   O
HO   OH   HO   CH$_2$OH

(1 mark for each correct diagram).

You don't need to learn the structure of fructose, but you do need to know that glucose and fructose are the monomers of sucrose.

1.3 Initially the sample is heated in a water bath (that's been brought to the boil) with Benedict's reagent to rule out the presence of reducing sugars *(1 mark)*. A new test sample is then heated in a water bath (that's been brought to the boil) with dilute hydrochloric acid *(1 mark)* and then neutralised with sodium hydrogencarbonate *(1 mark)*. Next the sample is heated with Benedict's reagent *(1 mark)*. The test sample would form a coloured (green/yellow/orange/brick red) precipitate if a non-reducing sugar was present *(1 mark)*.

1.4 Glycogen is a long, branched chain of α-glucose *(1 mark)*. Animals use it to store excess glucose *(1 mark)*. Many branches means that the glucose can be released quickly for energy *(1 mark)*. It is also a compact shape, so it is easy to store *(1 mark)*.

2.1 Add a few drops of sodium hydroxide solution to the test sample *(1 mark)*. Then add some copper(II) sulfate solution *(1 mark)*. If protein is present, the solution will turn purple *(1 mark)*. If there's no protein present, the solution will stay blue *(1 mark)*.

2.2 amino acid *(1 mark)*

R
|
H$_2$N—C—COOH
|
H   *(1 mark)*

2.3 The protein binds to pepsin's active site to form an enzyme-substrate complex *(1 mark)*. This lowers the activation energy for the breakdown of the protein (by putting strain on the peptide bonds, making them easier to break) *(1 mark)*. The reaction is catalysed and the products are released *(1 mark)*.

2.4 The tertiary structure is the 3D structure of the polypeptide chain *(1 mark)*, formed by hydrogen bonding and ionic bonding between different parts of the chain *(1 mark)*. Disulfide bridges can also be formed between cysteine R groups *(1 mark)*. The tertiary structure determines the shape of the active site of an enzyme *(1 mark)*. The shape of the active site makes the enzyme specific to its substrate *(1 mark)*.

3.1 *(1 mark for a value between pH 4 and pH 5)*

3.2 pH 1 and pH 9 *(1 mark)*. There is no reaction at these pH levels *(1 mark)*.

3.3 The shape of the active site has changed *(1 mark)* so it is no longer complementary in shape to the substrate, and will not bind to it to catalyse the reaction *(1 mark)*.

3.4 Any two from: e.g. temperature, substrate concentration, enzyme concentration *(1 mark for each correct variable)*.

3.5 A. The rate at which diglycerides and fatty acids are produced/the reaction rate is higher without the presence of orlistat *(1 mark)*.

3.6 Molecules of orlistat have a similar shape to triglycerides *(1 mark)*. They bind to the active sites of gastric lipase and block the entry of triglycerides *(1 mark)*. This means the reaction that produces diglycerides and fatty acids can't take place as quickly *(1 mark)*.

Topic 1B — More Biological Molecules

1. DNA and RNA

Page 53 — Application Questions
Q1 a) TGACAGCATCAGCTACGAT
   b) ACGTGGTACACCATTTAGC
Q2 a) 22
   b) 12
   c) 12
   If there are 34 base pairs in total and 22 of them contain adenine, then the other 12 must contain both cytosine and guanine — it's all to do with complementary base pairing.

Page 54 — Fact Recall Questions
Q1 It stores genetic information.
Q2 RNA and proteins.
Q3 Nucleotides
Q4 A = phosphate group, B = pentose/pentose sugar, C = nitrogen-containing organic base
Q5 A DNA nucleotide contains a phosphate group, the pentose sugar deoxyribose and a nitrogen-containing organic base.
Q6 adenine, guanine, cytosine and thymine
Q7 Phosphodiester bonds
Q8 Two DNA polynucleotide strands join together by hydrogen bonding between complementary base pairs — A with T and G with C. Two hydrogen bonds form between A and T, and three hydrogen bonds form between C and G. The antiparallel strands then twist round each other to form the DNA double helix.
Q9 ribose
Q10 adenine, guanine, cytosine and uracil
Q11 Any three from: e.g. DNA is double-stranded, whereas RNA is single-stranded / the pentose sugar in DNA is deoxyribose but it's ribose in RNA / DNA contains the base thymine, whereas RNA doesn't (it contains uracil instead) / molecules of RNA are relatively short compared to longer DNA molecules.
Q12 DNA has a relatively simple chemical composition.

2. DNA Replication

Page 56 — Application Questions
Q1

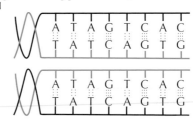

In semi-conservative replication of DNA, each of the new molecules of DNA contains a strand from the original molecule (shown in black in the diagram) and a new strand (green in the diagram).

Q2 AGTACCATGGATTT

Page 58 — Application Question
Q1 a) DNA in the two tubes were taken from bacteria that were grown in nutrient broths containing nitrogen isotopes of different weights. Tube A contained DNA with ^{14}N (light nitrogen) incorporated, whereas tube B contained DNA with ^{15}N (heavy nitrogen) incorporated. This meant that the sample in tube B settled further down the tube after being centrifuged because it was heavier.

   b) The DNA sample settled out in the middle of where the ^{14}N (light nitrogen) DNA settled out and where the ^{15}N (heavy nitrogen) DNA settled out. This is because the new bacterial DNA molecules contained one strand of the old DNA containing ^{15}N (heavy nitrogen) and one strand of new DNA containing ^{14}N (light nitrogen), as the new bacterial DNA had replicated semi-conservatively in the ^{14}N (light nitrogen).

   c) Tube D contains two bands. The lower band is at the same position as the band in tube C and the upper band is at the same position as the band in tube A. This is because the DNA molecules from tube C, which contained one strand of the ^{15}N (heavy nitrogen) DNA and one strand of the ^{14}N (light nitrogen) DNA had replicated for another generation in ^{14}N (light nitrogen). This meant that some of the molecules had ^{15}N DNA template strands with ^{14}N nucleotides incorporated onto new strands (these formed the lower band), and others had ^{14}N DNA template strands with ^{14}N nucleotides incorporated onto new strands (these formed the upper band).

Page 58 — Fact Recall Questions
Q1 It's where half of the new strands of DNA are from the original molecule of DNA.
Q2 DNA helicase, DNA polymerase
Q3 DNA helicase breaks the hydrogen bonds between bases on the two polynucleotide DNA strands. This makes the helix unwind to form two single strands.
Q4 Free-floating DNA nucleotides are attracted to their complementary exposed bases on each original template strand — A with T and C with G.

3. ATP
Page 60 — Application Questions
Q1 AMP is made from a molecule of adenine, a molecule of ribose and one phosphate group.

Q2 The breakdown/hydrolysis of ATP releases energy, so when this reaction/hydrolysis is coupled to the process of active transport it provides the energy for this process directly.

Page 60 — Fact Recall Questions
Q1 Adenosine triphosphate

Q2 A molecule of ATP is made from a molecule of adenine, a molecule of ribose and three phosphate groups.

Q3 a) ADP and P_i
b) hydrolysis
c) ATP hydrolase

Q4 a) It can be used to phosphorylate another compound/ added to another compound, which often makes the compound more reactive.
b) P_i

Q5 a) condensation
b) E.g. photosynthesis / respiration

4. Water
Page 63 — Fact Recall Questions
Q1 E.g. condensation and hydrolysis.

Q2 Because it has a slight negative charge on one side and a slight positive charge on the other.

Q3

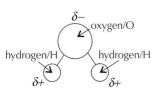

Q4 A weak bond between a slightly positively charged hydrogen atom in one molecule and a slightly negatively charged atom in another molecule.

Q5 A substance involved in a metabolic reaction.

Q6 Its polarity/the fact that it is a polar molecule.

Q7 Lots of heat is used to change it from a liquid to a gas.

Q8 Because when water is heated, a lot of the heat energy is used to break the hydrogen bonds between water molecules. This means there is less heat energy available to actually increase the temperature of the water.

Q9 a) The attraction between molecules of the same type (e.g. two water molecules).
b) Strong cohesion between water molecules allows water to travel in columns in the xylem tissue inside plants. Substances are transported around plants in this way.

5. Inorganic Ions
Page 65 — Fact Recall Questions
Q1 An ion that doesn't contain carbon.

Q2 They are present (in solution) in the cytoplasm of cells and in the body fluids of organisms.

Q3 Its specific properties.

Q4 a) Iron ions.
b) They bind to oxygen.

Q5 Hydrogen ions/H^+

Q6 a) Sodium ions/Na^+
b) Co-transport/co-transportation

Exam-style Questions — pages 66-67
1.1 ATP also contains a ribose molecule *(1 mark)* and a molecule of adenosine *(1 mark)*.

1.2 ATP synthase *(1 mark)*

1.3 E.g. ADP / AMP / a DNA nucleotide / a RNA nucleotide *(1 mark)*.

1.4 During ATP hydrolysis ATP is broken down into a molecule of ADP and a phosphate group/P_i *(1 mark)*. A phosphate bond is broken and this releases energy *(1 mark)*. This reaction is catalysed by ATP hydrolase *(1 mark)*.

1.5 ATP hydrolysis can be coupled to reactions that require energy so that energy can be supplied directly to the reaction and allow it to take place *(1 mark)*. DNA helicase must therefore require energy in order to unwind DNA molecules by breaking hydrogen bonds *(1 mark)*.

2.1 Water has a high latent heat of vaporisation *(1 mark)*, which means it carries away a lot of heat energy when it evaporates (vaporises) from a surface *(1 mark)*. So when sweat evaporates from the body it carries away heat energy, which cools the surface and helps to lower the temperature of the body *(1 mark)*.

2.2 Water is a polar molecule/has a slightly positively charged end and a slightly negatively charged end *(1 mark)*. The slightly negatively charged end of a water molecule will be attracted towards these positively charged sodium ions *(1 mark)*. The ions will become totally surrounded by water molecules and this means they are dissolved in water *(1 mark)*.

2.3 E.g. a molecule of glucose / an amino acid can be co-transported into a cell alongside sodium ions *(1 mark)*.

2.4 $45 \, g\,m^{-2}$ *(1 mark)*

2.5

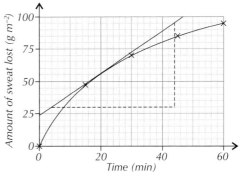

$65 \div 40 = \mathbf{1.6 \, g\,m^{-2}\,min^{-1}}$ *(1 mark for the correct answer and 1 mark for correct units)*
(Accept answers between $1.5 \, g\,m^{-2}\,min^{-1}$ and $1.8 \, g\,m^{-2}\,min^{-1}$.)

3.1 B, C, A, D *(1 mark)*

3.2 DNA polymerase *(1 mark)*

3.3 A condensation reaction *(1 mark)*.

3.4 It's where the base adenine (A) always pairs with thymine (T) and guanine (G) always pairs with cytosine (C) *(1 mark)*. Two hydrogen bonds form between A and T, and three hydrogen bonds form between C and G *(1 mark)*.

4.1 DNA stores genetic information while RNA transfers genetic information from the DNA to ribosomes *(1 mark)*.

4.2 In a DNA nucleotide part A is deoxyribose, whereas in an RNA nucleotide it is ribose *(1 mark)*.

4.3 Any two from: DNA is double stranded whereas RNA is single stranded *(1 mark)* / DNA contains thymine/T but this is replaced by uracil/U in RNA *(1 mark)* / RNA molecules are relatively short whereas DNA molecules are quite long *(1 mark)*.

Topic 2

Topic 2A — Cell Structure and Division

1. Eukaryotic Cells and Organelles
Page 74 — Application Questions
Q1 A = crista, B = outer membrane, C = matrix
Q2 Golgi apparatus
Q3 a) Mitochondria, to provide lots of energy for muscle contraction.
    b) E.g. they might have a lot of lysosomes to enable them to break down invading pathogens.
    c) E.g. ribosomes, rough endoplasmic reticulum, Golgi apparatus.
    You need to specify the rough endoplasmic reticulum in this answer (as the smooth endoplasmic reticulum is involved in lipid synthesis, not protein synthesis).
    d) E.g. They might have microvilli on their surface to increase the surface area for reabsorbing molecules.

Page 74 — Fact Recall Questions
Q1 To regulate movement of substances into and out of the cell. To respond to chemicals like hormones.
Q2 A = nuclear envelope, B = nucleolus, C = chromatin, D = nuclear pore.
Q3 The nucleus controls the cell's activities by controlling the transcription of DNA.
Q4 It is a group of fluid-filled membrane-bound flattened sacs.
Q5 Any one from: To digest invading cells. / To break down worn out components of the cell.
Q6 It synthesises and processes lipids.
Q7 A tissue is where similar cells are grouped together, whereas an organ is where different tissues are grouped together to perform a particular function.
Q8 An organ system is where different organs work together to carry out a particular function.

2. Prokaryotic Cells and Viruses
Page 77 — Application Questions
Q1 A = cell wall, B = capsule, C = plasmid, D = flagellum
Q2 Feature B (capsule) is a layer of slime that can help protect the bacterium from attack by the host's immune system. Feature D (flagellum) allows the bacteria to move through the gut.
Q3 The main genetic material floats free in the cytoplasm. It is one long coiled-up strand of circular DNA, which is not attached to any histones. Other genetic material is in the form of small loops of DNA called plasmids. These contain genes for things like antibiotic resistance.

Page 77 — Fact Recall Questions
Q1 In the cell wall.
Q2 Binary fission. The circular DNA and plasmids replicate. The main DNA loop is only replicated once but the plasmids can be replicated several times. The cell gets bigger and the DNA loops move to opposite poles of the cell. The cytoplasm begins to divide and new cell walls begin to form. The cytoplasm divides and two daughter cells are produced. Each daughter cell has one copy of the circular DNA but a variable number of copies of the plasmids.
Q3 The protein coat that surrounds the core of genetic material in a virus.
Q4 They allow a virus to attach to specific host cells, which have the complementary receptor proteins.

3. Analysis of Cell Components
Page 79 — Application Questions
Q1 a) size of image ÷ magnification = size of real object
       8 mm ÷ 3150 = **0.0025 mm**
    b) size of image ÷ magnification = size of real object
       18 mm ÷ 3150 = **0.0057 mm**
Q2 size of real object × magnification = size of image
    0.00002 mm × 40 = 0.0008 mm = 8×10^{-4} **mm**
Q3 size of image ÷ magnification = size of real object
    13 mm ÷ 7000 = 0.0019 mm
    Then times by 1000 to convert to μm
    0.0019 mm × 1000 = **1.9 μm**
Q4 size of real object × magnification = size of image
    0.023 μm × 1500 = 34.5 μm
    Then divide by 1000 to convert to mm
    34.5 μm ÷ 1000 = **0.035 mm**
Q5 a) size of image ÷ size of real object = magnification
       16 mm ÷ 2 mm = **× 8**
    b) size of real object × magnification = size of image
       3 mm × 50 = **150 mm**
Q6 First you need to convert 10 μm to millimetres by dividing by 1000:
    10 μm ÷ 1000 = 0.01 mm
    size of image ÷ size of real object = magnification
    10 mm ÷ 0.01 mm = **× 1000**

Page 83 — Application Questions
Q1 a) Optical microscope, as electron microscopes can only be used on dead specimens.
    b) SEM, as they can give 3-D images.
    c) Electron microscope (TEM/SEM) as the virus particles are smaller than the maximum resolution of optical microscopes.
Q2 a) nuclei, mitochondria, lysosomes, ER, ribosomes
    This is the filtered solution, so it should contain all the organelles.
    b) Nuclei
    Nuclei are the heaviest, so will separate out first.
    c) ER, ribosomes.
    The supernatant in this tube should contain everything except the nuclei (separated out in the first spin), mitochondria (separated out in the second spin) and the lysosomes (in the pellet in the bottom of Tube D).

Page 83 — Fact Recall Questions

Q1 magnification = size of image ÷ size of real object

Q2 Magnification is how much bigger the image is than the specimen. Resolution is how well a microscope can distinguish between two points that are close together.

Q3 a) 0.2 µm
   b) 0.0002 µm

Q4 Electron microscope

Q5 An electron microscope.
   Lysosomes are too small to be seen with an optical microscope — they're less than 0.2 µm in diameter (the maximum resolution of an optical microscope).

Q6 TEMs use electromagnets to focus a beam of electrons, which is then transmitted through the specimen. Denser parts of the specimen absorb more electrons, which makes them look darker on the image you end up with.

Q7 SEMs scan a beam of electrons across the specimen. This knocks off electrons from the specimen, which are gathered in a cathode ray tube to form an image.

Q8 Advantage: e.g. gives high resolution images, so can be used to look at small objects / the internal structure of organelles. Disadvantage: any one from, e.g. can only be used on thin specimens. / Can only be used on non-living specimens. / Produces black and white images. / Images may contain artefacts.

Q9 Any one from, e.g. can be used on thick specimens, whereas TEMs can't. / Can produce 3-D images, whereas TEMs can't.

Q10 A prepared microscope slide in which the specimen has been suspended in a drop of liquid.

Q11 Something you can see down the microscope that isn't part of the cell or specimen you are looking at.

Q12 They repeatedly prepared specimens in different ways. If an object could be seen with one preparation technique, but not another, it was more likely to be an artefact than an organelle.

Q13 By vibrating the cells, or by grinding the cells up in a blender. The homogenised cell solution is filtered through a gauze

Q14 The homogenised cell solution is filtered through a gauze to separate any large cell debris or tissue debris, like connective tissue, from the organelles.

4. Cell Division — Mitosis
Page 86 — Application Questions

Q1 a) B — because the chromosomes have lined up down the middle of the cell and are attached to spindle fibres.
   b) A — because the centromeres have divided, separating each pair of sister chromatids and the spindle fibres have contracted, pulling the chromatids to opposite poles of the spindle by their centromeres.
   To answer this you need to quickly go through each stage of mitosis in your head and think about the main thing that's happening, e.g. in metaphase all the chromosomes are in middle of the cell. Then ask yourself if you can see that in the photo.

Q2 a) 12-16 hours and 36-40 hours, because the mass of DNA doubles.
   b) 24 hours and 48 hours, because the mass of DNA halves.
   c) i) Two (at 24 and 48 hours) because the mass of the cell and its DNA doubles and halves twice.
      ii) At 72 hours.

Q3 12 out of 150 cells are in prophase. This suggests that the proportion of time the cells spend in prophase is 12/150th of the cell cycle. The cell cycle lasts 0.70 days, so 0.70 x 24 hours = 16.8 hours.
The cells spend (12 ÷ 150) x 16.8 = **1.3 hours in prophase**.

Page 87 — Application Question

Q1 a) synthesis / interphase
   b) mitosis
   Methotrexate stops A and G nucleotides from forming — these nucleotides are needed to make new strands of DNA during DNA synthesis. Spindle fibres separate chromosomes during mitosis.

Page 87 — Fact Recall Questions

Q1 The process that all body cells from multicellular organisms use to grow and divide.

Q2 For growth and for repairing damaged tissues.

Q3 Interphase

Q4 During prophase the chromosomes condense, getting shorter and fatter. The centrioles start moving to opposite ends of the cell, forming the spindle. The nuclear envelope breaks down and chromosomes lie free in the cytoplasm.

Q5 During telophase the chromatids reach the opposite poles on the spindle. They uncoil and become long and thin again. They're now called chromosomes again. A nuclear envelope forms around each group of chromosomes, so there are now two nuclei. The cytoplasm divides and there are now two daughter cells that are genetically identical to the original cell and to each other.

Q6 Division of the cell cytoplasm.

Q7 It's a tumour that invades surrounding tissues.

5. Investigating Mitosis
Page 91 — Application Questions

Q1 a) To make the chromosomes easier to see under the microscope.
   b) E.g. toluidine blue O / ethano-orcein / Feulgen stain
   c) The student should have put a coverslip over the top of the specimen and pushed down firmly, making sure that he didn't smear the coverslip sideways.
   d) The mitotic index for the root tip cells would be higher because they are part of a tissue that is undergoing a lot of growth — unlike the mature leaf.

Q2 a) 10 ÷ 6.5 = **1.5 µm**
   b) 14 × 1.5 = **21 µm**

Q3 a) (207 ÷ 750) x 100 = **27.6%**
   b) The tissue may be undergoing repair or cancerous growth may be occurring.
   c) (9.0 ÷ 200) = **0.045 mm**

Page 91 — Fact Recall Questions

Q1 The slide containing the specimen should first be clipped onto the slide. Then an objective lens should be selected and the coarse adjustment knob used to position the objective lens just above the slide. Finally, while looking down the eyepiece, the fine adjustment knob should be used to adjust the focus until a clear image of the specimen can be seen.

Q2 An eyepiece graticule is fitted onto the eyepiece. It's like a transparent ruler with numbers, but no units.

Q3 A stage micrometer is used to work out the value of the divisions on the eyepiece graticule at a particular magnification.

1.1 No. The microscope has a resolution of 200 nm/0.2 μm, which means it can't distinguish between objects that are smaller than 200 nm/0.2 μm — such as the ribosomes *(1 mark)*.

If you convert the diameter of the ribosomes and the resolution of the microscope into the same units, (e.g. both nm or both μm) it's easier to see that the ribosomes are too small for the microscope to pick up.

1.2 size of real object = size of image ÷ magnification
= 4 ÷ 100 = **0.04 mm/40 μm** *(1 mark)*

1.3 Any one from: e.g. ribosomes/rough endoplasmic reticulum as these are the site of protein synthesis. / Golgi apparatus because this processes and packages new proteins.
(1 mark for sensible choice of organelle, 1 mark for correct explanation)

1.4 Any five from: e.g. First the cell membranes are broken up by homogenisation to release the organelles into solution *(1 mark)*. The solution is kept ice cold to prevent enzymes breaking down the organelles / an isotonic solution is used to prevent damage to organelles by osmosis / a buffer solution is added to maintain the pH *(1 mark)*. The homogenised cell solution is then filtered through a gauze to separate any large cell debris or tissue debris from the organelles *(1 mark)*. Ultracentrifugation is then carried out to separate each organelle from the others *(1 mark)*. The cell fragments are poured into a tube and spun in a centrifuge to separate out the heaviest organelle, which remains in the pellet at the bottom of the tube, leaving the others suspended in the supernatant *(1 mark)*. This process is then repeated at higher and higher speeds to separate out all the organelles *(1 mark)*.
(Maximum of 5 marks available.)

2.1 Bacteria are prokaryotic cells, so the penicillin inhibits the synthesis of their cell walls, eventually leading to cell lysis and death *(1 mark)*. Human cells are eukaryotic animal cells, and so have no cell wall, so penicillin antibiotics leave these cells unaffected *(1 mark)*.

2.2 E.g. Antibiotics could target the capsule of prokaryotic cells, which human cells don't have *(1 mark)*. This would leave the prokaryotes more open to attack from the cells of the host's immune system *(1 mark)*.

The question asks for an example. Marks could be awarded for any example of a bacterial feature that human cells don't have and a sensible explanation of why it would be appropriate.

3.1 A is gap phase 1 because it contains 1 arbitrary unit of DNA *(1 mark)*. B is synthesis because the mass of DNA is increasing *(1 mark)*. C is gap phase 2 because it contains 2 arbitrary units of DNA *(1 mark)*.

The key to this question is to look at the amount of DNA at each stage on the graph and link that back to how the amount of DNA in a cell changes during the phases of interphase.

3.2 E.g. because phase A lasts longer *(1 mark)*.
If each phase lasted the same length of time, then each phase would have broadly the same number of cells.

4.1 The data shows a positive correlation between the activity of protein X and the percentage of cells dividing *(1 mark)*, but you can't tell from the data that the activity of protein X is causing the cells to divide — it might just be a coincidence / there might be other factors involved *(1 mark)*. Also the graph only shows data for one species of yeast so you can't apply any trend to other species of yeast *(1 mark)*.

4.2 E.g. cell division could be measured in yeast cells that do not produce this protein *(1 mark)*. The purpose of this would be to make sure that the change in the percentage of cells dividing is due to the activity of protein X and nothing else *(1 mark)*.

5.1 It is an organ because it is made up of lots of different tissues, such as the cornea and the retina *(1 mark)*, which work together to allow us to see *(1 mark)*.

5.2 A mutation in the gene for Rb means the Rb protein is not made / a faulty version of the Rb protein is made *(1 mark)*. This means the damaged cell goes through the cell cycle and divides *(1 mark)*. The cells continue to divide which can lead to the formation of a tumour *(1 mark)*.

Topic 2B — Cell Membranes

1. Cell Membranes — The Basics

Page 97 — Application Questions

Q1 a) E.g. to keep the enzymes needed for photosynthesis all in one place/to compartmentalise photosynthesis, making photosynthetic reactions more efficient.
b) E.g. to control what substances enter and leave the cell. / To enable cell signalling.

Q2 E.g. using carrier proteins/channel proteins in the membrane.

Q3 E.g. energy-releasing organelles require lots of substances (e.g. nutrients, enzymes, ATP) to travel across their membranes. Some of these substances will require help from proteins to get across the membrane, so these membranes will have a higher protein content.

Q4 Freezing the raspberries will have caused ice crystals to form and pierce the cell-surface membranes, making the membranes highly permeable when they thawed. This will have caused the red pigment to leak out of the raspberry cells as they defrosted.

Page 99 — Application Question

Q1 a) E.g. the size of the beetroot cubes. / The beetroot the cubes came from. / The volume of methanol solution the cubes were soaked in. / The temperature of the equipment and surroundings.
b) Any two from: e.g. it should be turned on and left for five minutes to stabilise. / It should be set up so it's using the correct (blue) filter / a wavelength of about 470 nm. / It should be calibrated to zero (using a cuvette containing distilled water).
c) A. As the concentration of methanol increased, more of the lipids in the beetroot's cell membranes would dissolve. This would cause the cells to lose their structure and become more permeable. More pigment would be released from the beetroot cubes, so the absorbance of the surrounding liquid would increase.

Page 99 — Fact Recall Questions

Q1 A = glycoprotein, B = glycolipid, C = cholesterol, D = protein channel, E = phospholipid (head)

Q2 Because the phospholipids are constantly moving.

Q3 Some of the proteins are fixed in position, others move sideways.

Q4 A protein with a carbohydrate attached.

Q5 'Hydrophilic' means 'attracts water'. Hydrophobic means 'repels water'.

Q6 The centre of the phospholipid bilayer is hydrophobic, so the membrane doesn't allow water-soluble substances through it.

Q7 Some proteins in the membrane allow the passage of large or charged particles that would otherwise find it difficult to cross the membrane.

Q8 Cholesterol helps make the membrane less fluid and more stable. It maintains shape of animal cells and creates a barrier to polar substances.

Q9 E.g. cut equal sized beetroot cubes and place each cube in a test tube. Add the same volume of water to each test tube, then place each test tube in a water bath set at a different temperature and leave them for the same length of time. Remove the beetroot cubes from each test tube and then use a colorimeter to measure the absorbance of the remaining liquid. This will indicate how much pigment has been released by each beetroot cube, and therefore how permeable the membrane is at each temperature tested.

2. Diffusion

Page 103 — Application Questions

Q1 The ink molecules are moving from an area of higher concentration (the original drop of ink) to an area of lower concentration (the surrounding water).

Q2 a) The distance the particles have to travel is further so the rate of diffusion will decrease.

    b) The surface area of the cell will increase, so the rate of diffusion will increase.

    c) The concentration gradient will increase, so the rate of diffusion will increase.

Q3 You could increase the concentration gradient of the particle and monitor the rate of diffusion. Facilitated diffusion requires proteins to transport particles across the cell membrane. There are a fixed number of proteins in the membrane. Once all the proteins are in use, increasing the concentration gradient won't increase the rate of facilitated diffusion any further, whereas increasing the concentration gradient will continue to increase the rate of simple diffusion.

Q4

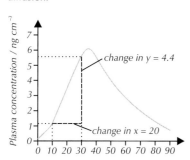

$$\text{Rate} = \frac{4.4}{20} = \mathbf{0.22\ ng\ cm^{-3}\ min^{-1}}$$

Your 'change in y' could have been anywhere between 4.2 and 4.6 giving you an answer between 0.21 and 0.23 ng cm⁻³ min⁻¹.

Page 103 — Fact Recall Questions

Q1 The net/passive movement of particles from an area of higher concentration to an area of lower concentration.

Q2 It's a passive process.

Q3 E.g. concentration gradient, surface area, thickness of the exchange surface

Q4 It's a passive process.

Q5 First, a large molecule attaches to a carrier protein in the membrane. Then, the protein changes shape. This releases the molecule on the opposite side of the membrane.

Q6 Channel proteins are proteins within a cell membrane that form pores.

Q7 Channel proteins allow charged particles to pass through a cell membrane via facilitated diffusion.

Q8 It would increase the rate of facilitated diffusion as it would allow more particles to be transported across the membrane at the same time.

3. Osmosis

Page 107 — Application Questions

Q1 a) Water molecules will move from the cheek cells into the salt solution.
     A -300 kPa solution has a higher water potential (it's less negative) than a -325 kPa solution.

    b) Water molecules will move into the apple slices out of the beaker of water.

    c) There will be no net movement of water molecules as the water potential in both solutions is the same/the solutions are isotonic.

Q2 a) The potato cells have a lower water potential than the sucrose solution, so they gain water by osmosis.

    b) The cells in both solutions will decrease in volume. This is because they have a higher water potential than the sucrose solutions, so will lose water by osmosis.

Q3 a) 1.5 M = 1500 mM.
     Scale factor = 1500 mM ÷ 125 mM = 12.
     30 ÷ 12 = 2.5.
     So she needs to use **2.5 cm³** of the original solution and 30 − 2.5 = **27.5 cm³** of distilled water.

    b) She is starting with 30 cm³ and diluting by a factor of 5. 30 cm³ ÷ 5 = **6 cm³**, so she would need to add 30 − 6 = **24 cm³** of distilled water to two test tubes. She would then use a pipette to take 6 cm³ from the 125 mM solution and add it to one of the test tubes containing 24 cm³ of distilled water. She would then mix the contents of this test tube thoroughly (to create one solution) before taking 6 cm³ of the solution and adding it to the distilled water in the remaining test tube and mixing thoroughly (to create the second solution).

Page 107 — Fact Recall Questions

Q1 Osmosis is the diffusion of water molecules across a partially permeable membrane, from an area of higher water potential to an area of lower water potential.

Q2 Water potential is the potential/likelihood of water molecules to diffuse out of or into a solution.

Q3 E.g. The water potential gradient (the higher the water potential gradient, the faster the rate of osmosis). The thickness of the exchange surface (the thinner the exchange surface, the faster the rate of osmosis). The surface area of the exchange surface (the larger the surface area, the faster the rate of osmosis).

Q4 E.g. cut equal sized chips from a potato. Divide the chips into groups of three and measure the mass of each group. Make up several different sucrose concentrations. Place each group of chips into a different sucrose solution and leave all the chips for the same length of time. Remove the chips and measure the mass of each group again. Record each group's percentage change in mass, then make a calibration curve by plotting the percentage change in mass against the concentration of the sucrose solution the group was in. Read off the concentration where the curve crosses the x-axis/where the percentage change in mass is 0. Look up the water potential for that concentration of solution in, for example, a text book to give you the water potential of the potato cells.

4. Active Transport
Page 111 — Application Questions

Q1 a) As the rate of sodium ion active transport increases, so does the rate of oxygen consumption.

b) Sodium ion active transport requires energy from ATP. As the rate of active transport increases, the rate of aerobic respiration must also increase in order to produce more ATP, which means the rate of oxygen consumption must increase too.

c) E.g. the rate of glucose consumption.

Q2 a) The I⁻ ion because it needs to move from an area of lower concentration to an area of higher concentration.

b) E.g. the co-transporter binds to an I⁻ ion and a Na⁺ ion. The Na⁺ ion moves across the membrane into the thyroid gland down its concentration gradient. This moves I⁻ across the membrane into the cell too, against its concentration gradient.

Page 111 — Fact Recall Questions

Q1 A hydrolysis reaction occurs which splits ATP into ADP and P_i / inorganic phosphate.

Q2 a) A molecule attaches to a carrier protein in the membrane. The protein then changes shape and releases the molecule on the opposite side of the membrane. The process requires energy.

b) Co-transporters bind two molecules at a time. The concentration gradient of one of the molecules is used to move the other molecule against its own concentration gradient.

Q3 Because sodium ions diffuse from the lumen of the ileum into the intestinal epithelium cells down their concentration gradient, through a sodium-glucose co-transporter protein. At the same time, the co-transporter carries glucose into the epithelium cell against its concentration gradient. Glucose is then able to diffuse into blood from the epithelial cell.

Q4 increase

Exam-style Questions — pages 113-114

1.1 Figure 2 because the lower water potential of the salt solution has caused water to move out of the cells down the water potential gradient *(1 mark)*. This has reduced the volume of the cells' cytoplasms *(1 mark)*.

1.2 Cell A because its membrane has the largest surface area, which increases the rate of osmosis *(1 mark)*.

1.3 The phospholipids are arranged in a bilayer *(1 mark)* with the hydrophilic heads facing outwards *(1 mark)* / the hydrophobic tails facing inwards *(1 mark)*.

1.4 glycoproteins *(1 mark)*

1.5 Cholesterol is responsible for giving cells rigidity / helping to maintain the shape of cells *(1 mark)*. Onion cells / plant cells have a cell wall which provides them with rigidity / helps to maintain their shape so they don't need as much cholesterol in their membranes as animal cells *(1 mark)*.

2.1 The movement of molecules usually from a low to high concentration *(1 mark)* using energy (from ATP) to do so *(1 mark)*.

2.2 It is a carrier protein/co-transporter *(1 mark)*, which binds glucose and sodium ions at the same time *(1 mark)*.

2.3 The centre of the phospholipid bilayer is hydrophobic *(1 mark)*. It forms a barrier to the diffusion of water-soluble substances including most polar molecules *(1 mark)*. Glucose is a polar molecule that can't diffuse directly across the membrane *(1 mark)*.

3.1 E.g. in case the cubes did not all start out at exactly the same mass *(1 mark)*. / To enable a fair comparison between the cubes *(1 mark)*.

3.2 16% (accept 15-17%) *(1 mark)*
Don't forget that pure water is always 0 kPa.

3.3 The water potential in these three solutions must have been lower than the water potential of the potato cells *(1 mark)* so water moved out of the cells by osmosis *(1 mark)*.

3.4 -425 kPa (accept any answer between -400 and -450 kPa) *(1 mark)*
Remember, all you need to do is read the water potential off the graph where the change in mass equals zero.

3.5 E.g. they could do repeats of the experiment for each concentration of sucrose solution and calculate a mean percentage change in mass *(1 mark)*.
There's more on precise results in the Practical and Maths Skills section at the front of this book.

3.6 Before 12 hours *(1 mark)* because the rate of osmosis will be faster due to the increase in surface area *(1 mark)*.

Topic 2C: Cells and The Immune System

1. Antigens
Page 115 — Fact Recall Questions
Q1 The molecules found on the surface of cells that can generate an immune response when detected by the body.
Q2 The immune system identifies them as foreign.

2. The Immune Response
Page 119 — Application Questions
Q1 a) Mouse A had 10 units, Mouse B had 10 000 units.
   b) Mouse B was already immune. You can tell this because the immune response was much quicker and stronger than the immune response of Mouse A.
   c) i) Day 20
      ii) The mouse's memory B-cells rapidly divided into plasma cells that produced the antibody needed to bind to the antigen. The mouse's memory T-cells rapidly divided into the correct type of T-cells to kill the cell carrying the antigen.
Q2 Antibodies will be generated against antigens on the surface of *S. pyogenes*. These will then bind to antigens on the surface of heart cells because the antibodies are very close to a complementary shape to the heart cell antigens. The immune system would then attack the heart cells and cause rheumatic fever.
The command word in this question is 'suggest', so you're not expected to know the exact answer. You're expected to use what you know about the immune system to come up with a possible explanation.

Page 119 — Fact Recall Questions
Q1 When activated by antigens presented by phagocytes, helper T-cells release chemical signals to activate phagocytes, cytotoxic T-cells and B-cells.
Q2 The function of plasma cells is to produce antibodies.
Q3 The cellular immune response involves the T-cells and other immune cells they interact with e.g. phagocytes. The humoral response involves B-cells, clonal selection and the production of monoclonal antibodies.
Q4 E.g. the primary response happens the first time a pathogen invades, the secondary response happens the second time a pathogen invades. / The primary response involves B and T-cells, the secondary response also involves memory cells. / There are symptoms with a primary response, but not with a secondary response.

3. Immunity and Vaccines
Page 122 — Application Questions
Q1 75% (accept answers in the range of 74-76%)
Q2 1000 cases
Q3 The number of cases decreased in a fluctuating pattern from a peak of around 6000 cases in 1960 to a peak of nearly 2000 cases around 1975. This is because more people were directly protected by the vaccine, and some people were protected by herd immunity.
Q4 a) Initially it increased slightly to about 80% of the population, and then decreased to around 50%.
   b) The number of cases increased from a peak of around 2000 cases in 1975 to a peak of around 4500 cases in 1983. This is because fewer people were directly protected by vaccination and fewer people were indirectly protected by herd immunity.
The question asks you to explain, so you need to give reasons why the decreased uptake of the vaccine caused the change in the number of cases.

Page 122 — Fact Recall Questions
Q1 Active immunity is the type of immunity you get when your immune system makes its own antibodies after being stimulated by an antigen.
Passive immunity is the type of immunity you get from being given antibodies made by a different organism — your immune system doesn't produce any antibodies of its own.
Q2 Vaccines contain antigens that cause your body to produce memory cells against a particular pathogen. This makes you immune.
Q3 Herd immunity is where unvaccinated people are protected because the occurrence of the disease is reduced by the number of people who are vaccinated.
Q4 Any two from: e.g. all vaccines are tested on animals and some people disagree with animal testing. / Testing vaccines on humans can be risky. / Some people don't want to take vaccines due to the risk of side effects, but they are still protected by herd immunity, which other people think is unfair. / If there was an epidemic of a new disease deciding who would receive a vaccine would be difficult.

4. Antigenic Variation
Page 123 — Application Questions
Q1 Antigenic variation is when the antigens on the surface of a pathogen change.
Q2 If the influenza virus undergoes antigenic variation the memory cells produced from the first infection will not recognise the different antigens. The immune system has to carry out a primary response to the new antigens. This takes time to get rid of the infection, which is why you get ill again.

5. Antibodies in Medicine
Page 127 — Application Questions
Q1 a) i) A
   ii) O
   Person 1 had a positive result with anti-antigen A because it reacted with the antigen A in her blood, but a negative result with anti-antigen B because she doesn't have any B antigens for it to react with. That means Person 1 must be blood type A. Person 3 had two negative results because they don't have A or B antigens — so they must be blood type O.
   b) i) No
   ii) Yes

Q2 a) To remove any unbound secondary antibody, so there won't be a false positive result if there are no primary antibodies present.
   b) The substrate will change colour, because there will have been (primary) antibodies to the gluten protein in the patient's serum. These will have bound to the gluten protein in the well, and then the secondary antibody will have bound to them. This means the enzyme that the substrate reacts with will be present in the well.
   c) E.g. to reduce the likelihood of getting a false result / to reduce the effect of random error / to make the results more precise.
   d) The control using antibodies should show a positive result (it's a positive control) — it shows that the secondary antibody will bind to an antibody specific to the gluten protein / that the enzyme will react with the substrate, so the result will be a colour change. The control using salt solution should show a negative result (it's a negative control) — it shows that all unbound secondary antibody is removed by washing the well plate / that the colour change is due to the presence of the enzyme and nothing else, so the result will be no colour change.

6. Interpreting Data About Vaccines and Antibodies
Page 129 — Application Questions
Q1 $12 \times 61 = $ **732**
Q2 Minor reactions are about five times more common than serious reactions. Serious reactions are about 120 times more common than Guillain-Barré syndrome.
   Rather than just saying it's more common, work out how much more common it is — manipulating data gets you higher marks in the exam.
Q3 No it does not support the idea that the influenza A vaccine increases the risk of Guillain-Barré syndrome.
   If the background rate is 1 per 100 000 people you would expect to see 10 cases per million people. The study only showed a rate of 0.1 cases per million people, which is far below the background rate.

7. HIV and Viruses
Pages 132-133 — Application Questions
Q1 a) 1995 because, e.g., after this year the number of people diagnosed with AIDS fell and the number of people living with HIV infection increased rapidly.
   b) Number of AIDS deaths in 1995 (thousands) = 50
   Number of AIDS deaths in 1998 (thousands) = 20

   $$\text{Percentage change} = \frac{(\text{final value} - \text{original value})}{\text{original value}} \times 100$$
   $$= -0.6 \times 100 = -60\%$$

   So percentage decrease = **60%**
   c) People with HIV develop AIDS when the number of helper T-cells in their bodies falls to a critically low level. HAART reduces the amount of HIV in the body, so the virus takes longer to destroy the same number of helper T-cells. This may increase the length of time it takes for HIV to progress to AIDS.

Q2 a) E.g. the virus infects and destroys helper T-cells that stimulate a B-cell response (to produce antibodies), so the overall immune response could be slower/ less efficient. / The antibodies produced by B-cells cannot reach the virus if it has entered a helper T-cell/becomes latent, so the immune response is less effective.
   b) The attachment proteins are antigens on the HIV membrane. The anti-HIV antibodies produced are complementary to the antigen, so if it changes shape the antibodies won't recognise it / bind to it.

Page 133 — Fact Recall Questions
Q1 HIV stands for human immunodeficiency virus.
Q2 It causes AIDS (Acquired Immunodeficiency Syndrome).
Q3 A = capsid, B = envelope, C = attachment/envelope protein, D = RNA
Q4 The viral attachment protein attaches to a receptor molecule on the cell membrane of the host helper T-cell. The capsid is then released into the cell, where it uncoats and releases RNA into the cell's cytoplasm. In the cell, reverse transcriptase is used to make a complementary strand of DNA from the viral RNA. Double-stranded DNA is made from this, which is inserted into the human DNA. Enzymes in the cell are used to make viral proteins from the inserted viral DNA. The viral proteins are assembled into new viruses, which bud from the cell and go on to infect other cells.
Q5 Antibiotics are designed to target bacterial enzymes and ribosomes, which are different to those in humans. Viruses do not have their own enzymes and ribosomes (they use those found in the host), so cannot be targeted in this way.

Exam-style Questions — pages 135-136

1.1

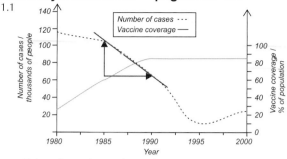

Number of cases ---
Vaccine coverage ——

Rate = change in *y* ÷ change in *x*
= (105 − 65) ÷ (1990 − 1985) = 40 ÷ 5
= **8 cases / thousands of people year⁻¹**

(*Accept any answer between 7 cases/thousands of people year⁻¹ and 9 cases / thousands of people year⁻¹.*)
(2 marks for the correct answer, 1 mark for evidence of the correct calculation)

1.2 The evidence does not support the conclusion. The data is for the whole world, not for the UK, so the pattern may not be true for the UK *(1 mark)*. The data covers between 1980-2000, not up to 2011 so the pattern may not be true in 2011 *(1 mark)*.

1.3 Any sensible answer, e.g. antigenic variation makes the vaccine ineffective *(1 mark)*.

1.4 It prevents them from suffering from the disease because the antibodies bind to the toxin and prevent it from causing muscle spasms *(1 mark)*. The injection does not contain pathogen antigens, so does not stimulate the production of memory cells *(1 mark)*.

2.1 When a phagocyte recognises the antigens on a pathogen, the cytoplasm of the phagocyte moves around the pathogen, engulfing it *(1 mark)*. The pathogen is now contained in a phagocytic vacuole inside the phagocyte *(1 mark)*.
A lysosome fuses with the phagocytic vacuole *(1 mark)* and the lysozymes inside the lysosome break down the pathogen *(1 mark)*.

2.2 Any five from: e.g. The phagocytes present foreign antigens from engulfed pathogens on their surface *(1 mark)*. Receptor proteins on the surface of helper T-cells bind to the antigens, activating the T-cells *(1 mark)*. Activated helper T-cells release chemical signals that activate phagocytes, cytotoxic T-cells and B-cells *(1 mark)*. When B-cells, which are covered in antibodies, meet an antigen with a complementary shape they bind to it *(1 mark)*. This, along with chemical signals released from helper T-cells, activates the B-cells *(1 mark)*. This is clonal selection *(1 mark)*. The B-cells then divide into plasma cells *(1 mark)*. The plasma cells then produce antibodies specific to the antigen (monoclonal antibodies) *(1 mark)*.
[Maximum of 5 marks available.]

3.1 They're antibodies produced from a single group of genetically identical B-cells / plasma cells *(1 mark)*. They're specific because their binding sites have a unique tertiary structure *(1 mark)* that only an antigen with a complementary shape can fit into *(1 mark)*.

3.2 An antibody has variable regions where the antigen binds *(1 mark)*. Each antibody has a different shaped variable region with a different tertiary structure *(1 mark)*. They also have a constant region that is the same in all antibodies *(1 mark)*. An antibody consists of light chains and heavy chains that are joined together by disulfide bridges *(1 mark)*.

3.3 Bupropion has a similar structure to amphetamine *(1 mark)*. So it may bind to the antibody that is complementary to amphetamine, causing a positive result *(1 mark)*.

3.4 E.g. monoclonal antibodies are made using animal cells, and some people disagree with using animals this way *(1 mark)*.

4.1 After the first infection their T-cells and B-cells produced memory cells *(1 mark)*. When they were exposed for a second time the memory B-cells divided into plasma cells that produced the right type of antibodies to destroy the virus *(1 mark)*. The memory T-cells divided into the correct type of T-cells to quickly destroy the virus *(1 mark)*.

4.2 E.g. helper T-cells release chemical signalling molecules to activate cytotoxic T-cells/phagocytes/B-cells *(1 mark)*. If the Spanish flu patients' helper T-cells released too many signalling molecules, it could have resulted in the over-activation of these other immune cells / more of these other immune cells to be activated than normal *(1 mark)*.

4.3 E.g. children and the elderly have weaker immune systems than young adults *(1 mark)* so fewer cytotoxic T-cells/phagocytes/B-cells were activated *(1 mark)*.

4.4 The neuraminidase and haemagglutinin antigens on the Asian flu strain were different from the antigens on the Spanish flu strain *(1 mark)*, so any memory cells created against H1N1 would not detect H2N2 *(1 mark)*. So the immune system would have to start from scratch and carry out a primary immune response if exposed to Asian flu *(1 mark)*.

Topic 3

Topic 3A: Exchange and Transport Systems

1. Size and Surface Area

Page 138 — Application Question

Q1 a) i) A — surface area = $6 \times 2 \times 2 = $ **24 cm²**

B — surface area = $(4 \times 4 \times 2) + (2 \times 2 \times 2)$
$= 32 + 8 = $ **40 cm²**

C — surface area = $4\pi r^2$
$= 4 \times \pi \times 2.5^2$
$= $ **79 cm²** (2 s.f.)

ii) A — volume = $2 \times 2 \times 2 = $ **8 cm³**

B — volume = $2 \times 4 \times 2 = $ **16 cm³**

C — volume = $\frac{4}{3} \pi r^3$
$= \frac{4}{3} \pi \times 2.5^3$
$= $ **65 cm³** (2 s.f.)

iii) A — SA:V = 24:8 (or 3:1)
B — SA:V = 40:16 (or 5:2 or 2.5:1)
C — SA:V = 79:65 (or 1.2:1)

You should have got the same answers for shape C whether you used π as 3.14 or the π button on your calculator. If an exam question specifies which value to use for π, make sure you do what it says.

b) A

Simplify all of the ratios to 1 in order to compare them, e.g. A = 3:1, B = 2.5:1 and C = 1.2:1 — it's then obvious that A is the largest ratio.

Pages 140-141 — Application Questions

Q1 a) Adélie penguin. The Adélie penguin would have the larger surface area : volume ratio because it's smaller than the Emperor penguin.

b) The Emperor penguin because its large size means it has a lower surface area to volume ratio than the Adélie penguin. This means it's harder for it to lose heat from its body / easier for it to retain heat in its body, so it'll be better suited to living in colder regions than the Adélie penguin.

c) The Adélie penguin because it has a more compact shape, and so has a lower surface area : volume ratio than the Rockhopper penguin. Therefore it won't lose heat as easily so it'll be better suited to living in colder regions than the Rockhopper penguin.

Q2 Small animals have a high surface area : volume ratio meaning they will lose heat easily in cold temperatures. Underground temperatures will be warmer than on the surface, so they go underground to keep warm.

Q3 Small birds. Smaller birds have a higher surface area : volume ratio so they will lose heat more quickly than larger birds. Therefore they are more likely to have adaptations to keep warm.

Q4 Large animals have a low surface area : volume ratio so they find it hard to lose heat. They are active at night because it is cooler.

Page 141 — Fact Recall Questions

Q1 a) Any two from: e.g. oxygen / nutrients / water.
b) E.g. carbon dioxide, urea.

Q2 Lower surface area : volume ratio.

Q3 Some cells are deep within the body so the distance between them and the outside environment is too great for diffusion to take place quickly. Larger animals have a low surface area : volume ratio. This means they don't have a large enough area exposed to the environment to be able to exchange all the substances they need quickly enough using diffusion.

Q4 A system in a multicellular organism that carries substances to and from individual cells.

Q5 High surface area : volume ratio.

Q6 An animal with a compact shape has a low surface area : volume ratio. This means they lose less heat. An animal with a less compact shape has a higher surface area : volume ratio. This means they lose heat more easily.

Q7 Any two from: e.g. they might have a higher metabolic rate. / They might hibernate. / They might have thick layers of fur.

Q8 Any two from: e.g. they might spend a lot of time in water. / They might have features that increase their surface area, e.g. large ears.

2. Gas Exchange

Page 145 — Application Questions

Q1 B. E.g. the leaf is curled with the stomata inside, protecting them from the wind so less water is lost. / There are lots of hairs on the epidermis to trap water vapour, reducing the concentration gradient of water between the leaf and the air. / The stomata are sunken in pits to trap water vapour, reducing evaporation by lowering the concentration gradient.

Q2 A concentration gradient would still be maintained between the water and the blood, but it would be less steep. This means the fish wouldn't be able to take in as much oxygen as they would in clean water.

Q3 a) It increases steadily.
To answer this question you need to look at the arrow head of the red line — it's pointing upwards so the oxygen concentration of the blood is increasing.
b) It decreases steadily.
c) 80%
d) Because at point X the oxygen concentration of the water is higher than in the blood (about 92 %) — so oxygen has diffused into the blood down its concentration gradient.

Page 145 — Fact Recall Questions

Q1 Any two from: they have a large surface area. / They're thin. / A steep concentration gradient is maintained across them.

Q2 Single-celled organisms can exchange gases directly through their cell-surface membrane. This has a large surface area, is thin and has a short diffusion pathway, so there's no need for a gas exchange system.

Q3 Each gill is made of lots of thin plates called gill filaments. These are covered in lots of tiny structures called lamellae. Lamellae have a thin surface layer of cells and a good blood supply.

Q4 The counter-current system works by maintaining a steep concentration gradient between the water and the blood along the entire length of the gill. Blood flows through the lamellae in one direction and water flows over the lamellae in the opposite direction. This means that water with a relatively high oxygen concentration always flows next to blood with a lower oxygen concentration. Oxygen then diffuses into the blood from the water down the concentration gradient.

Q5 The surface of the mesophyll cells in the leaf.

Q6 Through the stomata in the epidermis.

Q7 Through the spiracles on the surface of the insect's body.

Q8 Carbon dioxide from the cells moves down its concentration gradient through the tracheoles towards the spiracles to be released into the atmosphere.

Q9 A plant specially adapted for life in a warm, dry or windy habitat.

Q10 Any three from: stomata sunk in pits / curled leaves with stomata inside / a layer of hairs on the epidermis / a reduced number of stomata / waxy, waterproof cuticles on leaves and stems.

3. Gas Exchange in Humans
Page 149 — Application Questions

Q1 a) 1
b) A
c) Speed = distance ÷ time = 0.82 ÷ 2 = **0.41 mm s⁻¹**.
Always double-check the question to see if it tells you what units to use in your answer. If it doesn't say then make sure you pick a sensible unit.

Q2 Less air, and so less oxygen, would be inhaled in each breath. This means the concentration gradient of oxygen between the alveoli and the capillaries will be less steep, slowing the rate of diffusion.

Page 149 — Fact Recall Questions

Q1 The external intercostal and diaphragm muscles contract, which causes the ribcage to move upwards and outwards and the diaphragm to flatten.

Q2 During forced expiration, the external intercostal muscles relax and internal intercostal muscles contract, pulling the ribcage further down and in.

Q3 Oxygen diffuses out of the alveoli, across the alveolar epithelium and the capillary endothelium, and into haemoglobin in the blood.

Q4 Alveoli have a thin exchange surface, which means there's a short diffusion pathway. This speeds up the rate of diffusion into the blood. There is a large number of alveoli so there is a large surface area for gas exchange, which speeds up the rate of diffusion. There's also a steep concentration gradient of oxygen and carbon dioxide between the alveoli and the capillaries, which increases the rate of diffusion. This is constantly maintained by the flow of blood and ventilation.

4. The Effects of Lung Disease
Page 153 — Application Questions

Q1 Graph A, because the tidal volume is much lower.

Q2 a) The alveoli are enlarged/much larger in the diseased lungs than in the healthy lungs. / The alveoli in the diseased lungs have merged together. In the healthy lungs they're more distinct.
b) Having enlarged alveoli means there's a smaller surface area for gas exchange, slowing the rate of diffusion of oxygen into the blood. So a patient with emphysema would have a lower level of oxygen in the blood.

Q3 a) The data shows that before inhaling salbutamol, the median area of a bronchial cross-section in healthy volunteers was bigger than in the asthmatics — 29 mm² compared to 10 mm². Inhaling salbutamol reduced the area of the cross-section in healthy volunteers by 2 mm², but in asthmatics the area of the cross-section almost doubled to 18 mm².
b)
$$\text{percentage change} = \frac{\text{final} - \text{original}}{\text{original}} \times 100$$
$$= \frac{18 - 10}{10} \times 100$$
$$= \mathbf{80\%}$$
c) Salbutamol could be used in inhalers to relax the smooth muscles lining the bronchioles in asthmatics. During an asthma attack, the smooth muscle contracts, causing constriction of the airways. The graph shows that after inhaling salbutamol the bronchioles aren't as constricted, so the salbutamol must relax the muscles.

Page 153 — Fact Recall Questions

Q1 The maximum volume of air it is possible to breathe forcefully out of the lungs after a really deep breath in.

Q2 Scar tissue is thicker and less elastic than normal lung tissue. This means that the lungs are less able to expand and so can't hold as much air as normal, so the tidal volume is reduced.

Q3 Scar tissue is thicker than normal lung tissue, so diffusion of gases is slower.

Q4 Reduced air flow means that FEV_1 is severely reduced (i.e. less air can be breathed out in 1 second).

5. Interpreting Lung Disease Data
Page 157 — Application Questions

Q1 Male deaths due to COPD increased from just over 10 per 100 000 people in 1946 to almost 80 per 100 000 in 1972. It then slowly decreased to about 40 per 100 000 by 1998.

Q2 E.g. between about 1948 and 1969 there doesn't seem to be any correlation between female deaths from COPD and tobacco consumption. After this year the number of female deaths from COPD increases as tobacco consumption decreases (there's a negative correlation). This isn't enough to say that COPD in women is not caused by smoking though. Tobacco consumption in women might have risen while tobacco consumption in the overall population was decreasing, but you can't tell from this data. Also, female deaths from COPD could be increasing for other reasons, e.g. industrial causes, even if tobacco consumption is still a cause of the disease.

Q3 E.g. they could use it to help them decide whether there's a link between tobacco consumption and COPD and whether to impose legal restrictions on the sale/advertisement of tobacco products as a result.

6. Dissecting Gas Exchange Systems
Page 160-161 — Application Question
Q1 a) Because she could end up sucking up stale air from inside the lungs into her mouth.
    b) Put the lungs inside a plastic bag while she inflates them. *This helps prevent bacteria being released into the air.*
    c) The lungs would deflate by themselves because of the elastin in the walls of the alveoli.
    d) Lengthways, down the gaps in the C-shaped rings of cartilage.

Page 161 — Fact Recall Questions
Q1 E.g. check that they are clean, sharp and free from rust.
Q2 E.g. some people believe that it is morally wrong to kill animals just for dissections. Animals used for dissections may not be raised in a humane way/killed in a humane way.

Exam-style Questions — pages 162-163
1.1 A = lamellae *(1 mark)*. Lamellae increase the surface area of the gill for diffusion *(1 mark)*. They're also thin, which reduces the diffusion distance between the water and the blood *(1 mark)*.
1.2 It has a counter-current exchange system (to maintain a large concentration gradient of oxygen between the water and the blood *(1 mark)*.
1.3 Air enters through an insect's spiracles *(1 mark)*. Oxygen then diffuses down the tracheae and tracheoles, directly into respiring cells *(1 mark)*.
1.4 Any two from: they can close their spiracles to prevent water loss *(1 mark)*. / They have a waxy, waterproof cuticle all over their body to reduce evaporation *(1 mark)*. / They have hairs around their spiracles to trap moist air and reduce evaporation *(1 mark)*.
2.1 width of alveolus = width of image ÷ magnification
    = 9 mm ÷ 60
    = 0.15 mm × 1000 (to convert to micrometres)
    = **150 μm**
    (1 mark for correct calculation,
    2 marks for correct answer)
    The question tells you to give your answer in μm, so you need to remember to convert your answer from mm to μm. If you're a bit rusty on this, check out p. 78.
2.2 E.g. the walls of the alveoli have been destroyed in the diseased alveoli *(1 mark)*. Destruction of the alveolar walls reduces the surface area of the alveoli *(1 mark)*, so the rate of gaseous exchange would decrease *(1 mark)*.
2.3 There would be a steeper concentration gradient of oxygen between the alveoli and the capillaries *(1 mark)*. This would increase the rate of diffusion of oxygen into the blood *(1 mark)*.
3.1 E.g. peak expiratory flow rate is lower for the person with asthma/line B because the inflamed bronchioles restrict the amount of air that can pass through *(1 mark)*. / The expiratory flow rate decreases more rapidly for the person with asthma/line B as more air is exhaled because the constricted bronchioles reduce the flow of air out of the lungs *(1 mark)*. *(Accept reverse arguments about why the peak expiratory flow rate is higher for line A for 1 mark.)*
3.2 E.g. exercise may increase the strength of the respiratory muscles/the intercostal muscles and diaphragm *(1 mark)*. This would allow air to be exhaled more forcefully, increasing the peak expiratory flow *(1 mark)*.

4 In inspiration, the external intercostal and diaphragm muscles contract *(1 mark)*. This causes the ribcage to move upwards and outwards and the diaphragm to flatten, increasing the volume of thoracic cavity *(1 mark)*. As the volume of the thoracic cavity increases, the lung pressure decreases (to below atmospheric pressure), causing air to flow into the lungs *(1 mark)*. In expiration, the external intercostal and diaphragm muscles relax *(1 mark)*. The ribcage moves downwards and inwards and the diaphragm curves upwards/becomes dome-shaped again *(1 mark)*. The volume of the thoracic cavity decreases, causing the air pressure to increase (to above atmospheric pressure), forcing air out of the lungs *(1 mark)*.

5.1 surface area = $4\pi r^2$
                      = $4 \times \pi \times 0.7^2$
                      = 6 μm^2 (1 s.f.)
    volume   = $\frac{4}{3}\pi r^3$
                      = $\frac{4}{3}\pi \times 0.7^3$
                      = 1 μm^3 (1 s.f.)
    surface area : volume = **6 : 1**
    (2 marks for the correct ratio. 1 mark for either 6 or 1.)
5.2 Because it is a single-celled organism with a short diffusion pathway *(1 mark)* and a large surface area : volume ratio *(1 mark)*. This means it can exchange substances quickly across its cell-surface membrane/outer surface *(1 mark)*.
    To help you answer this question, think about why multicellular organisms do have a gas exchange system — it's because the diffusion pathway is too big and they have a small surface area : volume ratio, which makes diffusion too slow.

Topic 3B — More Exchange and Transport Systems

1. Digestion and Absorption
Page 167 — Application Questions
Q1 On the cell membranes of epithelial cells lining the ileum.
Q2 water, glucose, fructose
Q3 Sucrase catalyses the hydrolysis of sucrose into glucose and fructose. These smaller molecules/monosaccharides can then be absorbed across the ileum epithelium into the bloodstream.
    *Make sure you write the names of enzymes and their substrates really clearly — if the examiner mistakes an 'o' for an 'a' (so thinks you've written sucr**a**se rather than sucr**o**se) you may lose marks.*

Page 167 — Fact Recall Questions
Q1 A reaction that breaks bonds though the addition of water.
Q2 lipases
Q3 Once lipids have been broken down by lipase, the monoglycerides and fatty acids stick with the bile salts to form micelles.
Q4 Exopeptidases act to hydrolyse peptide bonds at the ends of protein molecules. They remove single amino acids from proteins.
Q5 The micelles break up, releasing the monoglycerides and fatty acids, which diffuse directly across the membrane because they are lipid soluble.
Q6 Sodium ions are actively transported out of the epithelial cells into the ileum itself. They then diffuse back into the cells through sodium-dependent transporter proteins in the epithelial cell membranes, carrying amino acids with them.

2. Haemoglobin

Page 172 — Application Questions

Q1 a) B. The dissociation curve would be further to the right after a bike ride than whilst watching television, because during the bike ride the man's respiration rate would have increased, raising the pCO_2. This increases the rate of oxygen unloading so the dissociation curve shifts right.

b) The Bohr effect.

Q2 Badger — A. In an underground sett the oxygen concentration will be low, so the badger's haemoglobin will have the highest affinity for oxygen compared to the other animals, so the dissociation curve is furthest to the left.

The badger needs to be able to get any available oxygen at a low pO_2. Its dissociation curve is furthest to the left meaning it loads oxygen more readily at a lower oxygen concentration.

Bush dog — C. Above ground there will be more oxygen than underground, so the bush dog's haemoglobin will have a lower affinity for oxygen than the badger's haemoglobin. The bush dog is more active than the brown-throated sloth, so it has a greater oxygen demand. This means its haemoglobin will also have a lower affinity for oxygen than the brown-throated sloth's, so its dissociation curve is furthest to the right.

Brown-throated sloth — B. Above ground there will be more oxygen than underground, so the brown-throated sloth's haemoglobin will have a lower affinity for oxygen than the badger's haemoglobin. However, the brown-throated sloth's oxygen demand won't be as high as the bush dog's, as the brown-throated sloth is less active. This means the brown-throated sloth's haemoglobin will have an affinity for oxygen (and therefore dissociation curve) that is between the badger's and the bush dog's.

Page 172 — Fact Recall Questions

Q1 To carry oxygen around the body.

Q2 In red blood cells.

Q3 four

Q4 Loading describes oxygen binding with/joining to haemoglobin, and unloading describes oxygen being released from/leaving haemoglobin.

Q5 oxyhaemoglobin

Q6 How saturated haemoglobin is with oxygen at any given partial pressure of oxygen.

Q7 It changes the shape of haemoglobin in a way that makes it easier for other oxygen molecules to join too.

Q8 In the alveoli / lungs. This is the site where oxygen first enters the blood so it has the highest concentration of oxygen.

3. The Circulatory System

Page 174 — Application Question

Q1 A — Vena cava
B — Renal vein
C — An arteriole
D — Renal artery
E — Aorta

Relative blood pressure is highest in the aorta as it has just left the heart. Relative blood pressure in the other blood vessels decreases as they get further away from the heart. The vessel with the lowest relative blood pressure is the vena cava as it is the last blood vessel before blood returns to the heart.

Page 176 — Application Questions

Q1 a) i) From the blood into the tissue fluid.

ii) E.g. water, oxygen and nutrients (like glucose and amino acids)

b) i) Venule end of the capillary bed.

ii) Arteriole end of the capillary bed.

Q2 The water potential of the capillary is higher because there is less albumin in the blood. This means less water is absorbed by osmosis back into the capillary at the venule end of the capillary bed, which leads to an increase in tissue fluid.

Page 176 — Fact Recall Questions

Q1 Mammals have a low surface area : volume ratio so they need a specialised mass transport system/a circulatory system to carry raw materials from specialised exchange organs to their body cells.

Q2 pulmonary vein, vena cava

Remember, that the blood vessels that carry blood into the heart do not supply the heart muscle with blood — the blood goes into the chambers of the heart. Only the coronary vessels supply the heart muscle itself.

Q3 pulmonary artery

Q4 renal artery

Q5 The (left and right) coronary arteries.

Q6 A — vein, B — capillary, C — artery, D — arteriole

Q7 An artery has a thick muscular wall with elastic tissue and a folded endothelium.

Q8 A blood vessel that branches off from an artery.

Q9 a) veins

b) To stop the backflow of blood.

Q10 Any two from: the walls are only one cell thick / they're always very near the cells in exchange tissues / there's a large number of them in exchange tissues.

Q11 The fluid that surrounds cells in tissues.

Q12 a) At the arteriole end the hydrostatic pressure inside the capillaries is higher than the hydrostatic pressure in the tissue fluid. This means fluid is forced out of the capillaries and into the spaces around the cells, forming tissue fluid.

b) At the venule end of the capillary bed, the water potential is lower in the capillary than it is in the tissue fluid. This means that some water re-enters the capillaries from the tissue fluid by osmosis.

4. The Heart
Page 181 — Application Questions
Q1 The left atrium is contracting.
Q2 Open. The left ventricle is contracting, so the pressure is higher in the ventricle than in the aorta, forcing the semi-lunar valve open.
Q3 The left ventricle is relaxing.
Q4 The left atrium is filling up.
At point D, the increase in atrial pressure can't be due to the left atrium contracting because the diagram shows that the left ventricle is relaxing — i.e. the left ventricle doesn't contract next. So you need to think about what happens in the left atrium as the left ventricle is relaxing — it's filling up with blood to prepare for the next atrial contraction.
Q5 Open. The ventricle is relaxing, increasing the volume and reducing the pressure in the chamber. The atrium has been filling, increasing the pressure in the chamber. So as the pressure in the atrium becomes higher than that in the ventricle, the atrioventricular valve will open.

Page 182 — Application Questions
Q1 stroke volume × heart rate = cardiac output
61 × 79 = **4819 cm³ min⁻¹**
Q2 cardiac output ÷ stroke volume = heart rate
5075 ÷ 72.5 = **70 bpm**
Q3 cardiac output ÷ heart rate = stroke volume
5175 ÷ 75 = **69 cm³**

Page 182 — Fact Recall Questions
Q1 right side
Q2 A — pulmonary artery
B — aorta
C — inferior vena cava
D — pulmonary vein
E — right atrium
F — semi-lunar valve
G — right atrioventricular valve
H — left ventricle
Q3 So that it can contract more powerfully, which means the blood can be pumped further and so travel all round the body. The less muscular right ventricle cannot contract as powerfully so cannot pump blood as far/only pumps blood to the lungs.
Q4 a) semi-lunar valves
b) They stop blood flowing back into the heart after the ventricles contract.
Q5 An ongoing sequence of contraction and relaxation of the atria and ventricles that keeps blood continuously circulating round the body.
Q6 The volume of the atria decreases and the pressure increases.

5. Cardiovascular Disease
Pages 187-188 — Application Question
Q1 a) It could decrease the number of new cases of CHD by 37 000 per year (accept 36 000 to 38 000).
Look carefully at the values on the y-axis — the projected annual change in the number of new cases of CHD is negative, which means there are fewer new cases of CHD.
b) There'd be 59 000 fewer new cases of CHD by reducing BMI, but only 41 000 fewer new cases by reducing tobacco use/exposure — so between the two there'd be 18 000 fewer new cases by reducing BMI.
c) Intervention 3 / reducing salt intake by 3 g per day. This is because this intervention is predicted to reduce the number of new cases of CHD per year by 110 000 — which is greater than any other intervention shown on the graph.
d) i)   The more salt intake is reduced by, the fewer new cases of CHD there are per year.
ii) A diet low in salt will decrease the risk of high blood pressure, which in turn will decrease the risk of damage to the coronary artery walls.
This means it's less likely that atheromas form in the coronary arteries, so the risk of CHD is reduced and it's likely that there'll be fewer new cases of CHD.
This question is asking you to explain why a low salt diet could lead to a lower risk of CHD — that's the opposite way round to how you've learnt it.

Page 188 — Fact Recall Questions
Q1 An atheroma is a fibrous plaque formed from the build up and hardening of white blood cells, lipids and connective tissue.
Q2 An atheroma partially blocks the lumen of an artery and restricts blood flow.
Q3 a) High blood pressure increases the risk of damage to the artery walls. Damaged walls have an increased risk of atheroma formation.
b) E.g. any three from: atheroma formation / being overweight / not exercising / excessive alcohol consumption / high salt diet.
Q4 a) E.g. any two from: diet high in saturated fat/salt / smoking / not exercising.
b) E.g. genetic predisposition / having high blood pressure as a result of another condition / some forms of diabetes / ethnicity / age / gender.

6. Transport in Plants — Xylem
Page 191 — Application Questions

Q1 a) 10 °C — $(15 + 12 + 14) \div 3 =$ **13.7 mm**
20 °C — $(19 + 16 + 19) \div 3 =$ **18 mm**
30 °C — $(25 + 22 + 23) \div 3 =$ **23.3 mm**

b) See graph below. The bubble would move approximately 21 mm in 10 minutes at 25 °C.

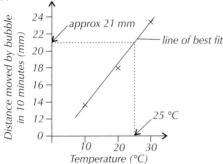

Q2 As the temperature increased, the distance moved by the bubble in 10 minutes increased too. This means the rate of transpiration increased with increasing temperatures, i.e. there is a positive correlation. At higher temperatures water molecules have more energy so they evaporate from the cells inside the leaf faster. This increases the water potential between the inside and outside of the leaf, making water diffuse out of the leaf faster.

Page 192 — Fact Recall Questions

Q1 xylem vessels

Q2 Water can move up a plant by cohesion and tension. Water evaporates from leaves at the top of the xylem. This creates tension which pulls more water into the leaf. As water molecules are cohesive, the whole column of water in the xylem moves upwards. More water then enters the stem through the roots.

Q3 a) An increase in wind increases transpiration rate. Lots of air movement blows away water molecules from around the stomata. This increases the water potential gradient, which increases the rate of transpiration.

b) Light intensity, temperature and humidity.

Q4 E.g. use a scalpel/razor blade to cut a thin cross-section of the stem. Place it in water to stop it drying out. Add a drop of water to a microscope slide and carefully add the stem section. Add a drop or two of stain (such as TBO) and leave for a short amount of time. Carefully apply a cover slip.

7. Transport in Plants — Phloem
Page 197 — Application Questions

Q1 a) E.g. meristems / leaves.

b) i) At the roots active transport is used to actively load solutes/assimilates into the sieve tubes. This lowers the water potential inside the sieve tubes, so water enters the tubes by osmosis.
Remember, water always flows from a higher water potential to a lower water potential.

ii) At the sink solutes/assimilates are removed from the phloem to be used up. This increases the water potential inside the sieve tubes, so water leaves the tubes by osmosis.

Q2 E.g. the radioactive carbon has been incorporated into organic substances produced by the plant during photosynthesis. The results show that these substances have been moved from the source in the leaves towards the sink in the roots because only the affected leaf and the upper part of the stem are black on the autoradiograph. This supports the mass flow hypothesis because solutes have been transported from areas of high pressure in the leaves to areas of lower pressure towards the root end of the stem. The solutes have not travelled into the other leaves, where the solute is also at a high concentration, because there is no pressure gradient in this direction.

Page 197 — Fact Recall Questions

Q1 Organic solutes, e.g. sugars/sucrose, amino acids.

Q2 It's the movement of solutes/assimilates to where they're needed in a plant.

Q3 In a plant a source is where solutes/assimilates are made, whereas a sink is where solutes/assimilates are used up.

Q4 If a ring of bark is removed from a woody stem, a bulge forms above the ring. If the fluid from the bulge is analysed, it will have a higher concentration of sugars than the fluid from below the ring. This is because the sugars can't move past the area where the bark has been removed — this is evidence that there can be a downward flow of sugars.

Q5 Sugar travels to many different sinks, not just to the one with the highest water potential, as the model would suggest. / The sieve plates would create a barrier to mass flow. A lot of pressure would be needed for the dissolved substances to get through at a reasonable rate.

Exam-style Questions — pages 199-200

1.1 In the first stage the atria contract, which decreases their volume *(1 mark)* and therefore increases the pressure in the atria *(1 mark)*.

1.2 Atrioventricular valves / AV valves *(1 mark)*. They prevent the back-flow of blood into the atria when the ventricles contract *(1 mark)*.

1.3 During stage one, the atrioventricular valves are open because the pressure in the atria is greater than that in the ventricles *(1 mark)*. During stage two, the atrioventricular valves are closed because the pressure in the ventricles is greater than that in the atria (*1 mark)*.

1.4 Because the atria are filling up with blood *(1 mark)*.

1.5 pulmonary artery *(1 mark)*

1.6 The walls of the pulmonary artery have elastic tissue to stretch and recoil as the heart beats *(1 mark)*. The inner lining/endothelium is folded, allowing the artery to stretch *(1 mark)*. Both of these features help to maintain the high pressure of the blood as it leaves the heart *(1 mark)*.

2.1 Reading off graph, distance moved by bubble in 5 minutes at 1.5 arbitrary units of light intensity = 15 mm
$15 \div 5 = \textbf{3 mm min}^{-1}$
(2 marks for the correct answer, otherwise 1 mark for showing a calculation of 'distance ÷ time')

2.2 The lighter it gets, the wider stomata open *(1 mark)*. This increases the evaporation rate from the leaves, which creates more tension in the xylem, pulling water into the leaves *(1 mark)*. The whole column of water moves up the xylem because water molecules are cohesive *(1 mark)*. The increased tension causes the water to move faster, meaning that the bubble moves further in a shorter amount of time *(1 mark)*.

2.3 E.g. the experiment should be repeated with a light intensity of zero *(1 mark)*.

3.1 Cardiovascular disease is a general term used to describe diseases associated with the heart and blood vessels *(1 mark)*.

3.2 control group *(1 mark)*

3.3 E.g. by taking a larger sample size *(1 mark)*. By making sure the men in the test group followed the dietary information *(1 mark)*.

3.4 The fats are emulsified by bile salts, forming small droplets *(1 mark)*. They are then broken down by lipases into monoglycerides and fatty acids *(1 mark)*. The monoglycerides and fatty acids stick with the bile salts forming micelles *(1 mark)*, which help move the monoglycerides and fatty acids towards the endothelium *(1 mark)*. There they are released and diffuse directly across the membrane *(1 mark)* because they are lipid soluble *(1 mark)*. [Maximum of 3 marks available.]

4.1 It is a protein with a quaternary structure consisting of four polypeptide chains *(1 mark)*. Each polypeptide chain has a haem group containing an iron ion *(1 mark)*.

4.2 Each animal's haemoglobin was 50% saturated at a lower pO_2 at high altitude than at sea level *(1 mark)*. This means that haemoglobin has a higher affinity for oxygen/ unloads oxygen less readily at high altitudes than at sea level *(1 mark)*. This suggests that the animals living at high altitudes live in environments with a lower oxygen concentration than those living at sea level *(1 mark)*.

5.1 phloem tissue *(1 mark)*

5.2 The phloem is involved in translocation/the movement of organic solutes in a plant *(1 mark)*. Translocation moves solutes from the source, where they are produced, to the sink, where they are used up *(1 mark)*.

5.3 Cutting a C-shaped ring in the bark reduces the volume of the phloem, limiting the amount of solutes that can be transported *(1 mark)*. The solutes normally travel from the leaves where they are produced, and flow through the plant *(1 mark)*. Cutting a C-shaped ring in the bark means that more solutes are retained in the upper part of the plant where the fruits are produced, which may lead to greater fruit production *(1 mark)*.

Topic 4

Topic 4A — DNA, RNA and Protein Synthesis

1. DNA

Page 201 — Fact Recall Questions
Q1 Eukaryotic chromosomes are thread-like structures made up of a long molecule of DNA wound around proteins called histones. The DNA and proteins are then coiled up to form a chromosome.
Q2 DNA in prokaryotic chromosomes is shorter than DNA in eukaryotic chromosomes and is also circular rather than linear. Also, the DNA isn't wound around histone proteins.

2. Genes and Chromosomes

Page 203 — Application Questions
Q1

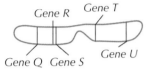

Homologous chromosomes are the same so all of the genes should be in the same place.
Q2 a) ACTGTATTGATCGAATGTCTA
This is the sequence of the exons only as these are the sections of the gene that actually determine the amino acid order.
b) 10
c) GC

Page 203 — Fact Recall Questions
Q1 A sequence of DNA bases that codes for either a polypeptide or functional RNA.
Q2 three
Q3 The complete set of genes in the cell.
Q4 The full range of proteins that the cell can produce.
Q5 Introns and multiple repeats.
Q6 exons
Q7 A different form of a gene.
Q8 A locus.

3. RNA and Protein Synthesis

Page 204 — Fact Recall Questions
Q1 mRNA carries the genetic code from the DNA to the ribosomes.
Q2 A group of three adjacent bases on an mRNA molecule.
Q3 Messenger RNA
Q4 Transfer RNA

4. Transcription and Translation

Page 206 — Application Questions
Q1 It will inhibit protein synthesis. By inhibiting RNA polymerase, α–amanitin will prevent the transcription of mRNA from DNA, preventing protein synthesis from taking place.
Q2 a) UCAAGCCUGCUCGGCUACGAGCAUUU
b) 6
One amino acid is coded for by three bases in an exon.

Page 208 — Application Questions
Q1 E.g. it may affect the function of the ribosomes, preventing them from translating mRNA into amino acids. This could prevent/impair protein synthesis.
You don't need to have learnt about Diamond-Blackfan anaemia to answer this question — so long as you know the process of translation, you can work out the answer.
Q2 It could result in a shorter amino acid sequence being produced, which would change the primary structure of the protein and therefore the 3D tertiary structure of the protein. This could affect the protein's function. This could happen because translation of the mRNA sequence only continues until a stop signal is reached. Any codons after the stop signal would not be translated into amino acids.

Page 208 — Fact Recall Questions
Q1 Transcription — takes place in the nucleus.
Translation — takes place at the ribosomes in the cytoplasm.
Q2 a) an enzyme
b) transcription
Q3 Because of complementary/specific base pairing.
Q4 Eukaryotic DNA contains introns/regions that don't code for amino acids. These get transcribed into pre-mRNA along with the exons/coding regions. Splicing removes the introns from pre-mRNA and joins together the exons to create mRNA ready for translation into a protein.
Q5 It doesn't contain introns.
Q6 tRNA molecules carry amino acids to the ribosome during translation.
Q7 ATP provides the energy needed for the bond between an amino acid and a tRNA molecule to form, allowing the tRNA to carry the amino acid to the ribosome.
Q8 A tRNA molecule with an anticodon that's complementary to a codon on the mRNA attaches itself to the mRNA by complementary base pairing. A second tRNA molecule attaches itself to the next codon on the mRNA in the same way, and so on.
Q9 Peptide bond

5. The Genetic Code and Nucleic Acids
Page 211 — Application Questions
Q1 UACUUUCAAAUAGCGCAU
Q2 TACAAAGTTGTTCGCATGTAT

Remember, DNA is a complementary sequence to mRNA and in DNA, T replaces U as a base.

Q3 UACGUAUAUGUAAAAGUU

tRNA codons also have a complementary sequence to mRNA codons, but tRNA still has U as a base.

Q4 Phe - Gln - Ile - His - Ala - Tyr

To answer this question, work out what the complementary mRNA codons would be first then match up the appropriate amino acids using the table.

Q5 The DNA sequence is missing the base triplets: CGC, TAT and GTT. The amino acid sequence is missing: Tyr and His.

Page 212 — Application Questions
Q1 Uracil is present as a base in mRNA but not DNA, so uracil can be used as a marker for RNA synthesis.
Q2 As the concentration of puromycin increased, the % inhibition of the development of respiration, leucine uptake and uracil uptake also increased. The development of respiration and leucine uptake were strongly inhibited, with uracil uptake being inhibited to a slightly lesser degree.
Q3 protein synthesis

Page 212 — Fact Recall Questions
Q1 Each triplet is read in sequence, separate from the triplet before it and after it — base triplets don't share their bases.
Q2 A base triplet that tells the cell when to start production of a particular protein.
Q3 universal

Exam-style Questions — page 214
1.1 RNA polymerase lines up free RNA nucleotides alongside exposed bases on the DNA template strand *(1 mark)*. The enzyme then moves along the DNA strand, assembling a complementary mRNA sequence from the RNA nucleotides by joining them together *(1 mark)*.
1.2 Genes in eukaryotic DNA contain introns (sections that don't code for amino acids) *(1 mark)*. After transcription the introns are removed from pre-mRNA strands by splicing, leaving only the exons (parts of the gene that code for amino acids) which form mRNA *(1 mark)*. So eukaryotic mRNA would be shorter than the DNA it was transcribed from *(1 mark)*.
2.1 The sequence of base triplets/codons in mRNA which code for specific amino acids *(1 mark)*.
2.2 It is universal because the same specific base triplets code for the same amino acids in all living things *(1 mark)*. It is degenerate because there are more possible combinations of triplets than there are amino acids *(1 mark)*.
2.3 (DNA sequence: CCT GTG CGT GGA GTG)
tRNA anticodons: CCU GUG CGU GGA GUG
(2 marks for 5 correct tRNA anticodons. Allow 1 mark if tRNA anticodons are correct but T hasn't been replaced with U.)

Remember, tRNA is complementary to a strand of mRNA — so it's just like DNA but with U replacing T.

2.4 tRNA is folded into a clover shape and held together by hydrogen bonds whereas mRNA is not *(1 mark)*. Three adjacent bases in mRNA form a codon whereas tRNA has three specific bases called an anticodon *(1 mark)*. tRNA has an amino acid binding site whereas mRNA does not *(1 mark)*.

2.5 ribosome *(1 mark)*
2.6 tRNA molecules carry amino acids to the ribosome *(1 mark)*. A tRNA molecule with an anticodon that's complementary to the first codon on the mRNA attaches itself to the mRNA by complementary base pairing *(1 mark)*. A second tRNA molecule attaches itself to the next codon on the mRNA in the same way and the two amino acids are joined by a peptide bond *(1 mark)*. The first tRNA molecule moves away, leaving its amino acid behind and this process continues and produces a polypeptide chain *(1 mark)*.

Always look at the number of available marks — the more marks there are, the more detailed your answer should be.

Topic 4B — Diversity and Selection

1. Meiosis and Genetic Variation
Pages 219-220 — Application Questions
Q1

Q2 E.g.

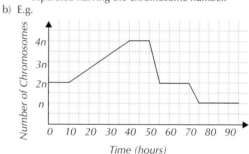

You should have drawn a single chromatid from each homologous pair — so there shouldn't be two orange chromatids and a red chromatid, for example.

Q3 a) After meiosis II, because there is only one chromatid of each chromosome.
   b) Between meiosis I and meiosis II, because there are no homologous pairs, but each chromosome has two sister chromatids.
   c) Before meiosis I, because there are homologous pairs of chromosomes.
Q4 a) i) The DNA is being replicated to produce two copies of each chromosome.
      ii) The DNA is condensing to form double-armed chromosomes and the chromosomes are arranging themselves into homologous pairs.
      iii) Meiosis I occurs — the homologous pairs are separated halving the chromosome number.
   b) E.g.

During this time period, meiosis II occurs and the sister chromatids are separated — halving the chromosome number again and generating haploid cells.

Page 220— Fact Recall Questions

Q1 a) diploid
   b) haploid
   c) diploid

Q2 a) The homologous pairs separate.
   b) The sister chromatids separate.

Q3 a) Crossing over and independent segregation of chromosomes.
   b) Crossing over is when chromatids twist around each other and bits of chromatid swap over. The resulting chromosomes contain the same genes but now have a different combination of alleles. This means that when the chromatids separate at meiosis II, each of the four daughter cells will contain chromatids with different alleles.
   Independent segregation is when the random separation of homologous pairs in meiosis I means that different combinations of maternal and paternal chromosomes go into each cell. This produces genetic variation in the gametes.

Q4 Mitosis produces cells with the same number of chromosomes as the parent cell, whereas meiosis produces cells with half the number of chromosomes as the parent cell. In mitosis daughter cells are genetically identical to each other and to the parent cell, whereas in meiosis daughter cells are genetically different from one another and the parent cell. Mitosis produces two daughter cells whereas, meiosis produces four daughter cells.

2. Mutations
Page 223 — Application Questions

Q1 a) G (in second triplet) has been deleted.
   b) leucine – glutamic acid – tyrosine
      leucine – serine
   c) The genetic code is degenerate, which means that some amino acids are coded for by more than one DNA triplet. In this example, TAT undergoes a substitution and becomes TAC. Both TAT and TAC code for tyrosine so the amino acid sequence produced stays the same.

Q2 a) chromosome non-disjunction
   b) Non-disjunction would mean that chromosome 18 fails to separate properly during meiosis, so one cell gets an extra copy of 18 and another gets none. When the gamete with the extra copy fuses to another gamete at fertilisation, the resulting zygote will have three copies of chromosome 18.
   c) E.g.

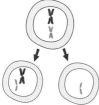

When the homologous pairs line up, the pair of sister chromatids making up chromosome 18 fail to separate.

Page 223 — Fact Recall Questions

Q1 Changes in the DNA base sequence of chromosomes.

Q2 E.g. deletions

Q3 a) They increase the rate of mutations occurring. / They increase the probability of mutations occurring.
   b) E.g. ultraviolet radiation / ionising radiation / X-rays / gamma rays

3. Genetic Diversity
Page 225 — Application Question

Q1 a) Population 1 is more genetically diverse because it has a relatively high frequency of three different alleles for flower colour / because population 2 has fewer different alleles for flower colour.
   b) Population 2 could have experienced an event in the past that caused a big reduction in its numbers. This could have meant that all the organisms with the purple allele (and lots with the pink allele) died before reproducing — causing the purple allele to be lost from the gene pool (and the frequency of the pink allele to be reduced). When the survivors reproduced, the new population would have been created without the purple allele (and a lower frequency of the pink allele).

Page 225 — Fact Recall Questions

Q1 Genetic diversity is the number of different alleles of genes in a species or population.

Q2 By mutations in the DNA forming new alleles. By different alleles being introduced into a population when individuals from another population migrate into it and reproduce / gene flow.

4. Natural Selection
Pages 227-228 — Application Questions

Q1 As the result of a mutation, some individuals in the population have a darker colouring that helps them to blend into their environment (wooded areas) better. This is beneficial because it helps them to avoid predators and sneak up on prey. So these individuals are more likely to survive, reproduce and pass on the allele for darker colouring. The frequency of the allele for darker colouring will increase in the population so that, after many generations, most organisms in the population will carry the allele for darker colouring.

Q2 Some individuals in the population have a mutated allele that gives them resistance to DDT. The population is exposed to DDT, killing the mosquitoes without the resistance allele. Individuals with the resistance allele survive, reproduce and pass on the allele. The frequency of the resistance allele will increase in the population so that, after many generations, most organisms in the population will carry the allele for DDT resistance.
See, I told you. It's the same answer whatever the adaptation — it helps them to survive, reproduce and pass on the allele for that adaptation. The frequency of the beneficial allele then increases in the population over many generations.

Q3 a) Behavioural adaptation — e.g. hunting in groups/pods. Physiological adaptation — reducing heart rate whilst diving. Anatomical adaptation — a thick layer of blubber.

b) E.g. Hunting in groups/pods helps killers whales to hunt food successfully, increasing their chances of survival. Reducing heart rate whilst diving helps the whales conserve oxygen, so they can last for longer underwater without breathing. This increases their chances of catching prey and so surviving.
A thick layer of blubber keeps them warm, so increases their chances of surviving in cold seas. / A think layer of blubber gives them a streamlined shape, so helps them to move more easily through water to catch their prey, increasing their chances of survival.

The important thing about all adaptations is that they increase an organism's chance of surviving and reproducing successfully.

Page 228 — Fact Recall Questions
Q1 Random mutations can result in a new allele being formed that is beneficial to the organism. This may then be selected for during natural selection.
Q2 Not all individuals are as likely to reproduce as each other. There's differential reproductive success in a population — individuals that have an allele that increases their chance of survival are more likely to survive, reproduce and pass on their genes (including the beneficial allele), than individuals with less advantageous alleles. This means that a greater proportion of the next generation inherits the beneficial allele. They, in turn, are more likely to survive, reproduce and pass on their genes. So the frequency of the beneficial allele increases from generation to generation.
Q3 An adaptation is a feature that increases an organism's chances of survival.
Q4 Physiological adaptations are processes inside an organism's body that increase its chance of survival.

5. The Effects of Selection
Page 230 — Application Question
Q1 a) Stabilising selection because the range of masses is being reduced towards the middle of the range.
b) E.g. light wolves are less likely to survive because they find it more difficult to keep warm in the snow/ find it difficult to move through heavy snow. Heavy wolves are also less likely to survive because they sink through the snow more easily/find it harder to hunt for food. Therefore, conditions are most favourable for medium-sized wolves, so the mass of wolves shifted towards the middle of the range.

You weren't expected to know the answer to this question, just to make sensible suggestions as to why smaller and larger wolves were less likely to survive.

Page 230 — Fact Recall Questions
Q1 Where individuals with alleles for characteristics of an extreme type are more likely to survive and reproduce.
Q2 Having full antibiotic resistance is a characteristic of an extreme type.

6. Investigating Selection
Page 232 — Application Question
Q1 a) E.g. sterilised water without antibiotic. It's used to make sure that the water the antibiotic is diluted in is not the reason for any change in turbidity, and hence bacterial growth changes.
b) Any two from: e.g. wear gloves and tie long hair back to prevent it from falling into anything. / Regularly disinfect work surfaces to minimise contamination. / Briefly flame the neck of the container of broth just after it's opened and just before it's closed. / Sterilise all glassware before and after use, e.g. in an autoclave.
c) Aseptic techniques are used to prevent contamination of cultures by unwanted microorganisms. This is important because contamination can affect the growth of the microorganism that you're working with. It's also important to avoid contamination with disease-causing microbes that could make you ill.
d) From 0 to 4 hours, the turbidity of the sample was increasing as the bacteria reproduced and the number in the sample increased. After the addition of the antibiotic at 4 hours, the turbidity remained the same. The antibiotic killed any bacteria present, stopping them reproducing any more and so turbidity stayed at the same level as before the addition of the antibiotic.

Pages 232-233 — Fact Recall Questions
Q1 E.g. antibiotics, antiseptics, disinfectants
Q2 distilled water, bacterial culture and nutrients
Q3 a) A clear patch in a lawn of bacteria where the bacteria can't grow.
b) It tells you how well an antibiotic/antimicrobial works. The larger the inhibition zone, the more bacteria were inhibited from growing.
Q4 Pass it through a hot Bunsen burner flame for 5 seconds.

Exam-style Questions — pages 234-235
1.1 Point 1 *(1 mark)* because the moss's chromosome number goes from diploid to haploid/the chromosome number halves *(1 mark)*.
1.2 Fertilisation *(1 mark)* because the haploid gametes fuse to form a diploid zygote/the chromosome number doubles *(1 mark)*.
1.3 Any one from: e.g. a genetic bottleneck occurred *(1 mark)*. / The founder effect meant there were only a small number of alleles in the initial gene pool *(1 mark)*. / Through stabilising selection favouring alleles towards the middle of the range and eliminating alleles at the extremes *(1 mark)*.
1.4 E.g. through the introduction of new alleles from gene mutations *(1 mark)*. Through new plants, carrying new alleles, being introduced to the population *(1 mark)*.
2.1 Crossing over *(1 mark)*
2.2 Independent segregation *(1 mark)*. When pairs of homologous chromosomes are separated during meiosis I, it's completely random which chromosome from each pair ends up in which daughter cell *(1 mark)*. So the daughter cells end up with different combinations of chromosomes, increasing genetic variation in potential offspring *(1 mark)*.

3 Mitosis produces two daughter cells, whereas meiosis produces four daughter cells *(1 mark)*. This is because mitosis only involves one division, whereas meiosis has two divisions *(1 mark)*. Mitosis produces cells with the same number of chromosomes as the parent cell, whereas meiosis produces cells with half the number of chromosomes as the parent cell *(1 mark)*. This is because mitosis only separates the sister chromatids, whereas meiosis separates the homologous pairs, then the sister chromatids *(1 mark)*. In mitosis, daughter cells are genetically identical to each other and to the parent cell, whereas in meiosis daughter cells are genetically different from one another and the parent cell *(1 mark)*. This is because there's no pairing or separating of homologous chromosomes in mitosis, and so no crossing over or independent segregation of chromosomes *(1 mark)*.

4.1 As a result of mutations, some individuals in a population have alleles for producing tetracycline-based antibiotics *(1 mark)*. This means they can kill other bacteria in the area, reducing competition for nutrients *(1 mark)*. So these bacteria are more likely to survive, reproduce and pass on their alleles to the next generation *(1 mark)*. After many generations the frequency of the beneficial allele increases in the population. / After many generations most bacteria in the population will have the alleles to produce tetracycline-based antibiotics *(1 mark)*.

4.2 Directional selection because that is where individuals with alleles for characteristics of an extreme type, such as antibiotic resistance, are more likely to survive and reproduce *(1 mark)*.

4.3 Any two from: e.g. they should all be the same breed of cattle. / The cattle should all be the same age. / The cattle should all be kept in the same type of environment. / None of the cattle should have been given any other antibiotics before the experiment started. *(1 mark for each correct answer, up to a maximum of 2 marks)*

4.4 To see what percentage of the *E. coli* present in the cows' stomachs were already resistant to tetracycline *(1 mark)*.

4.5 E.g. tetracycline resistance is present in some of the cattle who do not receive any antibiotics in their feed *(1 mark)* and in cattle that had antibiotics other than tetracycline added to their feed *(1 mark)*. Cattle that had both tetracycline and sulfamethazine added to their feed showed the most resistance to tetracycline/more resistance than cattle that had tetracycline alone added to their food *(1 mark)*.

Topic 4C — Diversity and Classification

1. Classification of Organisms
Page 238 — Application Questions
Q1 a) sharks
    b) salamanders
    c) i)   crocodiles
        ii) lizards
Q2

Taxon	
Domain	Eukarya
Kingdom	Animalia
Phylum	**Chordata**
Class	Mammalia
Order	Perrisodactyla
Family	Equidae
Genus	**Equus**
Species	**asinus**

Page 238 — Fact Recall Questions
Q1 Based on their evolutionary history.
Q2 Binomial naming system

2. Classification Using Courtship Behaviour
Page 240 — Application Questions
Q1 That fireflies 4 and 9 belong to the same species.
    Fireflies of the same species will have the same pattern of light pulses.
Q2 6
    Different species will have different patterns of light pulses.
Q3 Distantly. The patterns of light pulses produced by fireflies 1 and 3 are very different.
Q4 Yes. Fireflies 4 and 9 also start their display with three light pulses so probably belong to the same family.

Page 240 — Fact Recall Questions
Q1 Behaviour carried out by organisms to attract a mate of the right species.
Q2 Because it is species specific — only members of the same species will do and respond to that courtship behaviour.

3. Classification Using DNA or Proteins
Pages 242-243 — Application Questions
Q1 That horses are more closely related to humans than chickens.
Q2 a) Species A: TCGACGTGGGTAATCGAGC
        Species B: TCCACGTGTGTAATCGAGT
        Species C: ACGCCGAGTGTTATGGAGT
    b) 3
    c) 7
    Take your time with questions like this. Once you've got your answer, recount it to make sure it's right.
    d) Species B. There are fewer base differences in the DNA when comparing A and B than A and C.
    e) Species B. There are only 6 base differences between species C and B. This is fewer than for species C and A so species C and B are more closely related.
Q3 Species B. The higher relative fluorescence indicates that more anti-X antibody bound to cells from species B than to cells from A or C. This suggests that proteins from species B are most similar to those from species X, so B is most closely related to X.

4. Using Gene Technologies to Assess Genetic Diversity
Page 244 — Application Question
Q1 a) The scientist could compare the DNA base sequences of a gene controlling shell colour or pattern in individuals from a warm climate and individuals from a colder climate. Different alleles of the same gene have slightly different DNA base sequences, so by comparing the base sequences the scientist could determine how many alleles of the gene there are in each population. The scientist could repeat this for all the shell colour and pattern genes.
    b) By looking at the frequency of measurable or observable characteristics in a population.

Page 244 — Fact Recall Question
Q1 Gene technologies can give more accurate estimates of genetic diversity and make comparisons of genetic diversity easier to carry out.

5. Investigating Variation
Page 249 — Application Questions
Q1 a) i) The mean wing span is approximately 27 cm for species A and 31 cm for species B. Both curves follow a normal distribution. Species A has a higher standard deviation than species B.
   ii) Species A, because it has a higher standard deviation.
   b) $(31 - 27) \div 27 \times 100 = \textbf{14.8\%}$

   Make sure you're confident at calculating percentages — they're a common mathsy-type question that examiners like to ask.

Q2 Work out the mean length of snakes:
$\bar{x} = (177 + 182 + 190 + 187 + 191) \div 5 = 185.4$ cm
Work out $(x - \bar{x})^2$ for each snake length:
A $= (177 - 185.4)^2 = (-8.4)^2 = 70.56$,
B $= (182 - 185.4)^2 = (-3.4)^2 = 11.56$,
C $= (190 - 185.4)^2 = (4.6)^2 = 21.16$,
D $= (187 - 185.4)^2 = (1.6)^2 = 2.56$,
E $= (191 - 185.4)^2 = (5.6)^2 = 31.36$
Work out $\Sigma = (x - \bar{x})^2$:
$70.56 + 11.56 + 21.16 + 2.56 + 31.36 = 137.2$
Divide it by the number of values minus 1 ($n - 1$):
$137.2 \div 4 = 34.3$
Square root it:
$\sqrt{34.3} = \textbf{5.86 to 3 s.f.}$

Page 249 — Fact Recall Questions
Q1 Divide the total of all the values in your data by the number of values in your data.
Q2 Bell shaped
Q3 The spread of the values about the mean. / How much the values in a single sample vary.

6. Biodiversity
Pages 251-252 — Application Questions
Q1 a) 6
   The species richness is just the number of different insect species.
   b) i) Pond A
   $d = \dfrac{18 \times (18 - 1)}{6 + 20 + 2 + 6 + 0 + 12} = \dfrac{306}{46}$
   $= \textbf{6.65}$ (3 s.f.)
   ii) Pond B
   $d = \dfrac{54 \times (54 - 1)}{156 + 20 + 42 + 2 + 306 + 72} = \dfrac{2862}{598}$
   $= \textbf{4.79}$ (3 s.f.)

   If you have to calculate species diversity in the exam, always show your full working out. You may pick up a mark for showing you understand the equation if nothing else.
   c) Pond A. It has a higher diversity of insects, so it will be able to support a higher diversity of birds and amphibians.

Q2 a) i) Wood
$d = \dfrac{101 \times (101 - 1)}{210 + 306 + 272 + 342 + 72 + 56 + 42 + 56 + 0}$
$= \dfrac{10\,100}{1356} = \textbf{7.45}$ (3 s.f.)

ii) Town
$d = \dfrac{41 \times (41 - 1)}{0 + 6 + 2 + 0 + 0 + 2 + 380 + 30 + 20}$
$= \dfrac{1640}{440} = \textbf{3.73}$ (3 s.f.)

b) Comparing the number of species present in a community doesn't take into account the population size of each species. Species that are in a community in very small numbers shouldn't be treated the same as those with bigger populations. For example, the graph shows nine species of tree in the town and eight in the wood. However, eight of the nine tree species in the town are present only in small numbers. The tree species in the wood are all present in higher numbers. Calculating the index of diversity for the wood gives a much higher estimate of biodiversity than simply counting the number of species present.

Page 252 — Fact Recall Questions
Q1 The variety of living organisms in an area.
Q2 All the populations of different species in a habitat.

7. Agriculture and Biodiversity
Page 255 — Application Question
Q1 a)

Number of Crop Types	Rank	Diversity Index	Rank	Difference between ranks (d)	d^2
1	8	1.87	8	0	0
2	7	2.24	7	0	0
3	6	2.71	6	0	0
4	5	3.18	5	0	0
5	4	4.01	3	1	1
6	3	3.59	4	1	1
7	2	4.44	2	0	0
8	1	4.97	1	0	0

$r_s = 1 - \dfrac{6\Sigma d^2}{n(n^2 - 1)}$

$r_s = 1 - \dfrac{6\,(0 + 0 + 0 + 0 + 1 + 1 + 0 + 0)}{8\,(8^2 - 1)}$

$r_s = 1 - \dfrac{6 \times 2}{8 \times 63}$

$r_s = 1 - \dfrac{12}{504}$

$r_s = \textbf{0.976}$ (3 s.f.)

b) Positive
c) Rejected, because the result is higher than the critical value of 0.738.

Page 256 — Fact Recall Questions

Q1 a) It increases the area of land available for farming.

b) Woodland clearance and hedgerow removal reduce diversity by directly removing trees and hedgerow plants. This destroys habitats. Some species also lose their shelter and food source. This means that these species will die or be forced to migrate to another suitable area.

Q2 Both agriculture and biodiversity are important / provide us with important resources. A balance between agriculture and conservation is needed so we can keep farming and conserve biodiversity.

Exam-style Questions — pages 257-259

1.1 E.g. courtship behaviour is species specific *(1 mark)*. This reduces the probability of animals mating with different species and producing infertile offspring *(1 mark)*.

1.2 Length of phrase = 4 seconds

$60 \div 4 =$ **15 phrases/minute** *(1 mark)*

1.3 Songbirds A and C produce the same song *(1 mark)*. This suggests that they may be the same species *(1 mark)*.

1.4 E.g. she could calculate the Spearman's rank correlation coefficient *(1 mark)* as this would allow her to determine whether or not there is a correlation between song pitch and body size, as well as the direction/strength of the correlation *(1 mark)*.

2.1 It is present in all plants so any two species of plant can be compared by looking at RuBisCo *(1 mark)*.

2.2 Any one from, e.g. by comparing the amino acid sequence *(1 mark)*. The more similar the amino acid sequences the more closely related the species are *(1 mark)*. / By using immunological comparison *(1 mark)*. If two proteins are bound by the same antibody they must be similar and the two species must be closely related *(1 mark)*.

3.1 The index of diversity takes the number of individuals of each species into account, as well as the overall number of species — unlike species richness (which is just the number of species) *(1 mark)*. This gives a more accurate picture of biodiversity because species that are in a community in very small numbers aren't treated the same as those with bigger populations *(1 mark)*.

3.2 Farm A

$$d = \frac{47 \times (47 - 1)}{6 + 30 + 72 + 42 + 110 + 110}$$

$$= \frac{2162}{370} = \mathbf{5.84} \text{ (3 s.f.)}$$

(2 marks for correct answer, otherwise 1 mark for correct working)

Farm B

$$d = \frac{27 \times (27 - 1)}{132 + 2 + 12 + 30 + 6 + 0}$$

$$= \frac{702}{182} = \mathbf{3.86} \text{ (3 s.f.)}$$

(2 marks for correct answer, otherwise 1 mark for correct working)

3.3 Farm A. It has a higher index of diversity *(1 mark)* and using chemical herbicides tends to reduce the number and abundance of species *(1 mark)*.

3.4 E.g. they could include a sample of hedgerows on farms that do not use biological pesticides *(1 mark)*.

3.5 E.g it increases the area of farmland by turning lots of small fields into fewer large fields, which may increase crop production / make it easier to plant/harvest a lot of crops at once *(1 mark)*.

3.6 Hedgerow removal could reduce insect biodiversity *(1 mark)*. It destroys habitats, so insect species could lose their shelter and food sources *(1 mark)*. This could kill insects or force them migrate to other areas *(1 mark)*.

4.1 The method used was good because it used random samples, which helps to make sure the results aren't biased *(1 mark)*. The plants were grown in the same environment to control the variables, which increases the validity of the results *(1 mark)*. However, there was no control used, which decreases the validity of the results *(1 mark)* and they didn't repeat the experiment, which would have increased the precision of the results *(1 mark)*.

4.2 The mean number of hours survived without water was higher for species B than species A (168 hours compared to 120 hours), so species B would survive better in the area of Africa with low rainfall *(1 mark)*. However, the standard deviation is larger for species B than species A, so there is more variation in the results *(1 mark)*.

4.3 Gene Y, because the mean number of days survived without water is highest and the standard deviation is lowest *(1 mark)*.

Glossary

A

Accurate result
A result that is really close to the true answer.

Activation energy
The energy that needs to be supplied before a chemical reaction will start.

Active site
The part of an enzyme where a substrate molecule binds.

Active transport
Movement of molecules and ions across plasma membranes, usually against a concentration gradient. Requires energy.

Adaptation
A characteristic that increases an organism's chances of survival, e.g. antibiotic-resistance.

Affinity for oxygen
The tendency a molecule has to bind with oxygen.

Agglutination
The clumping together of cells, e.g. pathogens, red blood cells.

AIDS (acquired immunodeficiency syndrome)
A condition caused by HIV, in which the immune system deteriorates and eventually fails.

Allele
An alternative form of a gene.

Alveolus
A microscopic air sac in the lungs where gas exchange occurs.

Amino acid
A monomer of proteins.

Anomalous result
A measurement that falls outside the range of values you'd expect or any pattern you already have.

Antibiotic
A medicine that is designed to kill or inhibit the growth of bacteria (or sometimes fungi).

Antibiotic resistance
When bacteria are able to survive in the presence of antibiotics.

Antibody
A protein produced by B-cells in response to the presence of a pathogen.

Antigen
A molecule (usually a protein) that can trigger an immune response.

Antigenic variation
Where pathogens change their antigens.

Antigen-presenting cell
An immune system cell that processes and presents antigens on its surface to activate other immune system cells.

Antimicrobial substance
A substance designed to kill microorganisms, e.g. an antibiotic, antiseptic or disinfectant.

Artefact (microscope)
Something you can see on a microscope slide that isn't part of the specimen you're looking at, e.g. an air bubble.

Arteriole
A blood vessel that branches off an artery.

Aseptic technique
A technique used to prevent the unwanted growth or transfer of microorganisms.

Atheroma
A fibrous plaque caused by the build up and hardening of white blood cells, lipids and connective tissue.

ATP (adenosine triphosphate)
A molecule made up of adenine, a ribose sugar and three phosphate groups. It is the immediate source of energy in a cell.

ATP hydrolase
An enzyme which catalyses the hydrolysis of ATP into ADP and P_i.

ATP synthase
An enzyme which catalyses the synthesis of ATP from ADP and P_i.

Atrioventricular valve (AV)
A valve in the heart linking the atria to the ventricles.

Attachment protein (virus)
A protein on the surface of a virus that lets the virus cling onto a suitable host cell.

Autoradiography
A technique that reveals the location of radioactive tracers.

B

B-cell
A type of white blood cell involved in the immune response. It produces antibodies.

Base
A nitrogen-containing molecule that forms part of a DNA nucleotide.

Benedict's test
A biochemical test for the presence of sugars.

Bile salt
A type of salt produced by the liver to aid the digestion of lipids.

Binary fission
The process by which prokaryotic cells replicate.

Binomial system
The system used in classification for naming organisms using a two-part Latin name.

Biodiversity
The variety of living organisms in an area.

Biuret test
A biochemical test for the presence of polypeptides and proteins.

Bohr effect
An effect by which an increase of carbon dioxide in the blood results in a reduction of haemoglobin's affinity for oxygen.

C

Cancer
A tumour that invades surrounding tissue.

Capillary bed
A network of capillaries.

Capsid
The protein coat surrounding a virus's genetic material.

Capsule (cell)
A layer of secreted slime surrounding some prokaryotic cells.

Cardiac cycle
An ongoing sequence of contraction and relaxation of the atria and ventricles that keeps blood continuously circulating round the body.

Cardiac output
The volume of blood pumped by the heart per minute (measured in cm^3 per minute).

Cardiovascular disease
Any disease associated with the heart and blood vessels.

Carrier protein
A protein in a cell membrane that allows the facilitated diffusion of large molecules.

Catalyst
A chemical that speeds up a chemical reaction without being used up itself.

Causal relationship
Where a change in one variable causes a change in the other.

Cell cycle
The process that all body cells from multicellular organisms use to grow and divide.

Cell fractionation
A method that separates the organelles in a cell.

Cell-surface membrane
The membrane found on the surface of animal cells (and just inside the cell wall of other cells). Regulates the movement of substances into and out of the cell.

Cellular immune response
The immune response that involves T-cells and the other immune system cells they interact with, e.g. phagocytes.

Cellulose
A polysaccharide made of long, unbranched chains of β-glucose.

Cell wall
The outermost cell layer found in plant, algal and fungal cells.

Centromere
The point at which two strands of a chromosome are joined together.

Channel protein
A protein that forms a pore in a cell membrane and allows the facilitated diffusion of charged particles.

Chlorophyll
A green substance found in chloroplasts.

Chloroplast
An organelle present in plant and algal cells where photosynthesis occurs.

Cholesterol
A type of lipid present in cell membranes (except bacterial cell membranes).

Chromatid
One 'arm' of a double stranded chromosome.

Chromosome
A thread like structure made up of one long DNA molecule.

Chromosome non-disjunction
Failure of the chromosomes to separate properly during meiosis or mitosis.

Classification
The act of arranging organisms into groups.

Community
All the populations of different species in a habitat.

Competitive inhibitor
A molecule that has a similar shape to a substrate and blocks an enzyme's active site.

Complementary base pairing
Hydrogen bonding between specific pairs of bases on opposing polynucleotide strands.

Condensation reaction
A reaction that releases a molecule of water when it links molecules together.

Continuous data
Data that can take any value in a range.

Control group
A group in a study that is treated in exactly the same way as the experimental group, apart from the factor you're investigating.

Control variable
A variable you keep constant throughout an experiment.

Coronary artery
An artery supplying the heart muscle with blood.

Coronary heart disease
When the coronary arteries have lots of atheromas in them, which restricts blood flow to the heart.

Correlation
A relationship between two variables.

Co-transporter
A type of carrier protein that binds two molecules at the same time.

Counter-current system (fish)
The system in which blood flows in one direction and water flows in the opposite direction across the gills of a fish.

Courtship behaviour
Behaviour carried out by organisms to attract a mate of the right species.

Crossing over
When chromatids twist around each other and bits of them swap over during meiosis.

Cytokinesis
The division of the cytoplasm during eukaryotic cell division.

Cytoplasm
A gel-like substance where most of the chemical reactions in a cell happen.

Cytotoxic T-cell
A T-cell that kills abnormal or foreign cells.

Denatured
The point at which an enzyme no longer functions as a catalyst

Deoxyribose
The pentose sugar in DNA.

Dependent variable
The variable you measure in an experiment.

Dicotyledonous plant
A type of flowering plant, e.g. non-woody plants, bushes and trees.

Differential reproductive success
The fact that in any population, some individuals are more likely to survive and reproduce than others.

Diffusion (simple)
Net movement of particles from an area of higher concentration to an area of lower concentration.

Digestion
The process of breaking down food into substances that can be used by the body.

Dipeptidase
An endopeptidase enzyme that hydrolyses peptide bonds within a protein.

Dipeptide
A molecule formed from two amino acids.

Diploid
When a cell contains two copies of each chromosome.

Directional selection
When individuals with alleles for characteristics of an extreme type are more likely to survive, reproduce and pass on their alleles.

Disaccharidase
An enzyme that catalyses the hydrolysis of disaccharides.

Disaccharide
A molecule formed from two monosaccharides.

Discrete data
Numerical data that can only take certain values in a range.

DNA (deoxyribonucleic acid)
The molecule in cells that stores genetic information.

DNA helicase
An enzyme that breaks the hydrogen bonds between two polynucleotide DNA strands during DNA replication.

DNA polymerase
An enzyme that joins together the nucleotides on a new strand of DNA during DNA replication.

DNA sequencing
The process of determining the base order of a section of DNA.

Double-helix
The structure of a DNA molecule — two separate strands wound together in a spiral.

E

Emulsion test
A biochemical test for the presence of lipids.

Endopeptidase
An enzyme that hydrolyses peptide bonds within a protein.

Endoplasmic reticulum
A system of membranes enclosing a fluid-filled space. Involved with lipid and protein processing.

Endothelium
The inner lining of a blood vessel.

Enzyme
A protein that speeds up the rate of chemical reactions.

Enzyme-substrate complex
The intermediate formed when a substrate molecule binds to the active site of an enzyme.

Eukaryote
Organism made up of a cell (or cells) containing a nucleus, e.g. animals, plants, algae and fungi.

Evolution
The gradual change in species over time.

Exchange organ
An organ (e.g. the lungs) specialised to exchange substances.

Exon
A section of DNA within a gene that codes for amino acids.

Exopeptidase
An enzyme that hydrolyses the peptide bonds at the end of proteins to remove single amino acids.

Expiration
Breathing out.

F

Facilitated diffusion
The diffusion of particles through carrier proteins or channel proteins in the plasma membrane.

Fertilisation
When a haploid sperm fuses with a haploid egg to generate a diploid zygote.

Flagellum
A long, hair-like structure that rotates to move a cell.

Fluid mosaic model
Model describing the arrangement of molecules in a cell membrane.

Foreign antigen
An antigen not normally found in the body.

Founder effect
The reduction in genetic diversity that occurs when just a few organisms from a population start a new colony.

Functional RNA
RNA molecules that aren't mRNA, e.g. tRNA or the RNA found in ribosomes.

Gamete
A sex cell — e.g. the sperm cell in males or the egg cell in females.

Gas exchange
The process of taking in gases that are needed for life processes and getting rid of waste gases.

Gas exchange surface
A boundary between the outside environment and the internal environment of an organism, over which gas exchange occurs.

Gene
A section of DNA which codes for a protein.

Gene pool
The complete range of alleles in a population.

Genetic bottleneck
An event that causes a big reduction in a population and reduces genetic diversity.

Genetic code
The sequence of base triplets in mRNA which codes for specific amino acids.

Genetic diversity
The number of different alleles of genes in a species or population.

Genome
The complete set of genes in a cell.

Gill
The respiratory organ of a fish.

Gill filament
A thin plate in a fish's gill.

Glycogen
A polysaccharide made from a long, very branched chain of α-glucose.

Glycolipid
A lipid that has a carbohydrate attached.

Glycoprotein
A protein that has a carbohydrate attached.

Glycosidic bond
A bond formed between monosaccharides.

Golgi apparatus
A group of fluid-filled flattened sacs. Involved with processing and packaging lipids and proteins, and making lysosomes

Golgi vesicle
A small, fluid-filled sac produced by the Golgi apparatus, which stores and transports lipids and proteins.

Granum
A structure in chloroplasts formed from the stacking of thylakoid membranes

Guard cell
A cell that controls the opening and closing of stomata.

Haemoglobin
An oxygen-carrying protein found in red blood cells.

Haploid
When a cell contains one copy of each chromosome.

Helper T-cell
A T-cell that releases chemical signals to activate other immune system cells.

Herd immunity
Where unvaccinated people are protected because the occurrence of the disease is reduced by the number of people who are vaccinated.

Histone
Protein that DNA is wound around in order to fit into the nucleus.

HIV (human immunodeficiency virus)
A virus that affects the human immune system.

Homologous pair
A pair of matching chromosomes — each chromosome contains the same genes but could have different alleles.

Host cell
A cell inside which a virus replicates.

Humoral immune response
The immune response that involves B-cells, clonal selection and the production of antibodies.

Hydrolysis
A chemical reaction that uses a water molecule when it breaks bonds between molecules.

Hydrophilic
Attracts water.

Hydrophobic
Repels water.

Hydrostatic pressure
The pressure exerted by a liquid.

Hypothesis
A specific testable statement, based on a theory, about what will happen in a test situation.

Immunity
The ability to respond quickly to an infection.

Immunological comparison
Using antibodies to determine how similar proteins are.

Independent segregation
The random division of maternal and paternal chromosomes into daughter cells during meiosis.

Independent variable
The variable you change in an experiment.

Index of diversity
A measure of biodiversity that takes into account the number of species present in a community and the abundance of each species.

Inorganic ion
An ion (charged particle) that doesn't (usually) contain carbon.

Inspiration
Breathing in.

Interphase
A period of the cell cycle in which the cell grows and DNA is replicated.

Intron
A section of DNA within a gene that does not code for amino acids.

Iodine test
A biochemical test for the presence of starch.

Lamella (in chloroplasts)
A thin, flat piece of thylakoid membrane found in chloroplasts.

Lamella (in fish)
A tiny structure found on the gill filament in a fish.

Lipase
An enzyme that catalyses the hydrolysis of lipids.

Loading of oxygen (onto haemoglobin)
The action of an oxygen molecule binding with a haemoglobin molecule.

Locus
The position on a chromosome where a particular allele is found.

Lymphatic system
A network of tubes which transports excess tissue fluid back into the circulatory system.

Lysosome
A round organelle that contains digestive enzymes called lysozymes.

Magnification
How much bigger an image from a microscope is compared to the specimen.

Margin of error
The range in which the true value of a measurement lies.

Mass transport system
A system (e.g. the circulatory system) that carries substances to and from individual cells.

Mean
The average of the values collected in a sample, obtained by adding all the values together and dividing by the total number of values in the sample.

Meiosis
A type of cell division where a parent cell divides to create four genetically different haploid cells.

Memory cell
A white blood cell that remains in the body and remembers how to respond to infections.

Mesophyll cell
A type of plant cell present in a leaf and the main gas exchange surface in a plant.

Metabolic rate
The rate at which energy is used by an organism.

Micelle (digestion)
A microscopic structure composed of monoglycerides, fatty acids and bile salts.

Microfibril
A strong fibre formed by chains of cellulose linked together by hydrogen bonds.

Microvillus
A fold in the cell-surface membrane that increases the surface area.

Mitochondrion
An oval-shaped organelle with a double membrane. The site of anaerobic respiration.

Mitosis
A type of cell division where a parent cell divides to produce two genetically identical daughter cells.

Monoclonal antibody
An antibody produced from a single group of genetically identical B-cells.

Monomer
A small, basic molecular unit, e.g. amino acids and monosaccharides.

Monosaccharide
A monomer of carbohydrates.

mRNA (messenger RNA)
A type of RNA that is the template for protein synthesis. It carries the genetic code from the DNA to the ribosomes.

Multicellular organism
An organism that has more than one cell, e.g. a human.

Multiple repeat
A section of repetitive DNA found outside of genes — does not code for amino acids.

Mutagenic agent
Something that increases the rate of mutations in DNA.

Mutation
A change in the base sequence of an organism's DNA.

Myocardial infarction
A heart attack.

Natural selection
The process whereby an allele becomes common in a population because it codes for a characteristic that makes an organism more likely to survive, reproduce and pass on its genes to its offspring.

Negative control
An extra experiment set up to check that only the independent variable is affecting the dependent variable. It is not expected to have any effect.

Non-competitive inhibitor
A molecule that binds away from an enzyme's active site and alters the shape of the active site, so the substrate can no longer bind.

Non-reducing sugars
A class of monosaccharides and disaccharides.

Normal distribution
A bell-shaped curve symmetrical about the mean.

Nucleic acid
A polymer made from nucleotides, e.g. DNA and RNA.

Nucleolus
A structure within a nucleus that makes ribosomes.

Nucleotide
The monomer that makes up polynucleotides — consists of a pentose sugar, a phosphate group and a nitrogenous organic base.

Nucleus
An organelle that contains chromosomes and controls a eukaryotic cell's activities.

Null hypothesis
A hypothesis that suggests there's no correlation between the factors being investigated.

Organ
A group of different tissues that work together to perform a particular function.

Organ system
A group of organs that work together to carry out a particular function.

Organelle
A part of a cell, e.g. the nucleus.

Osmosis
Diffusion of water molecules across a partially permeable membrane, from an area of higher water potential to an area of lower water potential.

Oxygen dissociation curve
A curve on a graph that shows how saturated with oxygen haemoglobin is at any given partial pressure.

Oxyhaemoglobin
The molecule formed when oxygen binds to haemoglobin.

pCO$_2$
Partial pressure of carbon dioxide — a measure of carbon dioxide concentration.

pO$_2$
Partial pressure of oxygen — a measure of oxygen concentration.

Partially permeable membrane
A membrane that lets some molecules through it, but not others.

Pathogen
An organism that causes disease.

Peptidase
An enzyme that catalyses the hydrolysis of proteins.

Peptide bond
A bond formed between amino acids.

Phagocyte
A type of white blood cell that carries out phagocytosis, e.g. a macrophage.

Phagocytosis
The engulfment of pathogens.

Phloem
A tissue in plants that transports organic substances (e.g. sucrose) from their source to their sink.

Phospholipid
A lipid containing one molecule of glycerol attached to two fatty acids and a phosphate group. Main component of the cell membrane.

Phylogeny
The evolutionary history of groups of organisms.

Plasma cell
A type of B-cell that produces antibodies.

Plasma membrane
See cell-surface membrane.

Plasmid
A small loop of DNA in a cell, which is not part of the chromosomal DNA.

Plasmodesma
A small channel in a plant cell wall that connects neighbouring plant cells.

Polymer
A large, complex molecule composed of long chains of monomers, e.g. proteins and carbohydrates.

Polynucleotide
A long strand of nucleotides — two polynucleotide strands coil together to make the DNA double helix.

Polypeptide
A molecule formed from more than two amino acids.

Polysaccharide
A molecule formed from more than two monosaccharides.

Population sample
A small group of organisms used as a model for the whole population.

Positive control
An extra experiment set up to check what a positive result looks like.

Potometer
A special piece of apparatus used to estimate transpiration rates.

Precise result
A result that is close to the mean.

Prediction
See hypothesis.

pre-mRNA
mRNA in eukaryotes containing both introns and exons. It is spliced to form mRNA.

Primary immune response
The immune response triggered when a foreign antigen enters the body for the first time.

Prokaryote
Single-celled organism without a nucleus or membrane-bound organelles, e.g. bacteria.

Proteome
The full range of proteins a cell is able to produce.

Q

Qualitative test
A qualitative test tells you what's present, e.g. an acid or an alkali.

Quantitative test
A quantitative test tells you how much of something is present, e.g. an acid that's pH 2.46.

R

Random error
A difference in a measurement caused by an unpredictable factor, e.g. human error.

Reducing sugars
A class of monosaccharides and disaccharides.

Repeatable result
A result than can be repeated by the same person using the same method and equipment.

Reproducible result
A result that can be consistently reproduced in an independent experiment.

Resolution
How well a microscope distinguishes between two points close together.

Ribosome
A small organelle that makes proteins.

Risk factor
Anything that increases the chance of getting a disease.

RNA (ribonucleic acid)
A type of nucleic acid, similar to DNA but containing ribose instead of deoxyribose and uracil instead of thymine.

S

Sample size
The number of samples in the investigation, e.g. the number of people in a drug trial.

Saturated fatty acid
A fatty acid with no double bonds between its carbon atoms.

Secondary immune response
The immune response triggered when a foreign antigen enters the body for the second time.

Semi-conservative replication of DNA
Replication of DNA in which half of the new molecules of DNA are from the original piece of DNA.

Semi-lunar (SL) valve
A valve in the heart linking the ventricles to the aorta and pulmonary artery.

Serial dilution
The creation of a set of solutions that decrease in concentration by the same factor each time.

Sink (translocation)
A part of a plant where substances (e.g. sucrose and amino acids) are used up.

Sister chromatid
One of two identical copies of a chromosome joined together in the middle.

Source (translocation)
A part of a plant where substances needed by the plant (e.g. sucrose and amino acids) are produced.

Specialised cell
A cell adapted to carry out specific functions.

Species
A group of similar organisms able to reproduce to give fertile offspring.

Species richness
The number of different species in a community. A measure of biodiversity.

Specific base pairing
See complementary base pairing.

Spiracle
A pore on the surface of an insect.

Splicing
The removal of introns from pre-mRNA and the joining together of the exons to form mRNA.

Stabilising selection
Where individuals with alleles for characteristics towards the middle of the range are more likely to survive, reproduce and pass on their alleles.

Standard deviation
A measure of the spread of values about the mean.

Starch
A carbohydrate molecule made up of two polysaccharides — amylose and amylopectin.

Stoma
A pore in the epidermis of a plant leaf.

Stroke volume
The volume of blood pumped during each heartbeat (measured in cm^3).

Stroma
A thick fluid found in chloroplasts.

Substrate
A substance that interacts with an enzyme.

Sugar-phosphate backbone
Alternating sugar and phosphate groups joined together in a polynucleotide chain.

Supercoiling
The way that DNA is condensed to fit in the cell in prokaryotes.

Surface area:volume ratio
An organism or structure's surface area in relation to its volume.

T-cell
A type of white blood cell involved in the immune response. Some types activate B-cells and some kill pathogens directly.

Taxon
A group within a classification hierarchy, e.g. domain, kingdom.

Temporary mount
A method of preparing a microscope slide in which the specimen is suspended in a drop of liquid.

Theory
A possible explanation for something.

Thylakoid membrane
A membrane found inside chloroplasts, stacked up to form grana.

Tissue
A group of similar cells working together to perform a particular function.

Tissue fluid
The fluid that surrounds cells in tissues.

Toxin
A harmful molecule. Released by some pathogens.

Trachea (insects)
A pipe that carries air between the external environment and the inside of an insect's body.

Tracheole
A small pipe that branches off the trachea in an insect and is used for gas exchange.

Transcription
The first stage of protein synthesis, in which an mRNA copy of a gene is made from DNA.

Translation
The second stage of protein synthesis, in which amino acids are joined together by ribosomes to make a polypeptide chain (protein).

Translocation
The movement of solutes to where they're needed in a plant.

Transpiration
The evaporation of water from a plant's surface.

Triglyceride
A lipid containing one molecule of glycerol attached to three fatty acids.

Triplet
A series of three bases which codes for one amino acid in a protein.

tRNA (transfer RNA)
A type of RNA involved in translation. It carries the amino acids used to make proteins to the ribosomes.

Ultracentrifugation
A method where cell components are separated out using a centrifuge.

Uncertainty (in data)
The amount of error measurements might have.

Unloading of oxygen (from haemoglobin)
The action of an oxygen molecule being released from a haemoglobin molecule.

Unsaturated fatty acid
A fatty acid with at least one double bond between its carbon atoms.

Vaccination
The administering of a vaccine containing antigens to give immunity.

Vacuole
An organelle that contains cell sap (a weak solution of sugar and salts).

Valid result
A result that answers the original question and for which all the variables that could have affected it were controlled.

Variable
A quantity that has the potential to change, e.g. weight, temperature, concentration.

Variation
The differences that exist between individuals.

Ventilation
Breathing in and breathing out.

Virus
An acellular structure that invades and reproduces inside the cells of other organisms (causing disease).

Water potential
The likelihood of water molecules to diffuse into or out of solution.

Xerophyte
A plant specially adapted for life in a warm, dry or windy habitat.

Xylem
A tissue in plants that transports water and mineral ions up a plant from the roots to the leaves.

Zygote
The diploid cell formed when two gametes fuse during fertilisation.

Acknowledgements

AQA specification material is reproduced by permission of AQA.

Data acknowledgements

Graph of activity of protein X on mitosis on page 94 reprinted from Cell, 58 (2), Moreno S, Hayles J, Nurse P, 361-72, Copyright 1989, with permission from Elsevier.

Graph of whooping cough vaccine uptake on page 122 from Health in Scotland 2000, CMO Annual Report, September 2001. This information is licenced under the terms of the Open Government Licence http://www.nationalarchives.gov.uk/doc/open-government-licence/version/3/ (www.department.gov.uk/document, accessed November 2011).

MMR Graph on page 128 adapted from H. Honda, Y. Shimizu, M. Rutter. No effect of MMR withdrawal on the incidence of autism: a total population study. Journal of Child Psychology and Psychiatry 2005; 46(6):572-579.

Data used to construct Herceptin® graph on page 129 from M.J. Piccart-Gebhart, et al. Trastuzumab after Adjuvant Chemotherapy in HER2_positive Breast Cancer: NEJM 2005; 353: 1659-72.

Data used to construct Influenza A vaccine graph on page 129 from Xiao-Feng Liang et al. Safety of Influenza A (H1N1) Vaccine in Postmarketing Surveillance in China: N Engl J Med 2011; 364:638-647.

Data used to construct AIDS deaths and diagnoses graph on page 132 from Centers for Disease Control and Prevention (CDC), HIV Surveillance – United States, 1981-2008, Torian, et al., MMWR/June 3, 2011/Vol. 60/No. 21: 689-693.

Data used to construct tetanus graph on page 135 from http://www.who.int/immunization_monitoring/diseases/tetanus/en/index.html accessed November 2011.

Graph of normal lung function and obstructive lung disease on page 152 adapted from Johns Hopkins University School of Medicine's Interactive Respiratory Physiology. http://oac.med.jhmi.edu/res_phys/Encyclopedia/ForcedExpiration/ForcedExpiration.html, accessed April 2015. © Johns Hopkins University.

Data used to construct graph of bronchial cross-sectional areas on page 153: Beigelman-Aubry C, Capderou A, Grenier P A, et al. Mild intermittent asthma: CT assessment of bronchial cross-sectional area and lung attenuation at controlled lung volume. Radiology 2002;223:181-187. © 2011 by Radiological Society of North America.

Data used to construct smoking graph on page 154 from Cancer Research UK. http://www.cancerresearchuk.org/cancer-info/cancerstats/causes/tobacco-statistics/#Smoking, January 2015.

Data used to construct lung cancer graph on page 154 from Cancer Research UK. http://www.cancerresearchuk.org/cancer-info/cancerstats/types/lung/mortality/uk-lung-cancer-mortality-statistics, January 2015.

Data used to construct asthma and sulfur dioxide graphs on page 155. Source: National Statistics. Crown copyright material is reproduced under the terms of the open government licence http://www.nationalarchives.gov.uk/doc/open-government-licence/version/3/.

Graph of tobacco consumption and death rates for COPD on page 157. Source: AIHW, Australian Institute of Health and Welfare. Licenced for re-use under the creative commons licence http://creativecommons.org/licenses/by/3.0/au/.

Data used to construct the graph on page 186 from P.M. Ridker, et al. Comparison of C-reactive protein and low-density lipoprotein cholesterol levels in the prediction of first cardiovascular events. NEJM 2002; 347: 1557-65.

Acknowledgements

Data used to construct projected annual number of new CHD cases against interventions graph on page 188 from K. Bibbins-Domingo et al., Reductions in Cardiovascular Disease Projected from Modest Reductions in Dietary Salt: N Engl J Med. 2010 February 18; 362(7): 590–599.

Data in table on page 196 reproduced with permission from Plants in Action, http://plantsinaction.science. uq.edu.au, published by the Australian Society of Plant Scientists, accessed April 2015.

Data used in table of animal haemoglobin saturation on page 200 from Comparative Biochemistry and Physiology Part A Physiology, Vol number 113, Issue 4, F León-Velarde, C De Muizon, J A Palacios, D Clark, C Monge, Hemoglobin affinity and structure in high-altitude and sea-level carnivores from Peru, 407-411, Copyright 1996, with permission from Elsevier.

Data used to construct the table on the role of protein and nucleic acid synthesis on page 212 reproduced with kind permission from Robert E. Click, D. P. Hackett. PNAS 1963; 50 (2):243-250.

Data used to construct graph on E. coli and tetracycline resistance on page 235 © 2011 Mirzaagha et al; licensee BioMed Central Ltd. Distribution and characterization of ampicillin- and tetracycline-resistant Escherichia coli from feedlot cattle fed subtherapeutic antimicrobials: BMC Microbiol. 2011; 11: 78. Licenced for re-use under the creative commons licence http://creativecommons.org/licenses/by/2.0/

Table of critical values for Spearman's rank test on page 255 abridged from Significance Testing of the Spearman Rank Correlation Coefficient by Jerrold H Zar from the Journal of the American Statistical Association © 1972 Taylor & Francis, reprinted by the publisher Taylor & Francis Ltd, http://www.tandfonline.com

Photograph acknowledgements

Cover photo **Laguna Design**/Science Photo Library, p 3 (top) **Andrew Lambert Photography**/Science Photo Library, p 3 (bottom) **Tek Image**/Science Photo Library, p 22 (top) **Andrew Lambert Photography**/Science Photo Library, p 22 (bottom) **Andrew Lambert Photography**/Science Photo Library, p 25 **Biophoto Associates**/Science Photo Library, p 26 **Andrew Lambert Photography**/Science Photo Library, p 29 **Andrew Lambert Photography**/Science Photo Library, p 33 (top) **animate4.com**/Science Photo Library, p 33 (bottom) **Laguna Design**/Science Photo Library, p 34 **Andrew Lambert Photography**/Science Photo Library, p 36 **Clive Freeman, The Royal Institution**/Science Photo Library, p 53 Science Photo Library, p 54 **A. Barrington Brown**/Science Photo Library, p 57 **Andrew Brookes, National Physical Laboratory**/Science Photo Library, p 64 **Chemical Design**/Science Photo Library, p 69 **Omikron**/Science Photo Library, p 70 **Biophoto Associates**/Science Photo Library, p 71 (top) **Don W. Fawcett**/Science Photo Library, p 71 (middle) **Biology Pics**/Science Photo Library, p 71 (bottom) Science Photo Library, p 72 **Martin M. Rotker**/Science Photo Library, p 74 (left) **Don W. Fawcett**/Science Photo Library, p 74 (right) Science Photo Library, p 76 (top) **Eye of Science**/Science Photo Library, p 76 (bottom) **CNRI**/Science Photo Library, p 79 (top) **Steve Gschmeissner**/Science Photo Library, p 79 (middle) **NIAID/CDC**/Science Photo Library, p 79 (bottom) **CNRI**/Science Photo Library, p 80 (Fig. 1 top) © **Usere6035d91_515**/iStockphoto.com, p 80 (Fig. 1 bottom) **Dr. Fred Hossler/Visuals Unlimited, Inc.**/Science Photo Library, p 80 (Fig. 3 top) Science Photo Library, p 80 (Fig. 3 bottom) **Alfred Pasieka**/Science Photo Library, p 81 (top) © **lisafx**/iStockphoto.com, p 81 (bottom) **Louise Hughes**/Science Photo Library, p 82 **Tek Image**/Science Photo Library, p 85 (Fig. 2) **Pr. G. Gimenez-Martin**/Science Photo Library, p 85 (Fig. 3) **Pr. G. Gimenez-Martin**/Science Photo Library, p 85 (Fig. 4) **Pr. G. Gimenez-Martin**/Science Photo Library, p 85 (Fig. 5) **Pr. G. Gimenez-Martin**/Science Photo Library, p 85 (Fig. 6) **Pr. G. Gimenez-Martin**/Science Photo Library, p 86 **Steve Gschmeissner**/Science Photo Library, p 87 **Medical Photo NHS Lothian**/Science Photo Library, p 88 **Herve Conge, ISM**/Science Photo Library, p 89 © **David_Ahn**/iStockphoto.com, p 96 **Russell Kightley**/Science Photo Library, p 98 **Martyn F. Chillmaid**/Science Photo Library, p 101 **Science Picture Co**/Science Photo Library, p 103 **Andrew Lambert Photography**/Science Photo Library, p 106 **Charles D. Winters**/Science Photo Library, p 109 **Steve Gschmeissner**/Science Photo Library, p 113 (left) **J. C. Revy, ISM**/Science Photo Library, p 113 (right) **J. C. Revy, ISM**/Science Photo Library, p 117 Science Photo Library, p 118 **Phantatomix**/

Acknowledgements

Science Photo Library, p 123 **CNRI**/Science Photo Library, p 125 **Life In View**/Science Photo Library, p 126 **BSIP, Beranger**/Science Photo Library, p 131 **Thomas Deerinck, NCMIR**/Science Photo Library, p 137 **William Weber**/Science Photo Library, p 139 **Ami Images**/Science Photo Library, p 142 **Power and Syred**/Science Photo Library, p 143 **Power and Syred**/Science Photo Library, p 144 **Microfield Scientific Ltd**/Science Photo Library, p 145 (left) **Eye of Science**/Science Photo Library, p 145 (right) **Power and Syred**/Science Photo Library, p 146 **Innerspace Imaging**/Science Photo Library, p 147 **Science Vu, Visuals Unlimited**/Science Photo Library, p 150 **Du Cane Medical Imaging Ltd**/Science Photo Library, p 151 **Biodisc, Visuals Unlimited**/Science Photo Library, p 152 **John Thys/Reporters**/Science Photo Library, p 153 (top) **Dr Keith Wheeler**/Science Photo Library, p 153 (bottom) **Manfred Kage**/Science Photo Library, p 156 © **zoom-zoom**/iStockphoto.com, p 158 Science Photo Library, p 159 Science Photo Library, p 160 (top left) © **21bgil**/iStockphoto.com, p 160 (top right) **Herve Conge, ISM**/Science Photo Library, p 160 (bottom) **Dr Keith Wheeler**/Science Photo Library, p 162 (top) **Dr Keith Wheeler**/Science Photo Library, p 162 (Fig. 2 left) **Eye of Science**/Science Photo Library, p 162 (Fig. 2 right) **Dr Fred Hossler, Visuals Unlimited**/Science Photo Library, p 167 **Dr Keith Wheeler**/Science Photo Library, p 178 (top) **Science Picture Co**/Science Photo Library, p 178 (bottom) © **Alexandra Thompson**/iStockphoto.com, p 183 **BSIP VEM**/Science Photo Library, p 184 (top) Science Photo Library, p 184 (middle) **Professor P. M. Motta, G. Macchiarelli, S. A. Nottola**/Science Photo Library, p 184 (bottom) Science Photo Library, p 189 **Dr David Furness, Keele University**/Science Photo Library, p 192 **Biophoto Associates**/Science Photo Library, p 193 **Dr Keith Wheeler**/Science Photo Library, p 196 **Omikron**/Science Photo Library, p 203 **CNRI**/Science Photo Library, p 207 **Ramon Andrade 3DCiencia**/Science Photo Library, p 216 (top) **Adrian T. Sumner**/Science Photo Library, p 216 (bottom) **Pr. G. Gimenez-Martin**/Science Photo Library, p 217 **Adrian T. Sumner**/Science Photo Library, p 222 **Dept. of Clinical Cytogenetics, Addenbrookes Hospital**/Science Photo Library, p 224 **John Beatty**/Science Photo Library, p 227 (top) **David M. Schleser/Nature's Images**/Science Photo Library, p 227 (middle) **Duncan Shaw**/Science Photo Library, p 227 (bottom) **John Serrao**/Science Photo Library, p 231 **Michael Gabridge/Visuals Unlimited, Inc.**/Science Photo Library, p 232 **Martyn F. Chillmaid**/Science Photo Library, p 239 (top) © **Mariko Yuki**/Shutterstock, p 239 (middle) **B. G Thomson**/Science Photo Library, p 253 (top) **Kaj R. Svensson**/Science Photo Library

Every effort has been made to locate copyright holders and obtain permission to reproduce sources. For those sources where it has been difficult to trace the originator of the work, we would be grateful for information. If any copyright holder would like us to make an amendment to the acknowledgements, please notify us and we will gladly update the book at the next reprint. Thank you.

Index